DEVELOPMENTS IN FOOD COLOURS—1

THE DEVELOPMENTS SERIES

Developments in many fields of science and technology occur at such a pace that frequently there is a long delay before information about them becomes available and usually it is inconveniently scattered among several journals.

Developments Series books overcome these disadvantages by bringing together within one cover papers dealing with the latest trends and developments in a specific field of study and publishing them within *six months* of their being written.

Many subjects are covered by the series including food science and technology, polymer science, civil and public health engineering, pressure vessels, composite materials, concrete, building science, petroleum technology, geology, etc.

Information on other titles in the series will gladly be sent on application to the publisher.

DEVELOPMENTS IN FOOD COLOURS—1

Edited by

JOHN WALFORD

*Organics Division, Imperial Chemical Industries Ltd,
Blackley, Manchester, UK*

APPLIED SCIENCE PUBLISHERS LTD
LONDON

APPLIED SCIENCE PUBLISHERS LTD
RIPPLE ROAD, BARKING, ESSEX, ENGLAND

British Library Cataloguing in Publication Data

Developments in food colours.—(The developments
series)
1
1. Coloring matter in food
I. Walford, John II. Series
664'.06   TP456.C65

ISBN 0-85334-881-2

WITH 26 TABLES AND 71 ILLUSTRATIONS

© APPLIED SCIENCE PUBLISHERS LTD 1980

Printed in Great Britain by Galliard (Printers) Ltd. Great Yarmouth

PREFACE

There has been a continuing trend over the last few years to replace traditional synthetic colours for food with naturally derived or nature equivalent colours. Hence the 'natural' area is the one towards which most recent research activity has been directed, although the concept of synthetic polymeric colours where chromophores are leashed on to non-absorbable polymers has also been investigated and shows considerable potential.

For some time a need has existed for a single volume tracing both the progress of major developments in this field and also giving some indication of the likely future areas of research interest and activity. It is important that future legislative decisions should be made on the basis of available evidence and in full knowledge of the safety-in-use, technical and economic needs, constraints and possibilities. I hope that this volume will assist in providing a wider awareness of these factors.

I wish to record my sincere thanks to the contributors who have made the considerable range and depth of their experience in the food coloration field available for this venture, and also to the publisher's representative, Mr George Olley, who has been a consistent source of support and encouragement. I wish also to mention the staff of the Information and Library Service Department of Organics Division, ICI Ltd for their assistance in tracking down some of the more obscure sources of reference.

JOHN WALFORD

CONTENTS

LIST OF CONTRIBUTORS

P. Bridle

Long Ashton Research Station, University of Bristol, Long Ashton, Bristol BS18 9AF, UK.

J. Coulson

Pointing Ltd, Prudhoe, Northumberland NE42 6NJ, UK.

J. N. Counsell

Technology Centre, Roche Products Ltd, Chemicals Division, Dunstable, Bedfordshire LU6 1BG, UK.

J. J-P. Drake

The British Industrial Biological Research Association, Woodmansterne Road, Carshalton, Surrey SM5 4DS, UK.

K. McLaren

Instrumental Colour Systems Ltd, 13 Bone Lane, Newbury, Berkshire RG14 5TE, UK.

C. F. Timberlake

Long Ashton Research Station, University of Bristol, Long Ashton, Bristol BS18 9AF, UK.

J. Walford

Organics Division, Imperial Chemical Industries Ltd, PO Box 42, Hexagon House, Blackley, Manchester M9 3DA, UK.

Chapter 1

HISTORICAL DEVELOPMENT OF FOOD COLORATION

J. WALFORD

Organics Division, Imperial Chemical Industries Ltd, Blackley, Manchester, UK.

SUMMARY

The colouring of food is a long-established practice probably dating from prehistoric times, and the reasons for its continuing importance are discussed.

Early sources of colour were the naturally occurring animal, vegetable and mineral products, displaced only towards the end of the last century following development of the synthetic dyestuff industry. An insight is given into several coloration practices common in the period prior to the early legislation of the mid-19th century.

Basic approaches to the regulation of colour addition to food are illustrated by reference to developments in the UK and the USA. The important present-day aspects of manufacture and use are discussed and the trend away from synthetic colours towards the naturally derived and nature equivalent types is noted.

The practice of colouring food dates back to very early times. Until the middle of the nineteenth century, the only colouring matters available were derived from natural sources of animal, vegetable and mineral origin. Classical writers such as Pliny noted that in the days of the Roman Empire, both wine and bread were frequently coloured with such items as fruit berries and 'white earth'. Pliny also refers to the presence of meat inspectors in Athens and Rome.[1]

In Great Britain sugar was imported as a luxury from the twelfth century onwards and people delighted in the rosy and violet coloured varieties from Alexandria. The colouring matters used were probably those most ancient dyes Madder and Kermes, each giving a red shade, and Tyrian purple which are known to have been used in Egypt and the Mediterranean area for textile dyeing since biblical times.[2] A banquet in the late Middle Ages might well have been graced with a 'swan with silvered body and gilt beak served on a green pastry pond'.[3]

During the discovery of the New World, the explorer Alexander Von Humboldt concluded that cochineal was cultivated as early as the tenth century A. D. in Central America by the Toltecs[4] and later by the Aztecs. It seems possible that this colour was used in food.[5]

It is tempting to speculate that the first coloured foods were among those items prepared as ritual foods for consumption during religious festivals as well as simply to enliven a fairly monotonous diet. Later however, in more commercially minded times, colour was almost always introduced to mask the deficiencies of ingredients such as butter, eggs, chocolate and fruit.

It is clear from the extensive practice of food coloration that enjoyment of food is directly affected by colour as well as taste, odour and texture. Indeed, an unappetising colour may adversely affect digestion thus influencing the nutritional value of the food.

Food flavour and colour are clearly associated as has been amply demonstrated by many experiments. A recent one[6] involved presenting trained testers with white but chocolate flavoured ice-cream and brown but vanilla flavoured ice-cream. Asked to identify the flavours, the tasters' verdicts were almost without exception that the white ice-cream was vanilla and the brown was chocolate. Similar tests were carried out with children, using red and yellow jellies, variously flavoured. Regardless of the real flavours, the prevailing opinions were that the red jellies were strawberry and the yellow ones lemon. The problem extends into vegetables as well. For example, when presented with pale or brown cabbage, the immediate reaction is that it must be overcooked. When the above panel tasted a well-cooked sample artificially coloured brown, it was rated low on flavour. It is known also that the package colour of certain processed foods also helps to enhance perception of the appropriate flavour.

As a final illustration of the point, it is interesting to quote a case in which colour was left out of selected lines of popular foods by a leading firm of retailers in the UK. The items involved were canned garden peas, canned strawberries, and strawberry and raspberry jams. The peas without added colour were greenish grey or greenish yellow in colour and the canned strawberries pale straw coloured. The jams were brownish red which changed to a dull brown after a few months' storage.

Customer reaction was one of swift disapproval and sales suffered significantly. Later, following partial restoration of the colours, sales slowly regained their original level.[7]

Several surveys have been done on the extent of association between popular flavours and colours. One such list[8] compiled some years ago is given in Table 1.

TABLE 1
ASSOCIATION BETWEEN POPULAR FLAVOURS AND COLOURS

Apricot	Pale golden yellow	Mint	Yellow-green
Blackberry Blackcurrant	Dark bluish red	Orange	Bright reddish orange
Butterscotch	Golden brown	Peach	Light dull gold
Cassia	Dark red	Peppermint	White
Cherry	Bright bluish red	Pineapple	Greenish yellow
Chocolate	Dark reddish brown	Pistachio	Bright green
Clove	Light red	Plum	Reddish navy
Honey	Golden yellow	Prune	Dark navy
Lemon	Greenish or canary yellow	Raspberry	Bright bluish red
Liquorice	Dark blackish brown	Spearmint	Medium green
Lime	Bright bluish green	Strawberry	Bright bluish pink

Today, the reasons for adding colour to food are several fold.

1. To give an attractive appearance by replacing the natural colour destroyed during processing or anticipated storage conditions.
2. To give colour to those processed foods such as soft drinks, confectionery and ice-creams, which otherwise would have little or no colour.
3. To supplement the intensity of the natural colour where this is perceived to be weak.
4. To ensure batch to batch uniformity where raw materials of different source and varying colour intensity have been used.

With the continuing efforts to create novel synthesised foodstuffs, urgently needed to assist in feeding a rapidly increasing world population, it will remain important to improve food appearance and hence palatability. If the chances of meeting the criteria demanded for their acceptability are significantly improved by the addition of colour, flavour and the incorporation of texture, then a worthwhile contribution to solving a world food shortage problem could be made.

In most countries, the colours which are encountered today in food are the subject of strict legislative action, based on the twin criteria of toxicological harmlessness and demonstrated need. Only a small number, manufactured to exacting purity specifications are permitted. This has not always been the case of course.

In the Middle Ages, trade guilds exercised a close watch over the honesty of their members and the quality of the goods they sold. During the eighteenth and early years of the nineteenth century, however, when the Industrial Revolution was gaining momentum, there developed the increasingly widespread practice of food adulteration . This was associated with the massive social changes and population movements of that epoch. People accustomed to producing their own food and exchanging such produce for other foodstuffs, offered by trusted neighbours, now found themselves living and working in the rapidly growing cities and having to rely on food purchased from traders. Distribution methods simply could not keep up with demand and many unscrupulous traders took advantage of the shortages by selling increasingly more adulterated food, the use of colour being one of several instruments of adulteration.

In 1820, this situation was highlighted by the publication of a book by Frederic Accum.[9] Included in the book was a list of names of traders who had been convicted, together with an analysis of their wares. The book marked the first serious attempt to establish simple reliable analytical test methods to determine whether samples of food had been adulterated. This book caused quite a stir but it was not until the publication of supporting work by Hassall[10] in the 1850s that the public conscience was really aroused.

Some of the observations of Accum and Hassall make interesting reading. Wine and confectionery were two areas where colour was frequently used to deceive the consumer.

Anyone who has ever attempted the job of converting grapes into wine or chosen 'home brewing' as a hobby realises that wine making is an art rather than a science. According to Accum, it was indeed a 'black' art, or at least a 'highly coloured' art. In a chapter on adulteration of wine, he describes some colouring practices. '. . . Brazil Wood or the husks of elderberries or bilberries are employed to impart a deep rich purple tint to red port of a pale faint colour . . .' and that '. . . in this way a mixture of spoiled foreign and home-made wines is converted into the wretched compound frequently sold in this town [London] by the name of Genuine Old Port.' Accum also

complained that by these means '... A certain fraternity of chemical operators who work underground in caverns ... by the power of magical drugs and incantations raise under the streets of London the choicest products of the hills and valleys of France. They can squeeze Bordeaux (claret) out of the sloe and draw Champagne from an apple.'
Accum also mentions:

—tea leaves coloured with verdigris (copper acetate);
—Gloucester cheese contaminated with red lead which was itself an adulterant to the colour vermilion, often used to tint cheese;
—pickles boiled with a halfpence to make them green;
—confectionery contaminated with red lead and copper.

Much later, in a celebrated book,[11] F. A. Filby also has a word or two to say about wine. From *The Innkeepers and Butlers' Guide of 1805* he quotes a recipe for English Claret.

Take six gallons of water, two gallons of cyder and eight pounds of Malaga raisins, bruised; put them all together and let them stand close covered in a warm place for a fortnight, stirring it every other day very well. Then strain out the liquor into a clean cask and put to it a quart of barberries, a pint of juice of raspberries and a pint of juice of black cherries. Work it up with a little mustard seed and cover it with a piece of dough three or four days by the fireside and let it stand a week and bottle it off, and when it becomes fine and ripe it will become like common claret.

Perhaps today's Masters of Wine would describe it rather as 'uncommon claret'.
Another quote by Filby, this time from R. Shannon's *A Practical Treatise on Brewing, Distilling and Rectification,* also published in 1805, gives further handy hints on wine coloration.

Burnt sugar gives a fine amber colour from the lightest shade to the deepness of old brandy; oak chips the same and also an astringency. Yellow saunders a fine citron colour and grateful aromatic scent. Sassafras, a strawberry colour and a fine aromatic but peculiar scent. Red saunders, brazilli and logwood (give) red and purplish red with a sweet sub-astringent taste. To these colour ingredients, we may add turnsole, cochineal, mulberries, elderberries, brambleberries, barberries, etc. . . .

Some of Hassall's observations make more disturbing reading. He had analysed 101 samples of coloured sweets, the results of which he published in 1857.[10]

Yellows: 59 contained Lead Chromate, 11 Gamboge.
Reds:　　 12 Red Lead, 6 Cinnabar (Mercuric Sulphide).
Blues:　　 1 Indigo, 11 Prussian Blue (Ferric Ferrocyanide), 11 Antwerp Blue, 15 Artificial ultramarine (a double Silicate of Aluminium and Sodium with Sodium Sulphide).
Browns: 8 Vandyke Brown, Umber or Sienna.
Purple:　2 Prussian Blue.
Green:　　10 Brunswick Green (i.e. Prussian Blue mixed with Lead Chromate), 1 Copper Carbonate, 9 Copper Arsenite.

The rapid development of reliable methods of food analysis as begun by Accum and Hassall and the public outcry against these malpractices in food manufacture led quickly to the Adulteration of Food and Drink Act of 1860 which in turn was strengthened by the Public Health Act of 1875. As a result of the latter, local authorities were required to appoint public analysts and to institute regular sampling procedures in an attempt to detect adulterants 'injurious to health'.

With the advent of the modern dyestuffs manufacturing industry after the discovery of Perkin's Mauve in 1856, many new colours were synthesised and some were found technically suitable for use in food. These 'coal tar' colours, as they became known, provided a much brighter and wider range of shades and they rapidly supplanted the majority of the traditional colours, for several reasons.

Compared with the new synthetic colours, the natural colours suffered from:

Fastness deficiencies.
Restricted shade range.
High cost in use.
Low effective agent concentration.
Considerable batch to batch variation.
Distinctive aroma or spicy taste.

Some time after the introduction of synthetic colours, questions as to their suitability for food applications were raised. In some countries, e.g. the United Kingdom, a 'prohibited' list was devised while in others, e.g. the USA, a 'positive' list developed. The 'prohibited' list specifically precluded the use of certain colours believed to be injurious to health, e.g. in the UK Manchester Yellow, but by the same token allowed virtually any synthetic colours not on this list to be used in food. The 'positive' list approach was the opposite of this. Only those colours on the list were allowed for food use. The colours were selected on two criteria:

1. technical suitability;
2. toxicological harmlessness based on the knowledge available at the time.

UNITED KINGDOM

In the United Kingdom in the early 1920s, the time was considered right to examine the practice of food coloration in all its aspects. Accordingly a departmental committee was appointed by the Minister of Health in 1923 to enquire into the use of colouring matters and preservatives with the remit:

1. to examine whether the use of such materials for the preservation and colouring of food is injurious to health and if so in what quantities does their use become injurious.
2. to consider whether it should be required that the presence of such materials and the quantities present in food offered or exposed for sale should be declared.

In its report issued in 1924, the committee favoured the 'positive' list idea and recommended that each colouring matter should be considered individually. If the evidence demonstrated its harmless character, then it could be approved for food use if there was a demonstrated need.

In view of the large amount of detailed examination that this course of action implied, the government of the day decided on the 'prohibited' list approach. Under the Public Health (Preservatives, etc. in Food) Regulations, 1925, the following colours then known to be harmful were prohibited for use in food.[12]

1. Compounds of any of the listed metals.

   Antimony   Copper
   Arsenic   Lead
   Cadmium   Mercury
   Chromium   Zinc

2. The vegetable colouring matter—Gamboge.
3. Five 'coal-tar' colours.

   Picric Acid   Manchester Yellow
   Victoria Yellow   Aurantia
   Aurine

TABLE 2

Treatment Dye	3 M HCl	0·5 M $NaOH$	$SnCl_2 + HCl$	KCN
Gamboge	[a]	Brown	Decolorised	No visual reaction
Victoria Yellow	Paler yellow	Darker yellow	Decolorised	Red
Manchester Yellow	Paler yellow	Darker yellow	Decolorised	Red
Aurantia	Paler yellow	Little change	No visual reaction	No visual reaction
Aurine	Brown	Pink	No visual reaction	No visual reaction
Picric Acid	Pale yellow	Brown or darker yellow	Decolorised	No visual reaction

[a] Gamboge does not dye a fabric in an acid solution.

Several methods of detection of the five 'coal-tar' colours were published and the following is a simple scheme:[13]

Heat the coloured food with water and Sodium Sulphite slightly acidified with HCl and a piece of Nun's Veiling. If the fabric is dyed, squeeze out the moisture and observe the reactions obtained with parts of it and the indicated solutions [see Table 2]. The listed colour changes will occur in the presence of the respective colour.

From 1925 onwards, toxicological evidence gradually accrued on other synthetic colours which pointed to the possibility of a health hazard if used in food. Under particular suspicion were those colours having a similar chemical structure to those already prohibited. It was gradually realised that in common with the practice of the majority of the other developed countries, the 'prohibited' list concept should be abandoned in favour of the 'positive' list approach originally recommended in 1925.

In 1954 the Food Standards Committee of the Ministry of Food produced a report[12] which strongly supported this view and, further, gave its toxicological assessment on the suitability of those colours currently being used in food. The committee concluded that:

1. Public Health Regulation should be amended so as to permit a list of specified colours only.
2. These colours should be chosen for their toxicological harmlessness.
3. The generation of a permitted list was hampered by a lack of comprehensive biological and pharmacological evidence to enable a conclusive opinion to be formed on safety in use.
4. It was nevertheless possible to produce a tentative permitted list but that there was an urgent need for authoritative guidance on the tests to which colouring matters should be submitted in order to establish that their use in food would not present a health hazard.
5. The permitted list should be reviewed within five years in the light of new information.
6. Specifications for purity should be prescribed for each of the permitted colours.
7. Colours other than for marking purposes should not be permitted in milk or on meat, game, poultry, fish, fruit and raw or unprocessed vegetables. (Colours were already prohibited in bread.)
8. Notification of the presence in foods of added colour should be given to the purchaser.

The list of suitable colours proposed by the committee and subsequently modified by discussion with food colour manufacturers and users, formed the basis of the Colouring Matter in Food Regulations, 1957 (see Table 3).

After four or five years of operation of this permitted list, a formal review was conducted between 1961 and 1964, the resulting recommendations forming the basis of the 1966 regulations. In 1973 further regulations were published which gave effect to the UK obligations under the EEC Directive of 1962 dealing with the harmonisation of food colour lists within the Community. Comparison of the 1973 permitted list with that of 1957 is given in Table 3.

The latest development in the UK is a report[14] by the MAFF reviewing the 1973 regulations. This is an interim report and seeks further restriction of the use of colour in food. The final report will indicate the type and level of further restriction, perhaps specified colours for specified foods at maximum permitted levels, but meanwhile the interim report recommends:

1.   a prohibition of colour in baby and infant foods; and
2.   that new specifications for purity should be included in any future regulations. The report also calls for further toxicological studies on certain colours, the results of which must be available for review within five years.

USA

The food colour permitted list developed in a different way in the USA. The first national law was passed in 1906, much later than the UK laws of 1860 and 1875. A major reason for the delay was the conflict between federal authority and the assumed rights of individual states to enact their own food and drug control laws, according to local requirements.[15] With the rapid growth of industrial development from the middle of the nineteenth century onwards however, it became clear that if interstate commerce was not to be restricted unnecessarily, federal action was needed on food and drug law. The 1906 Pure Food and Drugs Act provided regulatory definitions for 'food and drugs' and prohibited their introduction into interstate commerce if misbranded or adulterated. The act prevented the use of many harmful chemicals and brought about great improvements in sanitation and labelling.

Out of almost 300 colours examined by the Bureau of Chemistry in the Department of Agriculture, the predecessor to today's FDA, the 1906 law

TABLE 3

COMPARISON OF UK FOOD COLOUR PERMITTED LISTS 1957 + 1973

Colour	1957 Status	1973 Status	CI number	EEC number	FDA number
Natural colours					
Riboflavin	−	+	No number	E101	+
Cochineal	+	+	75470	E120	+
Chlorophyll	+	+	75810	E140	+
Chlorophyll } Cu Complexes					
Chlorophyllin }	−	+	75810	E141	−
Caramel	+	+	No number	E150	+
Carbon Black	−	+	No number	E153	−
Carotenes	+	+	40820 / 40825 / 75120 / 75125 / 75130	E160	+
Beetroot Red	+	+	No number	E162	+
Anthocyanins	+	+	No number	E163	+
Vegetable Colours	+	+	No number	No number	+
TiO₂	+	+	77891	E171	+
Aluminium }	+	+	77000	E173	−
Silver } (Decoration only)		+	No number	E174	−
Gold	+	+	77480	E175	−
Pure Vegetable Colouring principle either isolated or synthesised	+	+	No number	No number	+

TABLE 3—*contd.*

Colour	1957 Status	1973 Status	CI number	EEC number	FDA number
Iron Oxide	+	+	77489 77491 77492 77499	E172	+
Ultramarine	+	−	77007	No number	−
Synthetic colours					
Oil Yellow GG	+	−	11920	—	—
Tartrazine	+	+	19140	E102	Yellow No 5
Quinoline Yellow	−	+	47005	E104	—
Naphthol Yellow S	+	−	10316	—	—
Yellow 2G	+	+	18965	—	—
Yellow RFS	+	−	13011	—	—
Yellow RY	+	−	14330	—	—
Oil Yellow XP	+	−	12740	—	—
Sunset Yellow FCF	+	+	15985	E110	Yellow No 6
Orange G	+	−	16230	—	—
Orange RN	+	−	15970	—	—
Ponceau MX	+	−	16150	—	—
Ponceau 4R	+	+	16255	E124	—
Carmoisine	+	+	14720	E122	—
Amaranth	+	+	16185	E123	—
Red 10B	+	−	17200	—	—
Erythrosine	+	+	45430	E127	Red No 3
Rhodamine B	+	−	45170	—	—

Red 2G	+	+	18050	−	−
Red 6B	+	−	18055	−	−
Red FB	+	−	14780	−	−
Ponceau SX	+	−	14700	−	−
Ponceau 3R	+	−	16155	−	−
Rhodamine 6G	+	−	45160	−	−
Patent Blue V	−	+	42051	E131	−
Blue VRS	+	−	42045	−	−
Indigo Carmine	+	+	73015	E132	Blue No 2
Brilliant Blue FCF	−	+	42090	−	Blue No 1
Violet 5BN	+	−	42650	−	−
Violet 6B	+	−	42640	−	−
Green S	+	+	44090	E142	−
Brown FK	+	+	−	−	−
Chocolate Brown FB	+	−	−	−	−
Chocolate Brown HT	+	+	20285	−	−
Black PN	+	+	28440	E151	−

Aluminium and calcium lakes of the water-soluble colours are also permitted.
+ Permitted.
− Not permitted.

TABLE 4
CHRONOLOGICAL HISTORY OF SYNTHETIC COLOURS IN THE USA

Year listed	Common name	FDA number	Colour index number	Year delisted	Currently permitted
1907	Ponceau 3R	Red No 1	16 155	1961	no
1907	Amaranth	Red No 2	16 185	1976	no
1907	Erythrosine	Red No 3	45 430	—	yes
1907	Orange I	Orange No 1	14 600	1956	no
1907	Naphthol Yellow S	Yellow No 1	10 316	1959	no
1907	Light Green SF yellowish	Green No 2	42 095	1966	no
1907	Indigotine	Blue No 2	73 015	—	yes
1916	Tartrazine	Yellow No 5	19 140	—	yes
1918	Sudan I	—	12 055	1918	no
1918	Butter Yellow	—	11 160	1918	no
1918	Yellow AB	Yellow No 3	11 380	1959	no
1918	Yellow OB	Yellow No 4	11 390	1959	no
1922	Guinea Green B	Green No 1	42 085	1966	no
1927	Fast Green FCF	Green No 3	42 053	—	yes
1929	Ponceau SX	Red No 4	14 700	1976	no
1929	Sunet Yellow FCF	Yellow No 6	15 985	—	yes
1929	Brilliant Blue FCF	Blue No 1	42 090	—	yes
1939	Naphthol Yellow S (K Salt)	Yellow No 2	10 316	1959	no
1939	Orange SS	Orange No 2	12 100	1956	no
1939	Oil Red XO	Red No 32	12 140	1956	no
1950	Benzyl Violet 4B	Violet No 1	42 640	1974	no
1959	Citrus Red No 2	Citrus Red No 2	12 156	—	yes
1966	Orange B	Orange B	19 235	1979	no
1971	Allura Red AC	Red No 40	16 035	—	yes

listed seven synthetic colours for food use (see Table 4), two of which, Erythrosine (FD and C Red No 3) and Indigotine (FD and C Blue No 2) remain on the permitted list to this day. Further listings occurred up to the late 1920s including several still permitted at the present time, i.e. Tartrazine, Fast Green FCF, Sunset Yellow FCF and Brilliant Blue FCF. By this time, however, loopholes in the 1906 law were beginning to be exploited and by the 1930s large-scale abuses, fostered by the social

TABLE 5

CODE OF USA FEDERAL REGULATIONS

COLOUR ADDITIVES FOR FOOD SUBJECT TO CERTIFICATION

Colour	Common name	Listing status
[a]FD and C Red No 3	Erythrosine	Permanent
[a]FD and C Blue No 2	Indigotine	Provisional
[a]FD and C Yellow No 5	Tartrazine	Permanent
[a]FD and C Green No 3	Fast Green FCF	Provisional
[a]FD and C Yellow No 6	Sunset Yellow FCF	Provisional
FD and C Blue No 1	Brilliant Blue FCF	Permanent
[b]Citrus Red No 2	Citrus Red No 2	Permanent
FD and C Red No 40	Allura Red AC	Permanent

Note: Aluminium and calcium lakes of the colours are also provisionally listed for general use.

[a] Further toxicological work in progress. Results must be evaluated by 31 January 1981 or colours will be delisted.

[b] For orange skins only.

upheaval of the depression years resulted in widespread public concern and criticism.

In 1933 the New Deal Government sponsored a new and much stronger law which after a five year debate was eventually enacted as the 1938 Federal Food, Drug and Cosmetic Act. This allowed the Food and Drug Administration to set standards of composition for foods known formally as Standards of Identity and Quality. The 1938 Act required that listed colours be 'harmless' although the burden of proof was placed on the government to demonstrate that the additives were in fact harmful. This was clearly an unsatisfactory state of affairs and in 1949 a Select Committee of the House of Representatives, the 'Delaney Committee' was appointed to investigate further the use of additives in food and cosmetics. The Committee took into account the reports of illness resulting from excessive use of certain colours which also prompted an FDA review of all the certified colours. Several were banned (Table 4) when it was considered that they could not be regarded as harmless when consumed in quantity. In 1958 the US Supreme Court found in favour of the FDA's interpretation that the term 'harmless' meant that a colour could not be used if it would cause harm at any level, even if it was not harmful at the level actually used. Subsequently, there appeared the Colour Additive Amendment of 1960 to permit the use of colours if they were safe at the level used. The manufacturer was made responsible for proving the safety of the colour.

TABLE 6
CODE OF USA FEDERAL REGULATIONS
LISTING OF FOOD COLOUR ADDITIVES EXEMPT FROM
CERTIFICATION

Annatto extract
Dehydrated beets (beet powder)
Ultramarine blue
Canthaxanthin
Caramel
β-Apo-8'-carotenal
β-Carotene
Cochineal extract: carmine
Toasted partially defatted cooked cottonseed flour
Ferrous gluconate
Grape skin extract (enocianina)
Synthetic iron oxide
Fruit juice
Vegetable juice
Dried algae meal
Tagetes (Aztec gold) meal and extract
Carrot oil
Corn endosperm oil
Paprika
Paprika oleoresin
Riboflavin
Saffron
Titanium dioxide
Turmeric
Turmeric oleoresin

The amendment established the concept of provisional listing in order to permit the continued use of all the colour additives that were in commercial use at the time the law was passed. The provisional listing was due to terminate after two and a half years, in January 1963, to allow the necessary toxicological tests to be carried out. Extension of the provisional listing was allowed beyond this date if toxicological work was still in progress, although the FDA Commissioner reserved the right to terminate the provisional listing whenever in his judgement such action was necessary to protect the public health.[16] Since 1960 several colours have been delisted (see Table 4) or had their use restricted because of safety questions.

The current FDA permitted food colour list is given in Tables 5 and 6. In Table 5 the majority of the certifiable colours still retain the status of provisional listing only. Further test work is being carried out and the results must have been evaluated by 31 January 1981, otherwise the colours will be delisted. If the available evidence confirms their safe use, the colours will be permanently listed until such time as further tests are called for.

The group of colours which do not require certification (Table 6) are of mainly natural origin. Some are permitted for general use but the majority are restricted to particular applications at specified maximum levels of use.

OTHER COUNTRIES

The development of food colour legislation in the rest of the world followed the same patterns as that in the UK and the USA. Those countries originally part of the British Empire tended, on independence, to adopt the Whitehall approach in many regulatory fields including food additive legislation, whereas countries in the USA's sphere of trade influence tended to follow the FDA lead. In continental Western Europe the situation is similar to that of the UK, but with a generally lower overall activity in food coloration. Although in Scandinavia, especially Sweden and Norway, there has been recent action (1978) to ban traditional synthetic food colours entirely, the widely acknowledged expertise and judgement of the EEC Scientific Committee for Food will have significant influence in shaping individual government action in the majority of Western European countries and it is not considered that the Committee will favour a total ban.

WORLD-WIDE PERMITTED LISTS

A world-wide attempt at the rationalisation of food colour legislation is being undertaken by the Joint Food and Agricultural Organisation and World Health Organisation (FAO/WHO) Codex Alimentarius Commission, as part of its programme of food additive specification and control. In the early 1960s it was considered vital by member governments of FAO/WHO to remove non-tariff barriers to trade caused by differing national food legislation. It was stressed that a major factor in this exercise was the need to establish proper safeguards for the health of the consumer. At the same time a framework of agreed principles could be provided which would enable developing countries, the majority of which are now member states of FAO/WHO, to be spared the difficulties and pitfalls of formulating their own legislation in isolation.

TABLE 7

EEC SCIENTIFIC COMMITTEE FOR FOOD: CLASSIFICATION OF FOOD COLOURS, 1975

Group 1 colours with established ADI	Group 2 colours with temporary ADI	Group 3 colours with no assigned ADI (a natural source)	Group 4 colours prohibited in food
Beta-apo-8′-carotenal	Amaranth	Anthocyanins	Alkanet
Beta-apo-8′-carotenic acid ethyl ester	Annatto extracts	Beet Red	Allura Red AC
Beta-carotene	Azorubine (Carmoisine)	Chlorophyll	Black 7984
Canthaxanthin	Brilliant Black BN	Curcumin	Burnt Umber
Caramel (non-ammonia)	Brilliant Blue FCF	Lycopene	Chocolate Brown FB
Chlorophyllin copper complex	Brown FK	Mixed $\alpha\beta\gamma$ Carotenes	Chrysoine S
Chlorophyllin cooper complex Na or K	Caramel (ammonia)	Xanthophylls	Fast Red E
Erythrosine	Chocolate Brown HT		Fast Yellow AB
Indigotine	Food Green S	For some alcoholic beverages	Indanthrene Blue RS
Iron oxides (+ hydrated iron oxides)	Patent Blue V	Cochineal and Carminic acid	Orange G
Red 2G	Ponceau 4R		Orange GGN
Sunset Yellow FCF	Quinoline Yellow		Orange RN
Tartrazine	Yellow 2G		Orchil and Orcein
			Ponceau 6R
			Scarlet GN
			Violet 6B

With these objectives in mind, the Codex Alimentarius Commission was set up and this in turn led to the formation of the Joint Expert Committee on Food Additives charged with advising the Commission on technical aspects. A framework for examination of food additives including colours was devised and provides a thorough procedure for the checking of safety-in-use of any additives which may be present in food. The major criteria include the establishment of a clear specification, the results of biological studies such as acute toxicity, biochemical effects, short- and long-term feeding studies, hypersensitivity and allergenicity reactions, reproduction, embryotoxicity, teratogenicity, carcinogenicity and mutagenicity tests.[17] This framework was closely followed by the EEC Scientific Committee for Food (SCF) when it undertook a toxicological review of all the member states' permitted colours. The SCF is an independent body of experts set up to advise the EEC Commission in much the same way that the Food Additives and Contaminants Committee (FACC) advises the UK Ministry of Agriculture Fisheries and Food (MAFF). The results of the SCF's deliberations appeared in June 1975[18] and on the basis of the evidence then available, split the colours into four groups using the concept of Acceptable Daily Intake (ADI). The ADI of a food additive is expressed in milligrams per kilogram bodyweight and is defined as the amount of a food additive that can be taken daily in the diet even over a lifetime without risk. ADIs incorporate a safety factor of at least 100. The full classification is given in Table 7 under the following general headings:

1. Permitted colours: established ADI
2. Permitted colours: temporary ADI
3. Permitted colours: no assigned ADI
4. Prohibited colours.

In the case of Group 2, colours with temporary ADI, further toxicological work was requested for evaluation by 1978, subsequently extended to 1981.

Many important colours are included in this group and the UK food industry, supported by the food colour manufacturers, took the initiative by identifying the colours it wished to retain, financing and commissioning the work to be done at the British Industrial Biological Research Association (BIBRA). The colours now undergoing tests are Food Green S, Brilliant Blue FCF, Chocolate Brown HT, Ponceau 4R, Amaranth and Carmoisine. The proposed tests should be completed and evaluated by 1981.

Test work on several other colours is in hand arranged by the European Continental Food Industry, i.e. Patent Blue V, Yellow 2G, and Brilliant

Black BN. Work has also been requested on caramel colour produced by the ammonia route.

With regard to Group 3, colours with no assigned ADI (natural source), a special situation exists. Most of these colours have been allowed onto permitted lists with minimal if any toxicological testing (cochineal is an exception). In the event of a significant increase in usage, defined by the EEC as a factor of 2 over the present level, the whole range of toxicological test work may be requested for continued colour listing. There is hence a self-limiting aspect to immediate large increase in usage of natural colours.

The series of tests required by the EEC and the USA are complementary in that all of the major synthetic food colours now permitted world-wide will be examined in the light of the latest requirements by either one authority or another. By the middle of 1981 a joint evaluation of these results could take place, leading to the possibility of a world-wide permitted list formulated with the participation of the EEC, the USA, and the FAO/WHO. In this manner a contribution should be made to a freer world-wide trade in foodstuffs while at the same time ensuring consumer health protection.

FOOD COLOUR MANUFACTURERS

In the UK, from the time of the Public Health (Preservatives, etc. in Food) Regulations of 1925, manufacturers began to offer food colours produced on plant dedicated to this purpose. This was in contrast to previous practice where suitable batches of colour from standard textile quality production were selected for food use.

Many water-soluble dyes had been examined and a group of colours, principally of the 'acid' dye type normally used for wool dyeing were selected on grounds of technical performance during food processing and storage conditions, e.g. Tartrazine, Sunset Yellow FCF and Carmoisine. Over the years colour manufacturers have carried out their own toxicological studies on specified colours, which in several instances, e.g. Benzopurpurine 4B and the Oil Yellows, have led the companies concerned to withdraw the colours from their foodstuff quality range when they were considered a safety hazard long before their use was prohibited by law. In Europe in the early 1950s, the manufacturers took the initiative in improving the quality of their food colours by tightening up on specification of pure dye contents and impurity clauses to provide products equal to the best available in the world which at that time were those manufactured in the USA.

Good Manufacturing Practice
Today, the manufacture of synthetic colours for food is concentrated in three world areas:
Europe, with 11 major producers;
North and Central America, 7 major producers;
Japan, 4 major producers.
Production capacity is known to exist in Eastern Europe and the People's Republic of China.
The colours are manufactured to a high level of quality, in many cases significantly better than required by law. Strict quality control is carried out in several vital areas which include the following:

1. Raw materials.
2. Reagents used in processing.
3. Solvents used in extraction or crystallisation.
4. Maintenance and cleanliness of manufacturing plant.
5. Unreacted intermediates.
6. By-products formed during some manufacture.

Comprehensive specifications are now required by all authorities responsible for food colour legislation. In many cases these now include maximum permitted levels for subsidiary dyes, unchanged intermediates and other specific organic compounds. Examples of proposed specifications are given in the recent MAFF Report on the 1973 UK Regulations.[14]

Food Colour Consumption
An estimate of the consumption of the traditional synthetic colours in 1977 and 1982 is given below (Table 8). The figures are based on several recent market reports.
In general, European and North American countries are expected to show a growth of around 2% p.a. with the South American, Asian and African markets showing higher growth rates in the 5–10% region.
For colours of natural origin, consumption figures are more difficult to estimate, although the recent FACC Report[14] stated that about 98% by weight of all colouring matter added to food in the UK comprises a wide range of caramel products. Carotenoids, both naturally derived and synthetically produced are the next most widely used.

Present-Day Food Colour Use
The traditional synthetic colours are still of great importance to the food

industry, finding use in virtually all branches. An up to date account of their use is given in Chapter 3.

Following the progressive reduction in the number of these synthetic colours permitted for use in food, attention has turned to the availability and possible application of natural colours as an alternative. The trend in government thinking towards the use of natural colours in place of

TABLE 8

CONSUMPTION OF SYNTHETIC
COLOURS FOR FOOD.
ESTIMATE IN METRIC TONNES OF PURE
COLOUR

Country	1977	1982
UK	450	495
Western Europe	1 050	1 160
Eastern Europe	200	240
USA	2 300	2 540
South America	540	870
Australasia	230	255
Asia	1 030	1 315
Africa	490	625
Total	6 290	7 500

synthetic colours, together with an increasing consumer interest in food additives gave impetus to the research.

In general, world legislation does not distinguish between naturally occurring colours permitted for use in food and their chemical equivalents produced by a synthetic route as long as the purity requirements are met. Hence much work has been done, especially in the USA, on both extraction of naturally occurring colours from their sources in nature as well as research into economic synthetic manufacturing routes. A considerable amount of work has also been undertaken on the application of natural colours in various food manufacturing processes in an attempt to improve their technical performance.

The major groups of natural and nature equivalent colours are briefly described here as an introduction to their fuller treatment given in the respective chapters.

Carotenoids
Of the naturally occurring and nature equivalent colours, the carotenoids

are considered the most useful in terms of technical performance. The main colouring constituent of carrots, carotene, was identified nearly 150 years ago, but it was not until the early 1950s that synthesis was perfected.[19] From then on the source of cartenoids for food colouring tended to shift from the natural extracts of plant materials to special application forms prepared by chemical syntheses. Although it has been reported that blues, greens and purples are obtainable in the laboratory by reacting carotenoids with selected proteins, this is not commercial at this stage, and nature identical carotenoids now available are confined to the yellow-orange-scarlet region of the spectrum and include in increasing order of redness: β-carotene, β-apo-8'-carotenal (C_{30} trans), ethyl-β-apo-8'-carotenoate (C_{30} trans), and canthaxanthin (trans). These compounds act mainly as colours but are also a source of vitamin A and are oxygen transporters in the body.

As isolated, they are water insoluble and only sparingly soluble in vegetable oils and fats. Fat-soluble preparations and water-dispersible suspensions have been developed for ease of use, the latter finding particular application in the soft drinks industry.

Carotenoids are very effective colouring agents with levels of addition of 1–10 ppm giving good results in such foods as margarine, fruit juices, salad dressing, ice-cream, cheese, pasta, cakes, icings and soups.

Anthocyanins
There has been considerable interest in the USA in the use of anthocyanins as food colours in view of the difficulties encountered in producing bluish-red shades following delisting of FD and C Red No 2 (Amaranth). Various sources of anthocyanins are available but only grape pigments are produced at present in amounts sufficiently large to be of commercial interest. The grape skin pigments are recovered as by-products of the wine and grape-juice industry and occur as complex mixtures of anthocyanins and other polyphenolic compounds. Hence robust purification processes are necessary.[20]

Other possible commercial sources are cranberries, roselle pigments from hibiscus flowers which can be grown in large quantities in the tropics, and miracle fruit, which in addition to being an anthocyanin source is also a taste modifier. It is possible that miracle fruit extract may eventually be permitted as a sweetener in the USA, the pigment being produced fairly cheaply as a by-product.

The fastness performance of anthocyanins is a problem. In acid solution, the colour is similar to Amaranth but above pH 4 anthocyanin becomes colourless unless the pigment is degraded first, when it remains a dull bluish red. Anthocyanins are also susceptible to oxidation, the action of ascorbic acid, metals and light.

Beet Colours

The red beet (*Beta vulgaris*) is a rich source of red pigments. The term Betalaine refers to the class of pigments found in the beet which consist of betacyanins and betaxanthins, the chromophore being a 1,7-diazaheptamethin system.[21] Betalaines occur in many other plants but red beet is the only plant cultivated in quantities which make colour extraction commercial. The stability of betalaines is fairly low compared with many other pigments. The colour is akin to raspberry between pH 3·0 and 7·0 becoming weaker and duller on either side of this range. The pigments have found uses in less technically demanding areas of food coloration such as gelatin desserts, soups, ice-creams and dairy products in general, and also in sherbets, meat and meat-based products.

Other Natural Colours

Colours from several other natural sources are used in food among them chlorophylls, cochineal and carminic acid, annatto turmeric, saffron and curcumin. Most of these colours have significant disadvantages in use such as cost, technical performance, or stray characteristic odour or peppery taste. Their use is hence fairly limited to specialised outlets.

REFERENCES

1. *Chambers Encyclopaedia*. 1972 Edition.
2. Lille, R. D., 'The Red Dyes used by Ancient Dyers: Their Probable Identity', *Journal of the Society of Dyers and Colourists*, **95**, February 1979, p. 57.
3. Bishop, M., *The Penguin Book of the Middle Ages*, 1971, p. 157, Penguin Books Ltd., Harmondsworth.
4. Pelham Wright, N., 'A Thousand Years of Cochineal: A Lost but Traditional Mexican Industry on its Way Back', *American Dyestuff Reporter*, 19 August 1963, p. 25.
5. Vaillant, G. C., *Aztecs of Mexico*, 1972, p. 142, Penguin Books Ltd., Harmondsworth.
6. Fox, H., *Food Industries of South Africa*, August 1976, p. 38.
7. Goldenberg, N., *Why Additives—The Safety of Foods*, Chapter 6, 'Colours—do we need them?' 1977, British Nutrition Foundation, London.

8. Nieman, C., *Food Colours Recently Authorised in 43 Countries*, 1961, Amsterdam.
9. Accum, F., *A Treatise on Adulteration of Food and Culinary Poisons*, 1820, London.
10. Hassall, A. H., *Food and its Adulterations: comprising the Reports of the Analytical Sanitary Commission of the Lancet 1857*, 1857, London.
11. Filby, F. A., *A History of Food Adulteration and Analysis*, 1934, London.
12. Ministry of Food, *Food Standards Committee Report on Colouring Matters*, 1954, HMSO, London, p. 4.
13. Liverseege, J. F., *Adulteration of Food and Drugs*, 1932, p. 78.
14. Ministry of Agriculture Fisheries and Food. *FACC Interim Report on the Review of the Colouring Matter in Food Regulations* 1973, HMSO, London.
15. Ministry of Agriculture Fisheries and Food. *Food Quality and Safety: A Century of Progress*, 1976, HMSO, London.
16. Anonymous, 'Why FDA Banned Red No. 2', *FDA Consumer*, April 1976, p. 18.
17. World Health Organisation, 'Toxicological Review of Certain Food Additives with a Review of General Principles and of Specifications', *WHO Technical Reports Series No. 539. 17th Report of the Joint FAO/WHO Expert Committee on Food Additives*, 1974, Geneva.
18. Commission of the European Communities, Directorate General for Agriculture, Scientific Committee for Food, *Report of the Scientific Committee for Food on the Revision of the Directive on Colouring Matters Authorised for Use in Foodstuffs Intended for Human Consumption*, 27 June 1975.
19. Roche Products, *Roche Carotenoids: Natural Food Colours*, 1971, p. 2, London.
20. Francis, F. J., 'Anthocyanins', Paper given at 173rd American Chemical Society Meeting, New Orleans, Louisiana, 21–25 March 1977.
21. Von Elbe, J. H., (1979) 'Betalaines as Food Colourants', Paper given at 173rd American Chemical Society National Meeting, New Orleans, Lousiana, 21–25 March 1977.

Chapter 2

FOOD COLORIMETRY

K. McLaren

Instrumental Colour Systems Ltd, Newbury, Berkshire, UK

SUMMARY

The light reflected or transmitted by an object can be measured by a spectrophotometer and the essential features of most modern instruments are described.

From the transmittance curves, the relative strengths of two colorants can be obtained and if curves of known colorants are plotted at different pH values, an unknown colorant can be easily identified.

To obtain numerical data directly related to perceived colour, reflectance or transmittance values have to be converted into tristimulus values using the CIE method first published in 1931. The instruments which do this directly by passing reflected or transmitted light through three or four filters are colorimeters which usually have a built-in microprocessor to perform the calculations involved.

A full description is given of the most recent development in colorimetry, the 1976 CIELAB uniform colour space and colour difference equation which is the most accurate method of quantifying the perceived variables of colour. It is rapidly becoming the internationally accepted method for object colours.

INTRODUCTION

The most important characteristic by which the quality of a food is judged is its appearance and the most important attribute of appearance is colour. Though colour is purely a subjective phenomenon, the sensations of the

27

observer, under normal conditions of viewing, are governed solely by the composition of the light entering the observer's eye from the object. The composition of this object light depends in the first instance on the spectral energy distribution of the illuminant and secondly on the spectral reflectance factor of the object itself, which is the ratio of the amount of light of a given wavelength reflected by the object to that reflected by a perfect white object, a theoretical concept termed the perfect reflecting diffuser. The basic instrument for measuring spectral reflectance factors, which are usually collectively called *reflectances* is the spectrophotometer which will be described later. Reflectances are usually expressed as percentages and often plotted with %R as ordinate and wavelength as abscissa over the range 400 nm (violet) to 700 nm (red). If the coloured object is transparent —for example, an aqueous solution of a food colorant—the corresponding value is *transmittance* or transmission factor.

The reflectance curve contains all the data governing perceived colour relating to the object but before any meaningful deductions can be made concerning the perceived colour these data have to be processed mathematically. The most useful transformations are those devised by the International Commission on Illumination, best known by the initials of the French translation, the CIE. Before these are discussed, however, there are two much simpler transformations which are useful in the analysis of food colorants as they permit the quantification of strength and the identification of a colorant.

THE DETERMINATION OF STRENGTH

If the transmittance of solutions of increasing strength of a food colorant is measured the height of the curve will be seen to fall at most wavelengths and in order to quantify the strength relationship between two specimens of the same colorant, the height of the curve at its lowest point, i.e. at the wavelength of maximum absorption, must be determined on a 0–1 scale. The logarithm to base 10 of the value is the *optical density* of the solution and this is linearly related to the strength of the colorant. Thus if the concentration (g/litre) of each specimen is the same then the strength of the sample as a percentage of that of the standard is given by:

$$\frac{\log_{10}(1/T) \text{ sample}}{\log_{10}(1/T) \text{ standard}} \times 100$$

COLORANT IDENTIFICATION

If transmittance data are determined for solutions of varying concentration of a single colorant, the shape of the transmittance curve varies as well as its height and this applies equally to the derived absorption and density curves. As the concentration of pure dye in a solution of an unknown dye is never known, these shapes cannot be used for identification purposes but the shape of the logarithm of the density curve is independent of concentration. If log-density curves have been plotted for all known food colorants under neutral acid and alkaline conditions then comparison of the shapes of the log-density curves of an unknown colorant prepared at the same pH values will usually provide a positive identification.

Further details concerning the use of these analytical techniques can be obtained from the book by Stearns listed in the bibliography at the end of this chapter.

THE CIE METHOD OF COLOUR MEASUREMENT

As the sensation of colour is purely subjective it is surprising that it is amenable to measurement but the scientific study of the phenomenon of colour has led first to a numerical definition of individual colours and later to a quantification of the various attributes of colour such as hue and brightness and the colour difference between sample and standard, which are so important commercially. This study, of course, began in 1666 when Isaac Newton disproved the accepted view handed down from the ancient Greek philosophers that light when pure was always white. It was not until 1802, however, that the next major discovery occurred. This was when Thomas Young suggested that the receptors in the retina involved in colour perception, the cones, were of three types only, one sensitive to the red end of the spectrum, another sensitive to the middle green portion and a third sensitive to the blue end. This was the trichromatic theory of colour vision but it was by no means universally accepted: the rival opponent-colour theory of Hering was more successful in explaining colour sensations. Today it is universally agreed that the mechanisms involved in colour perception are very complicated indeed but that the theory finally accepted must contain the essential elements of both the trichromatic and the opponent-colour theories.

Fortunately, the validity of the method of colour measurement which evolved did not depend on the correctness of the trichromatic theory but on the facts of colour mixture which the theory attempted to explain: these facts have never been in dispute.

ADDITIVE COLOUR MIXING

Colour measurement is based on a few simple facts:

1. Most colours can be perfectly matched by additively mixing the appropriate amounts of red, green and blue lights, the so-called additive primaries. This can be represented as a colour matching equation:

$$P \equiv a\text{R} + b\text{G} + c\text{B}$$

where a is the amount of a standardised red light R, etc., the $\equiv$ sign implying 'is matched by'. Observers with normal colour vision will agree quite closely as to the amounts required.

2. Every colour matching equation can be treated as though it were an algebraic equation. Therefore if a second stimulus Q is matched by d, e and f units of the primaries then

$$P + Q \equiv (a + d)\text{R} + (b + e)\text{G} + (c + f)\text{B}$$

3. If the amounts of R, G and B required to match light of each wavelength in turn in the visible spectrum are determined then the amounts required to match any stimulus whose spectral energy distribution is known can be calculated. This is the essentially simple concept of colour measurement first suggested by Clark Maxwell in 1860. If, for example, monochromatic yellow light of wavelength 570 nm is matched by a complex mixture of red, yellow, orange and green light and the amounts of every component radiation are known, then the amounts of the standardised red, green and blue primaries calculated to match the monochromatic stimulus will be the same as those calculated to match the heterochromatic stimulus. These amounts are termed the tristimulus values and they specify numerically the colour irrespective of its spectral composition.

Unfortunately, however, though the concept is simple, its implementation in practice was not. W. A. H. Rushton, who has spent many years attempting to determine the absorption curves of the three cone pigments in the retina, described the practical implementation as being 'like the square root of -1 in alternating current theory: it gives neat and exact answers to calculations by introducing a nearly incomprehensible concept of what is going on'.[1] These complications were introduced to get round another simple fact of colour mixing. Irrespective of the wavelength of the red, green and blue primaries few monochromatic regions of the spectrum could be perfectly matched: the hue and brightness could be matched but the colour of the monochromatic spectral light usually appeared more intense, or saturated, than the mixture even if monochromatic primaries were used, a fact first discovered by Newton. While this initially suggests that the method of colour measurement proposed by Maxwell was impossible, he discovered a very easy way to get round it: if the right amount of one of the primaries was added to the monochromatic spectral light, a perfect match could then be obtained by a specific mixture of the other two, e.g.

$$\lambda_{490} \not\equiv R + G + B$$

but

$$\lambda_{490} + R \equiv G + B$$

where λ_{490} is monochromatic blue–green light whose wavelength is 490 nm. As colour matching equations behave as algebraic equations, the last one can be re-written as:

$$\lambda_{490} \equiv G + B - R$$

Though one of the tristimulus values is now negative, this is just as valid a quantification of the colour of the actual amount of light of wavelength 490 nm as an all-positive set of tristimulus values is for a less saturated stimulus.

The tristimulus values of any stimulus are obtained by adding together those of each wavelength in turn and these negative numbers would have complicated computation in 1931 when only mechanical calculators were available and, in any case, would have been difficult to understand. The CIE therefore decided to make use of the algebraic nature of colour matching equations and to convert the mean of the R, G, B values obtained by Wright (ten observers) and Guild (seven observers) into the tristimulus values of three imaginary primaries X, Y, Z giving an all-positive set of values. In addition, these imaginary primaries were so chosen that the whole of the lightness or brightness of a stimulus was given by the Y value alone.

These data define the CIE 1931 standard colorimetric observer and, together with the spectral energy distributions of three light sources A, B and C representing respectively tungsten light, sunlight and north-sky daylight, enable tristimulus values to be calculated from reflectance curves. These data are still widely used but they have been supplemented by other data which should be used by any laboratory starting colour measurement for the first time. These additional data define another standard observer and an illuminant more representative of daylight.

THE CIE 1964 SUPPLEMENTARY STANDARD COLORIMETRIC OBSERVER

The colour matching experiments from which the 1931 standard observer data were derived employed a split field subtending an angle of 2° at the eye (the same as that of a two penny piece held at arms length) which is much smaller than is customary for colour appraisal. The field size for the 1964 data was 10° and, in addition, the data were much more accurate, particularly at the short-wave end.

ILLUMINANT D65

The 1931 Source C—representing north-sky light—was obtained by passing light from a tungsten filament lamp through solutions of cobalt and copper salts. Illuminant D65 is the spectral energy distribution of daylight whose correlated colour temperature is 6500 K, based on many measurements made in England, Canada and the USA.

THE CALCULATION OF TRISTIMULUS VALUES

To calculate the tristimulus values X, Y, Z of an object the reflectance, $R(\lambda)$, at a number of equally spaced wavelength intervals—usually 20 nm—expressed on a 0–1 scale must be multiplied by the spectral energy distribution of the chosen illuminant at the same wavelength, $E(\lambda)$, and then in turn by the three colour matching functions of the standard observer, $\bar{x}(\lambda)$, $\bar{y}(\lambda)$ and $\bar{z}(\lambda)$. These are then summed and normalised so that the Y value of a perfect white ($R = 1\cdot0$ at every wavelength) is 100·00. The tristimulus values are therefore:

$$X = K \sum R(\lambda)E(\lambda)\bar{x}(\lambda)$$
$$Y = K \sum R(\lambda)E(\lambda)\bar{y}(\lambda)$$
$$Z = K \sum R(\lambda)E(\lambda)\bar{z}(\lambda)$$

where

$$K = 100/\sum E(\lambda)\bar{y}(\lambda)$$

Calculation is simplified by pre-multiplying $E(\lambda)$ by $\bar{x}$, $\bar{y}$ and $\bar{z}(\lambda)$ and by K to give a set of weighted ordinates: tables of these are given in *Color Science* (Wyszecki and Stiles[2]) and in *Color in Business, Science and Industry* (Judd and Wyszecki[3]).

METAMERISM

Just as two lights of different spectral composition can have exactly the same colour so two objects can have exactly the same colour even though their reflectance or transmittance curves are different; this phenomenon is termed metamerism. When tristimulus values are calculated using the spectral energy distribution of the illuminant under which they match, they will be very similar and for this to happen, their reflectance or transmittance curves must cross in at least three points. Under a different illuminant the tristimulus values will be different, reflecting the main characteristic of metameric object colours—they often mis-match under certain illuminants. The difference in tristimulus values can be used to quantify the degree of metamerism by calculating colour differences which will be discussed later.

THE NATURE OF PERCEIVED COLOUR

The X, Y, Z tristimulus values of a stimulus, though they are only the amounts of three imaginary primaries, which would match the stimulus when viewed by the standard observer, are of the greatest value when they are used to quantify colour appearance. Before describing how they can be used for this purpose, however, it will be useful to consider the subjective aspects of colour appearance. Though many of the terms are used in everyday speech those using them do not necessarily agree as to their precise meanings, so therefore the meanings of the italicised terms given in the following paragraphs are those agreed by the CIE at its meeting in 1976.

In everyday speech the term *colour* is used, for example, to differentiate a colour television set from one whose images are confined to black, white and many intermediate shades of grey. This usage, however, implies that black, greys and white are not colours, but if not, what are they? The only way out of this semantic dilemma is to regard them as colours but as colours devoid of the attribute of *hue*, the technical term being *achromatic colours*: colours possessing hue are termed *chromatic*.

Hue is the most important attribute of colour but there are two others which are completely independent. The second variable is *lightness* a term widely used in everyday speech and in colorimetry it has the same meaning: it is that attribute whereby an object appears to reflect, if it is opaque or transmit if it is transparent, more or less of the incident light. For example, pale pinks and intense yellows both have high lightness; blacks and deep violets have low lightness.

The third variable is the strength of the chromatic response and in everyday speech this is indicated by qualifying the hue term with adjectives such as pale, pastel and light when the chromatic response is weak and full, and deep, intense and vivid, when it is strong. The new CIE term for this variable is *colourfulness* and it is subdivided according to whether the observer subconsciously judges the colourfulness of an area in relation to its intrinsic brightness or in relation to the average brightness of its surroundings. The first of these subdivisions is termed *saturation*, the second *perceived chroma*.

These distinctions are subtle and are only of importance because colour measurement can quantify both though in all probability the future will see the quantification of perceived chroma completely replacing that of saturation as far as object colours are concerned.

The fact that there are three independent variables of perceived colour means that a random collection of colours can only be arranged logically in three dimensions. Such an array is termed a colour space and several have been developed, the first in 1611. Every one has three features in common: the variable of lightness is aligned vertically; the various hues form a complete circle—red, orange, yellow, green, blue, violet, purple, red—centred on the vertical axis with colours of increasing saturation or chroma lying further out. This reflects the fact that the lightness variable is somewhat different from the other two and in fact it is a combination of hue and saturation/chroma which the unsophisticated observer means by colour. Hue and saturation together constitute the variable of *chromaticness*: unfortunately the combination of greater value to industry, i.e. hue and perceived chroma, has no term to describe it.

THE QUANTIFICATION OF COLOUR APPEARANCE

1. The *xy Y* Method

The *X, Y, Z* tristimulus values can be regarded as the axes of a three-dimensional space but interpreting the appearance of a colour whose location is known is very difficult. Though some indication of its lightness is given by its Y value, its chromaticness, which depends on XY and Z, is not readily deduced: it is, however, much easier if the XYZ values are converted into xy values. If we have a coloured light whose XYZ values are known and we compare its appearance with another light whose values are nX, nY and nZ

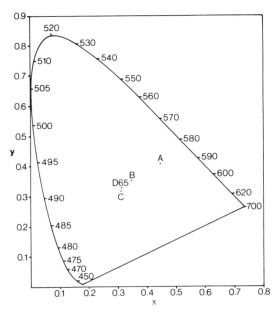

FIG. 1.   The CIE 1931 chromaticity diagram showing the spectrum locus/purple line and the positions of important illuminants.

where n is less than or greater than 1, the unsophisticated observer would say that they had the same colour, but one was brighter than the other. In CIE terms, they have different colours, they differ in brightness but have the same chromaticness. The similarity in chromaticness demands a set of numbers which are the same and these numbers are the ratios $X:Y:Z$. They are represented by the lower case letters x, y and z and are given by:

$$x = X/(X + Y + Z) \qquad y = Y/(X + Y + Z) \qquad z = Z/(X + Y + Z)$$

x, y and z are *chromaticity co-ordinates* and as $x + y + z = 1$, only two need be calculated, x and y having been the preferred choice since 1931. A plot of x against y is the chromaticity diagram, shown in Fig. 1. On this scale, the difference between the 2° and 10° observer diagrams would not be noticeable. The curve represents the spectrum locus, some wavelengths being indicated; the straight line joining the ends represents the locus of the purples; the positions of the illuminants are also indicated.

This diagram is capable of quantifying the chromaticness (hue and saturation) of any colour by its dominant wavelength and its excitation or colorimetric purity but the methods have not been a success: colours of the same hue often have markedly different dominant wavelengths and neither measure of purity reliably quantifies saturation: perceived chroma cannot be quantified. Similarly the Y value is not a reliable measure of perceived lightness: a grey which is midway between a black whose Y value would be about 5 and a white whose Y value would be about 90 would have a Y value of about 20 instead of 45–50. For these reasons the methods of calculating dominant wavelength and purity will not be given and interested readers should consult any of the textbooks listed in the appendix.

2. The CIELAB Method

An extremely successful method of quantifying the appearance of any surface colour was introduced by the CIE in 1976. This is to convert its XYZ tristimulus values into $L^*a^*b^*$ values using the following equations:

$$L^* = 116 \times f(Y/Y_n)$$

$$a^* = 500 \times f(X/X_n) - f(Y/Y_n)$$

$$b^* = 200 \times f(Y/Y_n) - f(Z/Z_n)$$

where X, Y and Z are the tristimulus values of standard and sample and X_n, Y_n and Z_n the tristimulus of the illuminant for the appropriate observer. When X/X_n, Y/Y_n or Z/Z_n is greater than 0·008 856 the function to be used is:

$$(X/X_n)^{1/3} - 16/116, \text{ etc.}$$

When X/X_n, Y/Y_n or Z/Z_n is equal to or less than 0·008 856, the function to be used is:

$$7·787 \times (X/X_n), \text{ etc.}$$

L^*, a^* and b^* are also the axes of a three-dimensional colour space which possesses the important advantages that its configuration is the same as those colour spaces derived by logically arranging colours visually which have already been mentioned. When these Cartesian co-ordinates are converted into the cylindrical co-ordinates L^*, C^* and h using the equations:

$$C^* = [(a^*)^2 + (b^*)^2]^{0.5}$$

$$h = \arctan b^*/a^*$$

these quantify the variables of the best-known visual colour space, that of Munsell. L^* is a measure of Munsell Value on a 0–100 scale and is termed *psychometric lightness*; C^* is a measure of Munsell Chroma and is termed

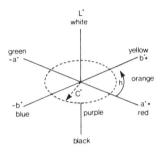

FIG. 2.   The configuration of CIELAB space showing the relationships between the three variables of perceived colours.

psychometric chroma; h is measured from the $a^* +$ axis and quantifies Munsell Hue: it is termed *hue-angle*.

Figure 2 is a diagram of CIELAB space showing the relationship between the various co-ordinates.

THE QUANTIFICATION OF COLOUR DIFFERENCES

The perceived difference in appearance between a specimen representing current production and one representing the standard, conveniently termed sample and standard, has always been a desirable target since colour measurement was introduced in 1931. If sample and standard are a perfect match then their XYZ values are identical: both are therefore located at the same point in XYZ space: their distance apart is therefore zero. If they are not a perfect match then their distance apart in XYZ space is finite and the greater the degree of mis-match the further apart sample and standard will be. Unfortunately the distance element in XYZ space cannot be used to quantify perceived colour differences because the range of distances representing equally perceptible colour differences is at least 30:1. Since

1936 many attempts have been made to transform XYZ values into the three axes which would define a more uniform space and each attempt has usually ended up as a colour difference equation enabling ΔE, the distance between sample and standard, to be calculated from their XYZ values. At least 25 different colour difference equations have been described of which 13 were in use in the USA in 1973, the 5 most important being ANLAB, FMC-2, Simon-Goodwin, Hunter Lab and CIE 1964.

The multiplicity of colour difference equations was most undesirable as accurate inter-conversion was rarely, if ever, possible and the CIE 1964 equation was put forward in a praiseworthy attempt to achieve uniformity of practice. Unfortunately, however, it failed because when studies were carried out to determine how well any equation correlated with the visual judgements of professional shade passers in industry it performed worse than several widely-used equations. These extensive studies resulted in a new colour difference equation, CIELAB, replacing the 1964 recommendation, this equation being based on the CIELAB uniform colour space already described viz.

$$\Delta E_{(CIELAB)} = [(\Delta L^*)^2 + (\Delta a^*)^2 + (\Delta b^*)^2]^{0.5}$$

The advantages that this equation has over all the others are as follows:

1. No other equation consistently gives a higher correlation coefficient against visual data;
2. It permits any colour difference to be split into three components viz.

    a lightness difference,

    $$\Delta L^* = L^*_{sample} - L^*_{standard}$$

    a chroma difference,

    $$\Delta C^* = C^*_{sample} - C^*_{standard}$$

    and a hue difference,

    $$\Delta H^* = [(\Delta E)^2 - (\Delta L^*)^2 - (\Delta C^*)^2]^{0.5}$$

    the numerical value of each component being in CIELAB units.
3. Calculating ΔE from XYZ values of sample and standard is much simpler than for any other equation.

For these reasons, therefore, CIELAB is likely to become internationally adopted by all industries concerned with object colours and this is well advanced in the case of textiles, plastics, paper and leather. It should therefore be the preferred choice for the food industry, both for foods themselves and for solutions of food colorants.

In 1976, the CIE also defined another colour space and colour difference equation, CIELUV, but this is primarly intended for industries involved with additive colour mixing, e.g. lighting and television.

THE QUANTIFICATION OF METAMERISM

To quantify metamerism, tristimulus values must be calculated for all the illuminants under which the metameric object colours will be critically judged. These will usually be daylight, tungsten light and the light from one or more fluorescent tubes. From the comprehensive tables of weights published by Stearns,[4] the following are a suitable choice:

$$10°/D65 \qquad 10°/A$$

From these tristimulus values, the colour difference between the two objects must be calculated for each of the illuminants: if this is markedly higher under any one illuminant this suggests that the closeness of the visual match when judged under that illuminant may be unacceptable.

COLOUR MEASURING INSTRUMENTS

1. Spectrophotometers
The spectrophotometer is the basic instrument for colour measurement and it enables spectral reflectance factors to be obtained at a number of wavelengths—at least 16—in the visible spectrum, each factor being the ratio of the amount of light of wavelength λ reflected by the specimen to that reflected by a perfect reflecting diffuser. In the case of solutions the corresponding factor is spectral transmittance which, although defined by the CIE as the ratio of transmitted to incident flux, is in practice the ratio of the flux transmitted by the specimen to that transmitted by the solvent under identical geometrical arrangements.

Spectrophotometers vary widely in design and the important features of a cross-section of the instruments currently available are given in Table 1. The significance of the various columns is as follows:

Optics
Spectrophotometers employing forward optics (F) irradiate the specimen

TABLE 1

Name of manufacturer	Address	Model name	Optics	Source	Beam	Plotting facilities	Effective band-width (nm)	Elapsed time (s)
Datacolor	Brandbachstrasse 10, Dietlikon bei Zurich, Switzerland	3500	R	X/C	D			6
		7080	R	X/C	D		10	8
Diano Corporation	8 Commonwealth Ave., Woburn, Mass 01801, USA	Diano/Hardy I	F	TH	D	R, T, D, LD	10	65
		II	F + R	TH/F	D	R, T, D, LD	10	65
		Chroma SCAN	R	TH/F	D	—	10	96
Hunter Associates Laboratory Inc.	9529 Lee Highway, Fairfax, Virginia 22030, USA	Match-Scan	F + R	TH/F	T	R, T, D, LD	2	9
		D54	R	TH/F	S	R, T	10	8
IBM	1000 Westchester Ave., White Plains, NY 10604, USA	IBM 7409	R	TH	D	R, T, D, LD	20	5
Instrumental Colour Systems Ltd	13 Bone Lane, Newbury, Berks., England	Micromatch	R	X/P	D	R, T		10
			R	X/P	D	R, T	20	
Macbeth	Drawer 950, Little Britan Road, Newburgh, NY12550, USA	MS-2000	R	X/P	D	R, T	20	7
Pretema	Birmensdorf-Zurich CH-8903, Switzerland	FM-4	R	X/C	D	R, T, D	10	20
Pye Unicam	York St., Cambridge, England	SP 8-100	F	TH	D	R, T	0·2	60
Zeiss	7082 Oberkochen, West Germany	RFC 3	R	TH or X/C	D	R, T	20	45

with near-monochromatic light. This is an entirely satisfactory arrangement providing no specimen is fluorescent, one advantage being that no
appreciable surface heating of the specimen occurs: heating can cause
colour changes. While synthetic food colorants are not fluorescent some
naturally-occurring colorants and other components of foods are. For
meaningful results with fluorescent specimens, the specimen must be
irradiated with polychromatic light, this arrangement being termed
reversed optics (R).

Source
In the case of spectrophotometers employing forward optics a tungsten
halogen (TH) lamp is entirely satisfactory. If a spectrophotometer
employing reversed optics is to be used to measure fluorescent specimens,
the spectral energy distribution of the incident radiation must resemble
Illuminant D65 in both the visible and near ultra-violet regions. This can be
achieved by passing the light from a tungsten halogen lamp through a blue
filter (TH/F) but this seriously reduces the total amount of light available
and may reduce the sensitivity of the instrument. A better method is to use
the light from a xenon arc with either continuous irradiation (X/C) or
pulsed irradiation (X/P). Continuous polychromatic irradiation from a
xenon source usually causes less specimen heating than that from a
tungsten halogen lamp while that from a pulsed xenon lamp cannot be
measured using conventional thermocouples.

Beam
Single beam (S) instruments are calibrated with white and black reference
standards and the amount of light reflected by the specimen in each
wavelength band is then measured. Any variations in light output, any
amplifier drift or other signal changes occurring between calibration and
measurement will inevitably reduce the precision of the results. In addition,
serious errors in measurement can occur because the specimen becomes
part of the sphere wall and therefore affects the composition of the light
incident on the specimen. This effect is non-linear and is therefore not
compensated by white and black calibration. The maximum error occurs at
mid-scale and increases with increasing specimen size relative to the sphere
diameter.

Both of these limitations are eliminated in double-beam instruments (D)
as at each wavelength the amount of light coming from a white reference
standard is measured immediately after that coming from the specimen and

the ratio determined by mechanical, electrical or computational methods. In a triple-beam instrument (T) the amount of light coming from a black reference standard is also measured at each wavelength and the measured values corrected accordingly.

Plotting Facilities

$$R = \text{reflectance}$$
$$T = \text{transmittance}$$
$$D = \text{density}$$
$$LD = \text{log density}$$

Effective Band-width

There are several different methods employed to select the spectral band in a spectrophotometer and these range from a monochromator (prism or grating) employing an effective slit width of 0·1 nm to 16 separate interference filters giving an effective band-width of 20 nm: instruments of the former type are termed 'continuous', those of the latter, 'abridged'. (Note: There is an instrument on the market which irradiates the specimen with monochromatic light at 436, 546, 585 and 640 nm thus measuring curve heights at four points. Though such information has proved of value in the food industry, it is misleading to describe the instrument as a 'multi-chromatic abridged reflectance spectrophotometer'. Data from it cannot be used to determine tristimulus values, strengths of solutions or dye identification.)

The distinction between continuous and abridged is rarely of importance when tristimulus values are being determined and is not necessarily important when density or log-density curves are being plotted. This is because in some continuous spectrophotometers, the plotted curve has been electrically or mechanically smoothed to pass through a limited number of points and hence, in such cases it is the effective band-width, rather than the type of spectral band selector, which is important. Spectrophotometers with an effective band-width greater than 10 nm are not suitable for density measurements. The value quoted in the table is the narrowest band-width when more than one can be selected.

Speed of Operation

The interval between starting the measurement cycle and having the required data displayed is important when many specimens have to be measured. In the case of the instruments listed this interval time can vary from about 5 to about 170 s but figures are not quoted as they can vary widely for a single instrument, being affected by scanning speed (when this is under the control of the operator) and by the type of output, i.e. visual display unit, print-out or graph plotter.

2. Tristimulus Colorimeters

As reflectance factors are often processed to give tristimulus values, instruments have been designed which measure these directly: such instruments are termed 'tristimulus colorimeters'. The basic design is usually the same: the specimen is irradiated with polychromatic light and that reflected is passed separately through three—occasionally four—filters in a photo-cell, the combination of the spectral energy distribution of the source, the transmission characteristics of the filters and the spectral response of the photo-cell being such that the three (or four) signals can be simply processed into XYZ tristimulus values.

The accuracy of such instruments is rarely comparable with that of a spectrophotometer but their precision is often better. This makes them particularly suitable for determining the colour difference between two specimens measured sequentially, the tristimulus values being converted into colour difference units. As the time required to perform the necessary calculations is many minutes, automatic calculating devices have been incorporated into colorimeters since 1960. At first these were analog but in 1973 a tristimulus colorimeter was interfaced to a digital computer. Today most colorimeters have a built-in microprocessor capable of determining colour differences using several equations and in some cases performing other functions such as automatic calibration.

The range of colorimeters on the market is so wide and developments are occurring so rapidly that it is impractical to describe available models. Table 2 therefore merely lists the major manufacturers from whom full details can be obtained.

3. Visual Colorimeters

(a) *Subtractive*

Visual colorimeters based on subtractive colour mixing have long been associated with the food industry, the first being developed by J. W. Lovibond, a brewer, for measuring the colour of beer. The direct descendants of this instrument, the Lovibond Tintometer, are manufactured by The Tintometer Co. Ltd, Waterloo Road, Salisbury, Wiltshire, England and are widely used in the food industry.

The basic principle of the instrument is to pass white light through a

TABLE 2
MANUFACTURERS OF COLORIMETERS AND COLOUR DIFFERENCE METERS

Name	Address
Gardner Laboratory Inc.	PO Box 5728, Bethesda, Maryland 20014, USA
Hunter Associates Laboratory Inc.	9529 Lee Highway, Fairfax, Virginia 22030, USA
Instrumental Colour Systems Ltd	13 Bone Lane, Newbury, Berks. RG14 5TE, England
Macbeth	Drawer 950, Little Britain Road, Newburgh, NY 12550, USA
Manufacturers Engineering and Equipment Corp.	250 Titus Avenue, Warrington, Pennsylvania, USA
Neotec	1132 Taft Street, Rockville, Maryland 20852, USA
Zeiss	7082 Oberkochen, West Germany

combination of red, yellow and blue glass filters until a visual match is obtained against the sample which may be either liquid or solid. There are 25 red, 25 yellow and 22 blue filters and many specifications for edible oils, etc. are given in Lovibond units of red, yellow and blue. If the specification is in units of red and yellow only the need for visual matching can be eliminated by using the Lovibond Automatic Tintometer which employs a photocell to measure the optical density at two points in the spectrum approximately equivalent to Lovibond red and yellow filters: two dials then display the units of each.

The Flexible Optic Tintometer has a small illuminating and viewing head connected to the case of the instrument by fibre optics and is thus useful for measuring samples not readily placed over a conventional aperture.

The Lovibond Schofield Tintometer employs the standard filters but incorporates refinements which allow the conversion of Lovibond units into XYZ values graphically.

(b) Additive
A visual colorimeter based on additive colour mixing was developed by the US Department of Agriculture in 1946. It consists of a disc on which varying areas of Munsell cards are mounted and then spun at a speed sufficient to eliminate flicker, the colour of the disc then appearing uniform. By varying the cards chosen and the areas exposed a match is obtained against the adjacent solid sample. The XYZ values of this sample under the

illuminant used are the weighted averages of those of all the cards on the disc. This method is widely used in the USA, the equipment being manufactured by Macbeth, Drawer 950, Little Britain Road, Newburgh, NY 12550, USA.

REFERENCES

1. Rushton, 'Visual Pigments and Color Blindness', *Scientific American*, 1975, **232**(3), 64–74.
2. Wyszecki and Stiles, *Color Science*, 1966, John Wiley & Sons, New York.
3. Judd and Wyszecki, *Color in Business, Science and Industry*, 1975, John Wiley & Sons, New York.
4. Stearns, *The Practice of Absorption Spectrophotometry*, 1969, John Wiley & Sons, New York.

BIBLIOGRAPHY

Billmeyer and Saltzman, *Principles of Color Technology*, 1966, John Wiley & Sons, New York.
Francis and Clydesdale, *Food Colorimetry, Theory and Applications*, 1975, Avi Publishing Co. Inc., Westport, Conn. USA.
Hunter, *The Measurement of Appearance*, 1975, John Wiley & Sons, New York.
Wright, *The Measurement of Colour*, 1964, Hilger & Watts, London.

Chapter 3

SYNTHETIC ORGANIC COLOURS FOR FOOD

J. COULSON

Pointing Ltd, Prudhoe, Northumberland, UK

SUMMARY

Synthetic organic colours have been used to enhance the appearance of foodstuffs for a hundred years and they remain the most important group of colourants in use in the food and drink industries.

The chemical compositions, physical properties, and methods of manufacture of the major classes of water-soluble, permitted synthetic food colours and their lakes are considered. The manufacturing plants and processes utilised, the product specifications, and the quality control procedures carried out on the food colours are all designed to ensure that products are obtained having well defined compositions and of a quality suitable for use in foodstuffs. The stabilities of the synthetic food colours towards the conditions prevailing in food processing are considered and their applications in a wide range of food products are discussed.

INTRODUCTION

In modern food processing a wide range of physical and chemical conditions are encountered which very often destroy any inherent natural colour in the foodstuff. The addition of colour is, therefore, essential to restore an acceptable appearance and it plays a significant part in our enjoyment of food. The consumer associates each foodstuff with a particular colour, thus it is desirable psychologically[1] for processed food, in its finished state, to resemble the colour of the natural product. The use of synthetic organic colours has been recognised for many years as the most

47

reliable and economical method of restoring something of the food's original shade to the processed product, such as in canned fruit and vegetables. In addition, there are sound economic reasons for the addition of food colour for improving and standardising the appearance of wholesome foods varying in colour and attractiveness, such as in preserves and vegetable protein products, so that waste is avoided. Equally as important, is the use of colour in those products that have little or no natural colour present, such as mineral waters, dessert powders, table jellies, ice-lollies, sugar confectionery and pickles. Without the addition of colour, these products would completely lack eye-appeal and would become unpalatable regardless of their flavour and texture.

Since the discovery of dye synthesis in 1856, the natural colour extracts, which were used for centuries for colouring food, have been extensively replaced by synthetic dyes. These dyes are coloured substances that can be applied in solution or dispersion to the food as substrate, thus giving it a coloured appearance. Usually the dyes have an affinity for the foodstuff and are readily absorbed from solution. The synthetic organic colours are superior to the natural dye extracts in tinctorial power, consistency of strength, range and brilliance of shade, stability, ease of application and cost effectiveness. Many of the synthetic colouring materials thus selected for use in foods, however, and the manner in which they were employed, left much to be desired from a safety viewpoint. As toxicological and analytical techniques improved, regulations were, therefore, introduced to control the use of these added food colourings.

SYNTHETIC COLOURS USED IN FOOD

Classification of Synthetic Colours for Food
The classifications used are those of the EEC, the USA and the UK. The E references are the numbers allotted in the EEC Directive of 23.10.62 (as amended) to the colouring matters listed in Annex I to that Directive.[2] The FD and C numbers are those of the currently permitted food colours in the USA, while the colours formerly listed as FD and C colours are also classified. The current and former CI Food Colour Numbers of the Colour Index (CI) of the Society of Dyers and Colourists (UK) and the American Association of Textile Chemists and Colorists (USA) are included in the classification along with the 1971 CI Numbers.

Class of Synthetic Colours for Food
For the purposes of this chapter the synthetic organic colours permitted in

the EEC and the USA for food use (Appendix 1) have been grouped into the following classes according to their chemical structure:

Monoazo, Disazo, Trisazo.
Triarylmethane.
Xanthene.
Quinoline.
Indigoid.

Synthetic organic colours permitted outside the EEC and the USA and the more important formerly permitted colours for food use (Appendix 2) have been grouped into the following classes according to their chemical structure:

Nitro.
Monoazo, Disazo.
Triarylmethane
Xanthene.
Anthraquinone.

In addition the colours have been divided into water-soluble, oil-soluble, insoluble (pigment) and surface marking colour groups.

Description of Synthetic Colours for Food
Water solubility is conferred on many dyes by the presence of at least one salt-forming group. The most common is the sulphonic acid group, $—SO_3H$, but the presence of a carboxylic acid group, $—CO_2H$, in the colour molecule may also confer water solubility. These dyes are usually isolated as their sodium salts. They have coloured anions and are known as anionic dyes. Dyes containing basic groups, such as $—NH_2$, $—NH \cdot CH_3$ and $—N(CH_3)_2$, form water-soluble salts with acids. These are the cationic dyes and the coloured ion is positively charged. If both acidic and basic groups are present in the colour molecule then an internal salt or zwitterion is formed.

Oil-soluble or solvent-soluble colours lack salt-forming groups and are insoluble in water. Pigments are the colours having no affinity for most substrates. They are thus generally insoluble in water, oils, fats and solvents so they colour by dispersion in the food medium. Lake colours are the most important group of food colour pigments.

Azo Food Colours
In the Azo group of colours the chromophoric system consists essentially of the azo group (Fig. 1) in association with one or more aromatic systems.

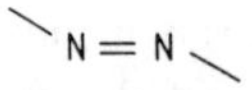

FIG. 1.   Azo group.

There may be one or more azo groups present in the colour molecule, these are the Monoazo, Disazo, Trisazo, Tetrakisazo and Polyazo dyes according to whether there are 1, 2, 3, 4 or more azo groups present. The range of shades covered by the Azo group of food colours is very wide and includes red, orange, yellow, blue, violet, brown and black. Azo dyes having a green shade are very limited and none are used as food colours.

The Azo colours containing a pyrazolone residue (Azo, Pyrazole) do not possess a true azo linkage.[3] They exist rather as a keto-hydrazine tautomer (Fig. 2).

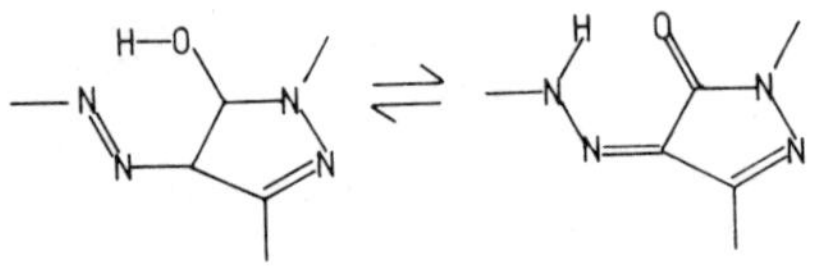

FIG. 2.   Keto–hydrazine tautomer structure of Azo pyrazolone colours.

Triarylmethane Food Colours

Triarylmethane colours are distinguished by their brilliance of colour and high tinctorial strength, but they have poor light-fastness properties. The chromophoric system consists of a central carbon atom joined to three aromatic rings generally with hydroxyl, amino and substituted amino

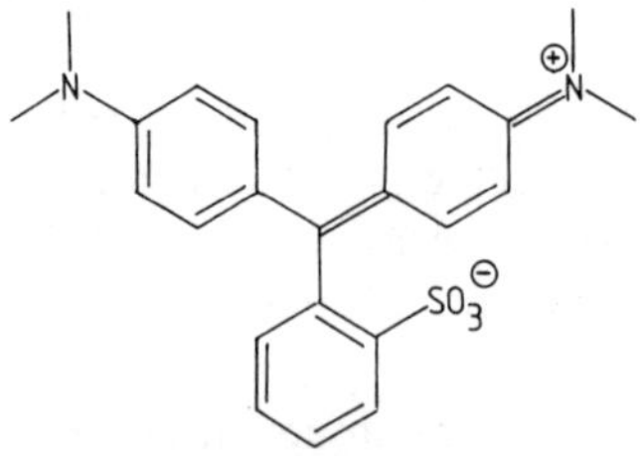

FIG. 3.   Triarylmethane chromophoric system.

substituents in the *para* position acting as auxochromes (e.g. Fig. 3). The Triarylmethane food colours are generally bright green and blue in shade but red and violet hues are also available.

Xanthene Food Colours

In the Xanthene group of colours the chromophoric system is the xanthene

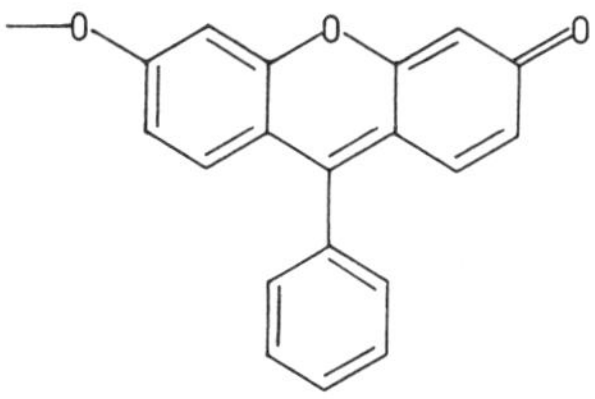

FIG. 4. Xanthene chromophoric system with phenyl substituents.

or dibenzo-1,4-pyran heterocyclic ring system with amino or hydroxyl groups in the *meta* position with respect to the oxygen bridge. Generally a further aromatic ring is attached to the xanthene system (e.g. Fig. 4), analogous to the Triarylmethane dyes. The shade of the dyestuff depends on the other substituents and auxochromes present in the molecule. The group gives rise to brilliant red and greenish yellow dyes with fluorescence present in some of the colours. Erythrosine is the only Xanthene dye permitted in the EEC or the USA for use in food colouring.

Quinoline Food Colours
In Quinoline dyes the chromophoric system is the quinophthalone or 2-(2-quinolyl)-1,3-indandione heterocyclic ring system (Fig. 5). In addition the Quinoline dyes invariably contain a small amount of the isomeric phthalyl derivatives (Fig. 6). Bright greenish yellow shades with poor light fastness are characteristic of the group. Quinoline Yellow is the only dye in this group of importance for use in food coloration.

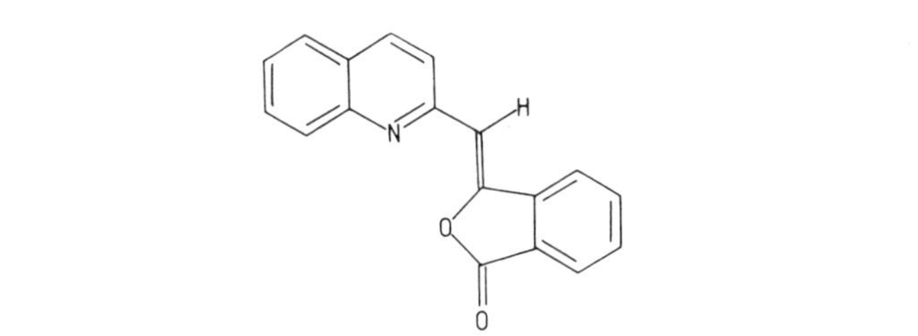

FIG. 5.   Structure of Quinoline colours.

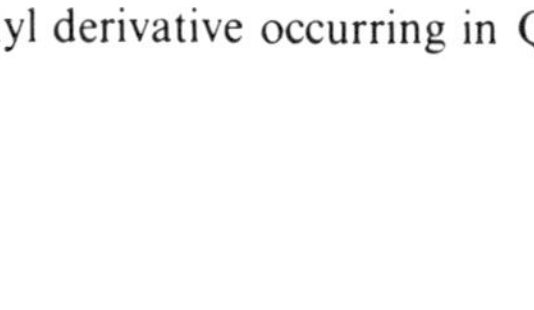

FIG. 6.   Phthalyl derivative occurring in Quinoline colours.

Indigoid Food Colours

The Indigoid group of food colours is based on synthetic equivalents of naturally occurring Indigo (1971 CI No 75780). Colour is due to a resonance hybrid of structures (Fig. 7) or a tetrapole structure (Fig. 8). In their crystalline state, at least, they are normally in the *trans* configuration. The only food colour of importance in this group is Indigo Carmine.

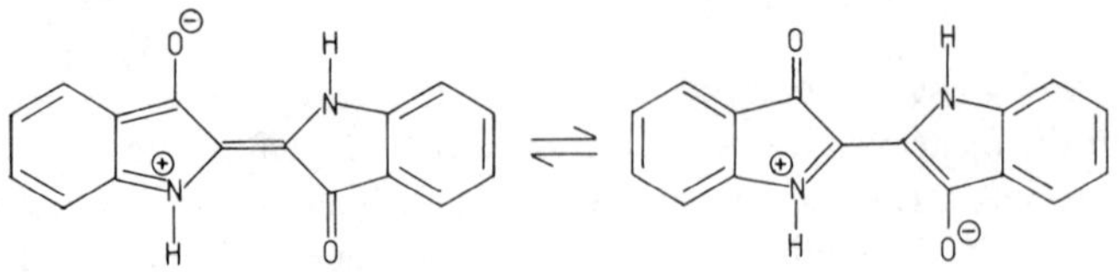

FIG. 7.   Resonance hybrid structure of Indigo.

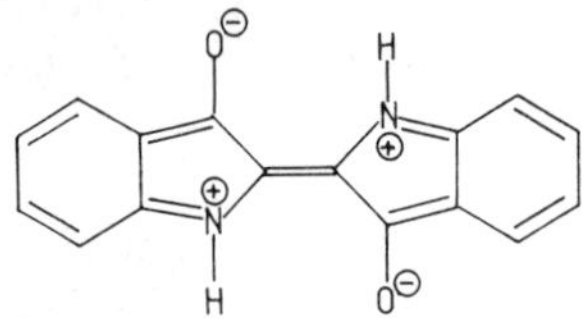

FIG. 8.   Tetrapole structure of Indigo.

MANUFACTURE OF SYNTHETIC ORGANIC COLOURS FOR FOOD

Manufacture of Azo Food Colours

The manufacture of an Azo dye by azo coupling is generally a batch operation consisting essentially of reacting (coupling) a diazotised primary aromatic amine (diazo component) with a coupling component (usually an aromatic amine, hydroxy compound or keto compound capable of enolisation) in an electrophilic aromatic substitution reaction, shown schematically by the convention:

Amine → Coupling Component

The dis-, tris-, tetrakis- and poly-azo compounds are manufactured by either using a diamine or polyfunctional coupling component as starting material or by repeating the process with an aminoazo compound, such as shown schematically in Fig. 9 by the conventions:

Amine $\longrightarrow$ Coupling component 1
      $\longrightarrow$ Coupling component 2

Amine 1 $\longrightarrow$
          Coupling component
Amine 2 $\longrightarrow$

Amine $\longrightarrow$ Coupling component 1 $\longrightarrow$ Coupling component 2

FIG. 9.   Manufacture of colours containing multiple azo groups.

As diazonium ions are relatively weak electrophilic reagents, the aromatic coupling components must carry powerful electron donor groups, such as —OH, —NH$_2$, —NHCH$_3$, and —N(CH$_3$)$_2$.

Generally an acidic solution of the aromatic amine is converted into the diazonium at 0–5 °C by addition of sodium nitrite:

$$Ar—NH_2 + 2HX + NaO \cdot NO \rightarrow Ar—N_2^{\oplus}X^{\ominus} + NaX + 2H_2O$$

where X = Cl, Br, NO$_3$, HSO$_4$, etc.,

The rate determining step is nitrosation of the amine (Fig. 10), the actual nitrosating species, which may be NO$^+$, NOCl, H$_2$O$^{\oplus}$ $\rightarrow$ NO or N$_2$O$_3$, varying according to the conditions. At low acidities and in sulphuric acid of less than about 85 % strength, it is probable that O$_2$N $\cdot$ NO is the effective agent; in sulphuric acid of higher than 85 % strength it is HO$_3$S $\cdot$ O $\cdot$ NO, while in HCl it is Cl $\cdot$ NO (Fig. 10).

With primary amines the nitrosamine is first formed but is quickly transformed, presumably via the diazohydroxide, into the diazonium ion.

Excess sodium nitrite must be avoided during the reaction as it reduces the stability of the diazonium ion and may react with the diazo compound

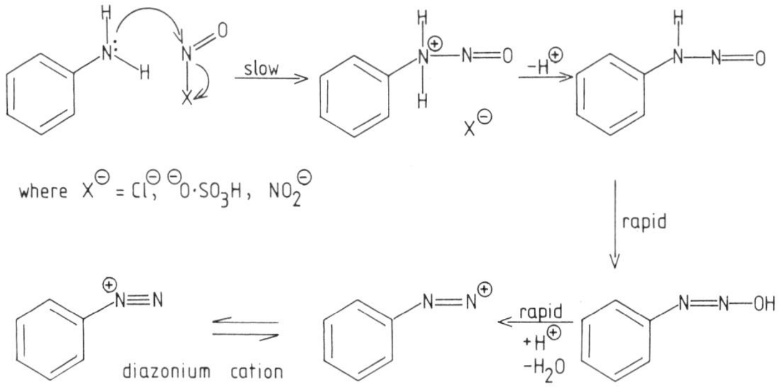

FIG. 10.   Mechanism of diazotisation.

or coupling component in the subsequent reactions. An excess of nitrite can be detected by starch–potassium iodide paper and can be destroyed with sulphamic acid.

$$HO \cdot NO + HO_3 \cdot NH_2 \rightarrow H_2SO_4 + N_2 + H_2O$$

The various naphthylaminosulphonic acids are sparingly soluble in water, but they may be diazotised directly by precipitating them in the finely divided free acid form from their aqueous sodium salt solutions followed by addition of sodium nitrite.

Diazotisation of aromatic amines containing sulphonic groups in an acid medium is often difficult and in these cases an inverse or reversed method can be used. Thus the amine is dissolved in the requisite amount of alkali and sodium nitrite is added to the almost neutral solution. This mixture is then added, with stirring, to iced mineral acid. Concentrated sulphuric acid can be used as a reaction medium in enamelled or glassed steel vessels for diazotisation, in which case the nitrosating agent is nitrosylsulphuric acid. Alternatively one can diazotise in glacial acetic acid using amyl nitrite.

Meanwhile the calculated quantity of coupling component is dissolved in alkaline solution (the phenolate ion, Ar—O$^\ominus$, and the free amine, Ar—NH$_2$, react more readily than the free phenol, Ar—OH, and the ammonium ion, Ar—NH$_3^\oplus$) and cooled to the optimum coupling temperature. Enols, such as pyrazolone derivatives, may also be used as the coupling components.

There is an optimum pH region for reaction of each diazo/coupling component combination. This region lies between pH 4–9 for aromatic amines as coupling components, but between pH 7–9 for enols and around

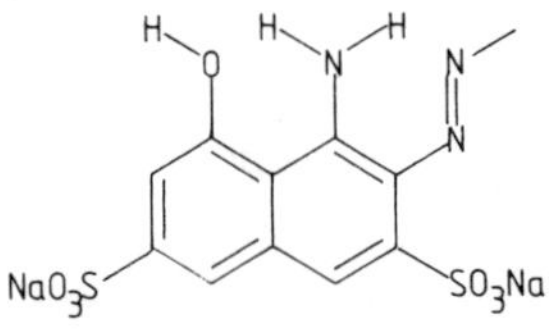

FIG. 11. Products of acidic coupling of H-acid.

pH 9 for phenols. For coupling between a phenol and an o-diazophenol, then pH 9–12 is the optimum. When there is a possibility of coupling at more than one position the pH must be chosen to favour the product required. Thus with 5-amino-4-hydroxynaphthalene-2,7-disulphonic acid (H-acid) coupling in acid takes place in the ring containing the amino group at the 6-position (Fig. 11), while in strong alkali coupling takes place in the ring containing the hydroxyl group at the 3-position (Fig. 12). Raising the temperature does not, generally, improve the coupling reaction as diazo decomposition rates increase faster than coupling reactions. Temperatures below 10 °C are, therefore, preferred, but if a fairly stable diazo compound is concerned one can operate at temperatures as high as 40 °C.

Since diazo compounds are usually unstable and may be explosive, when dry or in suspension, they are not normally isolated but are run directly into

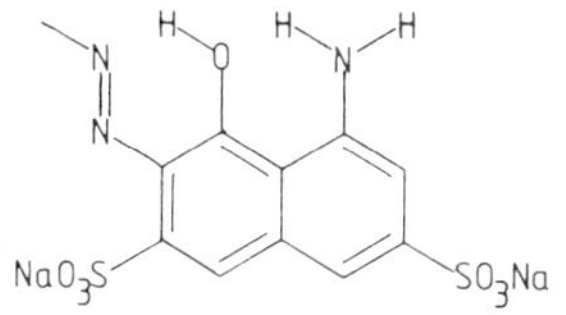

FIG. 12.   Products of alkaline coupling of H-acid.

the agitated solution of the coupling component. In acid couplings the rate of addition of the diazo component is not usually critical, and in some cases, it is advantageous to add the coupling component to the agitated diazo solution. When coupling in alkaline media, however, the amount of uncoupled diazo component must be kept to a minimum. The progress of the reaction is followed by spotting the reaction product onto filter paper and allowing it to diffuse into adjacent spots of solutions of selected diazo and coupling components. Coloration at the intersection with the former shows the presence of excess coupling component, or at the intersection with the latter, excess diazo component. Colour formation in both zones or in the general outspread shows that coupling is taking place very slowly, in which case pyridine may be used as a catalyst, particularly for polyazo dyes.

At the completion of coupling the dyestuff solution is heated to 70 °C and screened to remove insoluble material. The dyestuff is then generally isolated by salting out with sodium chloride and the colour is filtered in a press or other filtration unit, such as a pressure filter or centrifuge.

The product is washed with water, brine or solvent and air-blown to remove as much mother liquor as possible. Successful filtration depends on the dyestuff having been precipitated in the right physical form. The exact conditions for the isolation of each dyestuff have to be determined by experimenting with the isolation volume, pH, quantity of salt added, temperature when salt is added and cooling rate. An efficient filtration and washing regime is critical in food dyestuff manufacture to free the colour from impurities.

The wet filter-cake is transferred to the drier, which may be of the tray type or a more efficient vacuum-drier, spray-drier or fluid-bed drier. The dried filter-cake undergoes a preliminary chopping and sieving to a size suitable for use as a granule or for entry to the fine grinder to reduce it to the appropriate mesh size for powder colour. A detailed analysis is conducted on the bulked, ground powder colour at this stage and it is blended, in an efficient mixer, with other batches of the

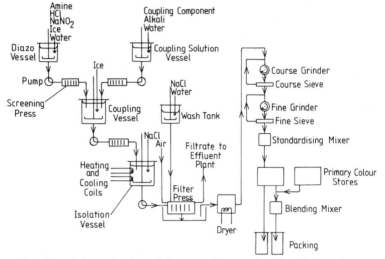

FIG. 13. Schematic plan of the manufacture of an Azo food colour.

same primary colour to obtain a standardised product. Once again the composition of this standardised primary colour must be ascertained to confirm its compliance with required specifications. The specification requirements of the various countries in which the colour may be used must be met, and for this reason the colour manufacturer's own specification is frequently the most severe. In addition, at this stage, samples of the colour may be sent for certification by the FDA.

The dry powder colours are hygroscopic and are, therefore, stored under dry conditions in well-sealed containers to avoid absorption of moisture. A schematic plan of the manufacture of an Azo food colour is shown in Fig. 13.

Manufacture of Triarylmethane Food Colours
The synthesis of Triarylmethane colours proceeds stepwise from mono- via

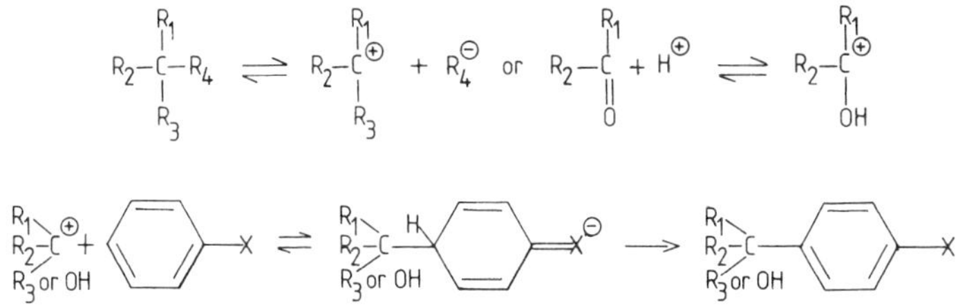

FIG. 14. Above: Synthesis of Triarylmethane colours: Formation of carbonium ion. Below: Synthesis of Triarylmethane colours: Reaction of carbonium ion.

di- to tri-arylcarbonium compounds. Materials containing a central carbon atom as electrophilic reaction centre are reacted with an aromatic nucleophile (Fig. 14). This reaction can be repeated up to three times provided that the central carbon atom remains sufficiently electrophilic. The number of hydrogen atoms attached to the central carbon atom of the electrophilic reagent indicates the number of oxidation steps necessary to produce the triarylcarbonium dye (Fig. 15).

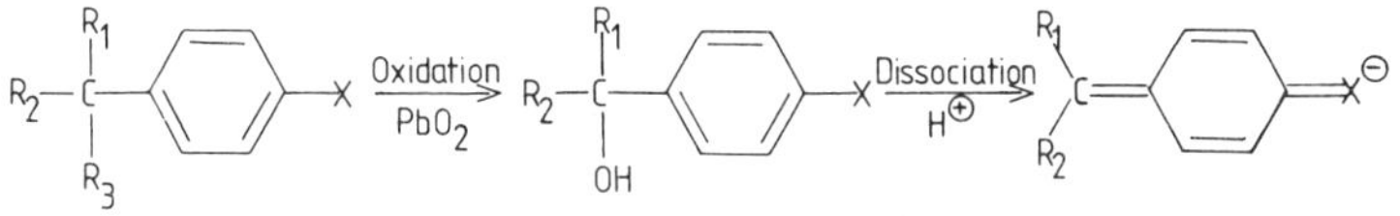

FIG. 15. Synthesis of Triarylmethane colours: Colour formation by oxidation.

The most widely used electrophilic reagents are phosgene, $R_1 = R_2$ = Cl; formaldehyde, $R_1 = R_2 = H$; chloroform, $R_1 = R_2 = R_3 = Cl$, R_4 = H and aromatic aldehydes or ketones, $R_1 = $ aryl, $R_2 = H$ or aryl.

Symmetrical triarylmethane dyes are mainly synthesised in one operation by reaction of an electrophilic reagent, $R_1R_2R_3C^{\oplus}$ or $R_1R_2C^{\oplus}OH$, with three molecules of an aromatic nucleophile, Ph—X, and lead dioxide. With unsymmetrical dyes the intermediate products,

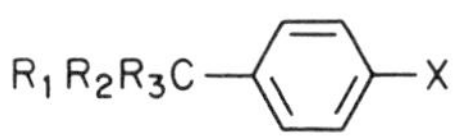

are often isolated so that they can again react, as $R_1R_2R_3C^{\oplus}$ or $R_1R_2C^{\oplus}OH$, with another aromatic nucleophile, Ph—X.

Generally, manufacture of Triarylmethane dyes consists of condensing an aromatic aldehyde with two molecules of an N,N-dialkylaniline in water by stirring with two-thirds of a molecule of hydrochloric acid or sulphuric acid

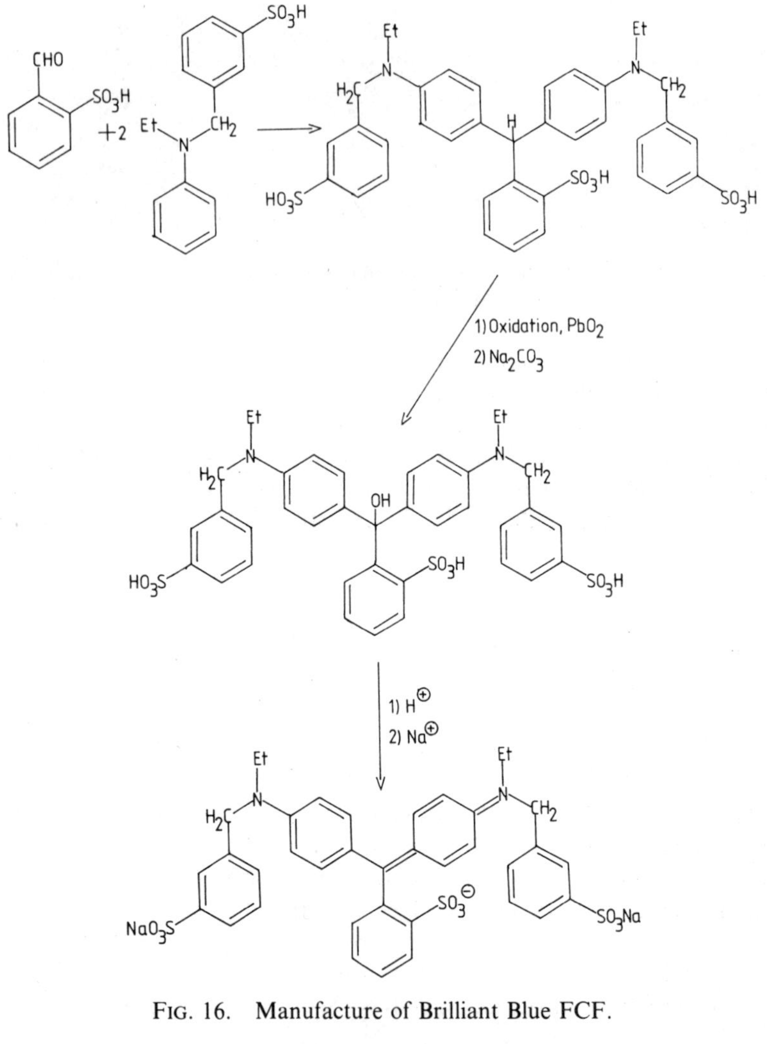

FIG. 16.   Manufacture of Brilliant Blue FCF.

as condensing agent, under reflux at 100 °C for 10 h. At the end of the reaction the mixture is made alkaline with sodium carbonate, and then steam distilled to remove excess of alkyl aniline. The residual leuco-base is filtered off, dissolved in ice-cold dilute hydrochloric acid and oxidised with the theoretical quantity of freshly prepared lead dioxide (prepared by the action of hypochlorite on lead sulphate) with vigorous stirring. Lead sulphate is then precipitated with sodium sulphate and removed by filtration. The clear filtrate is boiled, and treated with sodium carbonate to precipitate the carbinol base. The base is converted into the Triarylmethane dye by the action of acid, and is generally isolated as the sodium salt (Fig. 16).

Alternatively, the Triphenylmethane dyes are manufactured by condensing a bis-dialkylaminobenzhydrol with a benzene- or hydroxybenzene- (or naphthalene- or hydroxynaphthalene-) sulphonic acid. Thus Green S is

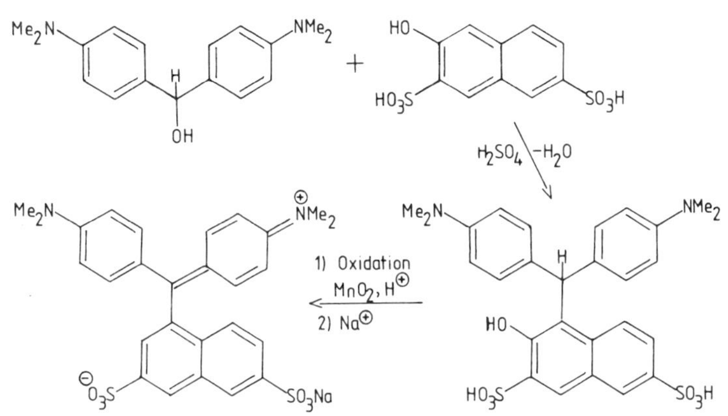

FIG. 17. Manufacture of Green S.

manufactured by first condensing bis-dimethylaminobenzhydrol with 2-hydroxynaphthalene-3,6-disulphonic acid in the presence of concentrated sulphuric acid, with the elimination of a molecule of water, to give the leucobase. Oxidation with manganese dioxide in weakly acid solution then gives the Triarylmethane dyestuff (Fig. 17). The benzhydrol is prepared by oxidation of the tetra-alkyldiaminodiphenylmethane with manganese dioxide and sulphuric acid, and it is used, without isolation, as a moist filtercake after centrifuging, for the condensation with 2-hydroxynaphthalene-3,6-disulphonic acid. Finely divided manganese dioxide for such operations is freshly prepared from manganese sulphate and potassium permanganate in sodium carbonate solution.

Manufacture of Xanthene Food Colours
The condensation of resorcinol with phthalic anhydride by fusion in the presence of concentrated sulphuric acid or zinc chloride, with the elimination of two molecules of water, gives Fluorescein (1971 CI No 45350). Treatment of a boiling alcoholic solution of Fluorescein with iodine

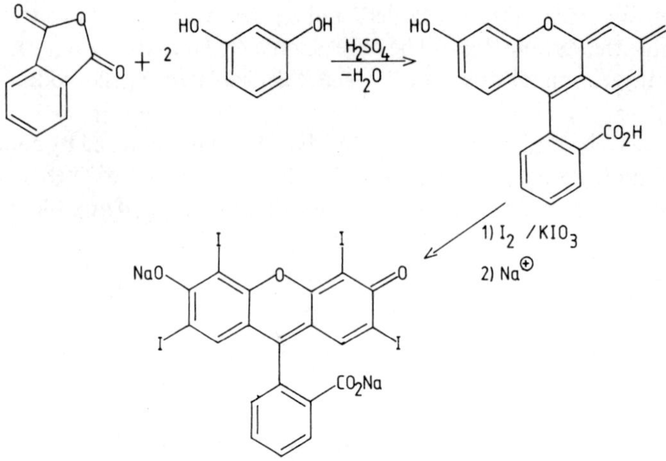

FIG. 18.   Manufacture of Erythrosine.

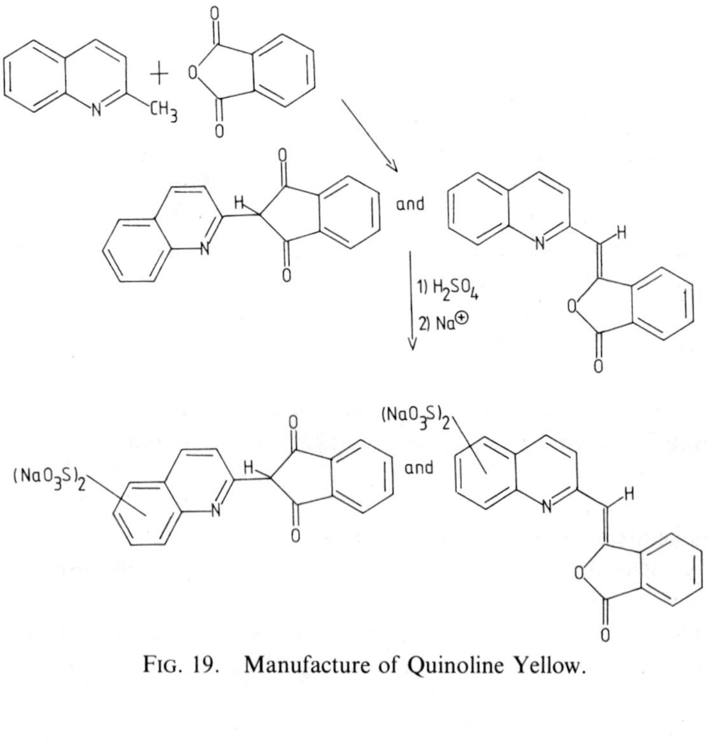

FIG. 19.   Manufacture of Quinoline Yellow.

and potassium iodate affords Erythrosine (Fig. 18), the only Xanthene dye permitted for food use in the EEC or the USA.

Manufacture of Quinoline Food Colours

Quinoline Yellow, the only permitted Quinoline food colour, is manufactured by condensation of quinaldine (2-methyl-quinoline) with phthalic anhydride by fusion at about 220 °C in the presence of zinc chloride, and sulphonation of the product with oleum at around 90 °C (Fig. 19). Sulphonation occurs in the quinoline ring and the disulphonated product predominates.

In some cases 6-methylquinaldine is used in combination with quinaldine in the fusion with phthalic anhydride. The Quinoline Yellow then formed by sulphonation contains a proportion of material substituted in the 6-position (Fig. 20).

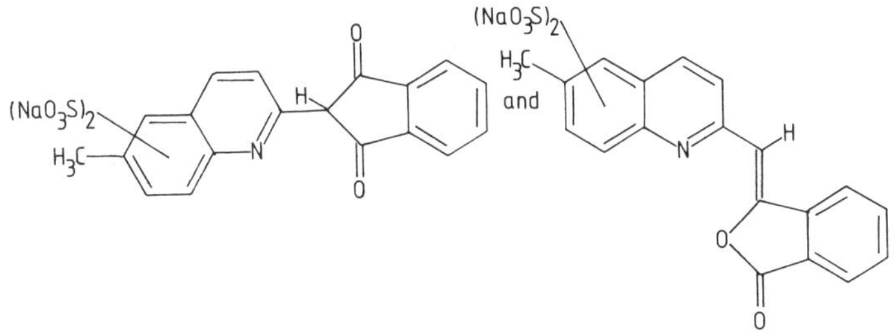

FIG. 20.   6-Methyl component of Quinoline Yellow.

Manufacture of Indigoid Food Colours

In the manufacture of Indigo Carmine, the only permitted Indigoid food colour, Indigo (1971 CI No 73000) is sulphonated with concentrated sulphuric acid at around 90 °C. Indigo Carmine is the 5,5'-disulphonated product and is isolated as the sodium salt. Indigo itself is manufactured by two important routes. In the first method aniline is converted into phenylglycine by reaction with formaldehyde and sodium bisulphate, then with sodium cyanide, followed by hydrolysis of the nitrile (Fig. 21). Sodium phenylglycinate is fused with two moles of potassium hydroxide, one mole of sodium hydroxide and two moles of sodamide at 222 °C for 5 h under pressure in the inert atmosphere provided by the liberation of ammonia.

Alternatively, sodium phenylglycinate can be fused with metallic sodium while dry ammonia is passed into the reaction mixture. The fusion mass, in either case, is discharged into ice and water, and the indoxyl formed is

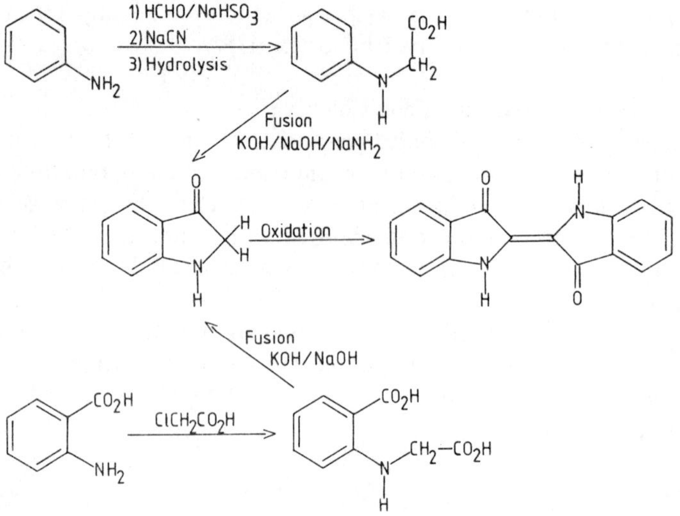

FIG. 21.   Manufacture of Indigo.

oxidised to Indigo by blowing air into the mixture. Following filtration, the press-cake is slurried with water, acidified, refiltered and washed.

The second method of manufacture commences with the more expensive anthranilic acid, which is converted into phenylglycine-*o*-carboxylic acid by reaction with chloroacetic acid (Fig. 21). Fusion with sodium hydroxide affords indoxyl which is then converted to Indigo as before.

Manufacturing Plant Used for Food Colours

The manufacture of food colours is carried out on a batch rather than a continuous process basis. Equipment is usually multipurpose, thus ease of cleaning between batches of different products is vital to eliminate cross-contamination. The reaction media used in dyestuff manufacture are highly corrosive and particular care has to be taken to eliminate contact with surfaces that are not resistant to the conditions. In addition, airborne contamination in the form of dust particles or corrosive or toxic fumes, must be controlled.

In Azo dye manufacture rubber-, plastic- or tile-lined or enamelled mild steel enclosed vessels are suitable. All product contact with mild steel, copper, zinc and aluminium should be avoided, so the rubber or plastic coating of agitators, baffles, heating and cooling coils, temperature and pH sensors, centrifugal pumps and transfer lines is essential. The use of stainless steel, glassed steel or enamel may reduce even further the possibility of surface damage and product adsorption but these finishes are generally more expensive.

Condensation or fusion reactions at elevated temperatures, and in some cases at elevated pressures or under inert atmospheres, are required during the manufacture of Triarylmethane, Xanthene, Quinoline and Indigoid colours. In these cases agitated pressure vessels are used: they are constructed in some cases of cast iron but more usually, now, of glassed steel.

Sulphonation at elevated temperatures with concentrated sulphuric acid or oleum is an essential part of the manufacture of Triarylmethane, Quinoline and Indigoid food colours and for the manufacture of intermediates for the Azo dyestuffs. Glassed steel vessels are becoming the standard for sulphonation reactions to ensure the elimination of heavy metal contamination of the food colours. Similarly, oxidation reactions during Triarylmethane manufacture and halogenation reactions in the manufacture of Xanthene food colours are now performed in coated, generally glassed steel, vessels.

Filtration, drying, grinding and blending plant should also be constructed of materials resistant to corrosion and easy to clean. Thus the use of rubber-lined or polypropylene filter-presses or of coated or stainless steel pressure filters and centrifuges is the norm for food colour manufacture. Similarly, fan assisted tray-driers and spray-driers have contact parts constructed of stainless steel. Once the product is in a dry form then fewer problems occur with adsorption onto and corrosion of contact surfaces but the attrition of surfaces in the grinders used to manufacture powder colour is another potential source of heavy metal contamination. This can be reduced to minimal levels by constructing all contact parts in stainless steel. In addition, the use of magnetic screens following grinding of the powder colour reduces further the possibility of contamination with iron particles.

Dust reduction equipment is essential during dyestuff manufacture to eliminate product cross-contamination and to protect the process worker and the environment. Thus, product driers, grinders, sieves, blenders and packaging equipment are serviced by efficient cyclone or bag-filter airborne-particle collection systems.

Reaction vessels should be fitted with systems to reduce any corrosive or toxic fumes entering the atmosphere. This is achieved by purging air-tight vessels or by ducting fumes to scrubbers where undesirable materials are washed out of the air stream before venting to the atmosphere.

Effluent treatment is an essential part of any dyestuff manufacturing operation.[4] Organic materials, as measured by chemical oxygen demand (COD) and biochemical oxygen demand (BOD), and suspended solids in the effluent must be maintained below levels permitted by the local Water Authorities. This is achieved by adsorption of any colour in the effluent on activated carbon, or destroying the colour by reductive or oxidative methods, followed by biochemical degradation of almost all of the organic material and precipitation in settling tanks. In some cases quantitative precipitation of sodium sulphate followed by filtration and dumping is the only method of meeting suspended solids and sulphate content specifications for the effluent.

Regular inspections of food colour manufacturing plant are carried out by both national and international authorities. Thus in the UK, inspections are carried out by officials from the Department of Health, Safety and Social Security (DHSS) and, in cases where colours are manufactured for certification and use in food in the USA, by the FDA. These inspections ensure that good manufacturing practice, of a standard for food grade materials, is being carried out and that hygiene and safety standards are being maintained.

SPECIFICATIONS FOR FOOD COLOURS

In most countries there is not only a list of permitted food colours but there are also specifications of purity for each permitted colour.

In the UK the specifications of purity prescribed in the current Colouring Matter in Food Regulations[5] are, for the most part, those included in the EEC Directive on Colouring Matters.[2] The FACC[6] consider that these specifications are far from satisfactory in that they contain no minimum limit for total content of the dye and give little indication as to the nature and levels of subsidiary dyes, residues of starting materials, intermediates or other contaminants. The FACC have, therefore, recommended that specifications should normally consist of a minimum colour and maximum impurity levels as follows:

Subsidiary-dyes content.
Sodium chloride and sodium sulphate content.
Unchanged intermediates content.
Breakdown products content.
Free aromatic amine content.
Trace metal content, including arsenic, lead and occasionally also cadmium, chromium and mercury.

Volatile matter.
Water-insoluble matter.
Diethyl ether extractable matter.

Introduction of new specifications of this type in the UK would be subject to their adoption by the EEC as a whole, but the FDA already uses similar specifications for food colours in the USA.

REGISTRATION AND CERTIFICATION OF FOOD COLOURS

A number of countries, including Colombia, Indonesia, Taiwan and Thailand, require registration of permitted food colours. Under this system a manufacturer's food colour is examined by the local authorities against their own specifications and allocated a registration number if it is acceptable. The number is quoted on each consignment of the colour to enable the local authorities to control the use of food additives.

In the USA, the system is more strict in that every batch of food colour is tested by the FDA against their specifications. The colour manufacturer sends a sample representing a quoted weight of a production batch requiring certification analysis to the FDA laboratories in Washington DC along with the registration fee. Upon completion of the analysis and satisfactory results, a certified lot number is assigned by the FDA to the batch of colour. A certificate stating compliance with the regulations and giving the results of the analysis is issued to the colour manufacturer. The specifications that the synthetic organic food colours must meet for certification are listed under Code of Federal Regulations, Title 21, Food and Drugs, Chapter 1, Part 74, Subpart A, Section 74.101 to 74.705 for permanently listed colours and Part 82, Subparts A and B, Section 82.3 to 82.706 for provisionally listed colours.

QUALITY ASSURANCE OF FOOD COLOURS

The importance of quality assurance in the manufacture of food colours cannot be over emphasised. It is imperative that the raw materials employed, the manufacturing process itself, and the dyestuffs produced, are all rigorously controlled.

High standards of manufacturing practice must be maintained to ensure that stringent chemical specifications are met and that the product is bacteriologically of food quality.

Chemical raw materials are controlled by analysis against specifications and also by conversion into the finished colour in the laboratory and carrying out detailed analysis on that colour against specifications. At the same time, accurate strength determinations of raw materials allow quantitative control over the stoichiometric reactions and minimise the occurrence of unchanged raw material in the product.

Process quality control is maintained at critical stages of manufacture. Thus during Azo colour manufacture, tests will be carried out to assess the extent of diazotisation, coupling, product isolation and washing efficiency, by taking aliquot samples which are worked-up in the laboratory in a corresponding manner to the main batch.

The quality assurance of raw materials, processes and products is carried out in well equipped analytical laboratories by chemical, biochemical and instrumental methods of analysis. Classical chemical and gravimetric methods of analysis such as titanous chloride titration for dye content measurement, sulphate and chloride content determinations, moisture contents and diethyl ether extractable matter, are still used on a routine basis.

These have been supplemented by the use of well-established spectroscopic techniques, such as ultra-violet, visible, infra-red, nuclear magnetic resonance, X-ray fluorescence and atomic absorption spectroscopies, to assist in recognition and quantification of raw materials, reaction intermediates, heavy metal contaminants and products. The use of separation techniques, including gas–liquid chromatography, column chromatography on powdered cellulose, alumina or silica, thin-layer and paper chromatographies and, more recently, high performance liquid chromatography (HPLC) with gradient elution, are particularly important, for identification and quantitative comparison with standards, in view of the complex nature of the products and the need to specify very low levels of impurities.[7] The FDA, in particular, uses HPLC as the major analytical tool to enforce its strict control of foodstuff dye quality.

Quantitative bacteriological specifications for food colours are not yet in general use but manufacturers conduct their own testing. Bacteriological control of food colours is carried out by taking samples from processing equipment and of manufactured dyes and subjecting them to total plate counts and estimates of yeasts, moulds and coliforms.

Physical properties of food colours, apart from those specified by legislation, are also subjected to testing by food manufacturers. These include particle size measurements, frequently specified in terms of percentage of colour either passing through or retained by standard mesh-sizes of sieves. Solubility measurements are regularly made on food colours and these are particularly important for Sunset Yellow FCF, which is prone to precipitation on storage in the presence of calcium ions. The final check on a food colour is its shade. Although the physical appearance of a water-soluble colour is not important in the dry state, its shade in solution is critical. Tristimulus colorimetry[1] may be used as a guide to variations in hue, but the most accurate method of assessing samples is to view in solution by eye against a standard solution in natural Northern light.

BLENDED FOOD COLOURS

An extremely wide range of blended or secondary shades may be prepared by intimate blending of mixtures of primary food colour powders. Blend constituents are selected that have been found to be most stable under the processing and storage conditions of the food they are to colour and to comply with the national legislation of the countries in which the food is to be sold. Blended colours may be full primary colour dye strength or may contain approved diluents, such as sodium chloride or sodium sulphate, to tailor them to needs of the food processor. The quality assurance of colour blends is generally controlled by shade in solution and comparison with a standard.

PHYSICAL FORM OF FOOD COLOURS

Food colours are available in traditional dry powder form as primary or blended colours. These water-soluble colours generally have a particle size such that not less than 99% pass through a 60-mesh sieve.

More finely ground powders, or micro-ground colour, can be obtained when the colour is to be used in the dry state in products such as dry drink powders, instant desserts, cake mixes and soups. In these cases 99% of the colour may be required to pass through a 200-mesh sieve. Plating grade colours are extremely finely ground dyes, generally 95% passing through a 325-mesh sieve. They tend to be soft in texture and are bright in shade in the dry mixes.

In order to avoid the dust problems experienced by the food processor in handling fine powder colour, the primary colours are also available in granular form. As well as eliminating dust contamination, the granules possess improved flow characteristics and are more convenient to weigh and dose into food formulations. The granules resist crushing under their own weight during storage and have relatively high bulk density making them cheaper to transport. At the same time, they retain good water-solubility characteristics. Food colour granules are prepared by chopping the dried filter-cake and sieving the product to the desired range of particle sizes. Granules may also be produced by agglomeration of the powder colour. This is achieved by re-wetting powder colour in a tilting pan agglomerator, followed by drying of the granules to an acceptable moisture level. Spray-drying of filter-cake slurry may also be used to produce a small non-dusting particle with similar properties to the food colour granules.

Food colours are also available in extremely dilute form either as aqueous solutions or gelled cubes and sticks. They are convenient for the food manufacturer but are relatively more expensive to use.

LAKE COLOURS

Precipitation of water-soluble colours, generally with an aluminium salt, but in some cases with calcium or magnesium salts, onto a substrate of alumina hydrate (aluminium hydroxide) forms water-insoluble pigments called lakes. Lakes may be prepared from all classes of water-soluble food colours including Azo, Triarylmethane, Xanthene, Quinoline and Indigoid dyes.

Legislation on Lake Colours

Lake colours are permitted for use in food in the EEC, the USA and in most countries which permit the use of synthetic organic food colours. They are not currently permitted in Denmark. In the USA lakes are provisionally listed for use in food by the FDA until 31 January 1981, while further toxicity studies are conducted. The FDA has requested comments on the definition, nomenclature, safety and specification of lakes and announced its intention to propose regulations leading to permanent listing.[8] The FDA require all lakes to be certified for food use.

The aluminium lakes, which are the most widely used, are manufactured at various strengths between 10% and 40% dye content. Tinctorial strengths of lakes are, however, not proportional to dye content, and the shade of a lake varies with dye content. For general food applications the mid-range dye-content lakes (around 20% dye content) are the most useful, while for tablet coatings and food packaging the concentrated lakes of around 40% dye content are recommended.

Manufacture of Lake Colours

A water-soluble food colour is precipitated as its aluminium salt onto alumina by addition of aluminium chloride (Fig. 22). The alumina substrate is usually prepared *in situ* from a solution of an aluminium salt by addition of sodium hydroxide, carbonate or bicarbonate. If aluminium sulphate is used, then the alumina must be washed with water to remove as much sulphate ion as possible, as it prevents total absorption of the

$$3(\text{Dye} - SO_3Na) + AlCl_3 \longrightarrow (\text{Dye} - SO_3^{\ominus})_3 Al^{3\oplus}\downarrow + 3NaCl$$
$$\text{deposited onto}$$
$$Al_2O_3 \cdot 3H_2O$$

FIG. 22.   Manufacture of lake colours.

dyestuff. The calculated quantity of the dye, to achieve the required dye content, is run into the alumina slurry and aluminium chloride solution is added to the stirred slurry to effect laking. Once all of the dye has been absorbed the slurry is washed free from soluble salts by decantation, then filtered and rewashed in a filter-press. The filter-cake is dried and ground to the desired particle size. A very wide range of shades may then be produced by intimate blending of the individual lakes.

The manner of precipitation of the alumina hydrate and the conditions under which the dye is added to the slurry are important and determine the shade, particle size, dispersibility, hardness, and even the tinctorial strength of the lake.

The colouring action of lakes is by dispersion in food and thus the physical appearance of the dry lake powder is of vital importance. The particle size must be sufficiently small to achieve, at economical usage levels, adequate covering of all the product mass to be coloured. Thus the lake colours are ground to an individual particle size of around 1 to $5\,\mu\text{m}$, while agglomerates of particles may be $45\,\mu\text{m}$ or more. Even finer grinding can be achieved, resulting in lakes of greater covering power, but the bulk density of the powder rapidly decreases and handling properties deteriorate.

Specifications for Lake Colours

Specifications for the purity of lake colours vary from country to country. In the USA lake colours must conform to the following specification. Soluble chlorides and sulphates, as the sodium salts, shall not be more than 2%. Inorganic matter, insoluble in hydrochloric acid, shall not be more than 0·5%. In addition, certified lakes in the USA may only be manufactured from previously certified batches of water-soluble colours. In most other countries the same specifications for subsidiary dyes, unchanged intermediates, breakdown products and metallic contamination apply to lake colours as are specified for the corresponding water-soluble colours. The lake colour manufacturers also generally specify dye content and some physical properties including particle size and shade. Particle size specifications for lake colours are generally 100% through a 200-mesh sieve and up to 99·9% through a 325-mesh sieve by the wet sieving method. The specific gravity of lake colours varies somewhat but is generally 0·08 to 0·14 for sifted material and 0·14 to 0·24 for material that has been tamped down.

The shade of the lake is matched against a standard sample.

Lake Colour Usage

Lake colours are insoluble in water, oils, fats and other solvents. They have, therefore, numerous application advantages over water-soluble colour.

1. Colouring oil and fat-based mixes, such as cakes, biscuits, icings, fillings, chocolate substitutes, salad dressings and snack foods, where the presence of water is undesirable.
2. Colouring sugar crystals, frosting sugars and film-coated sweets for confectionery.
3. Colouring compressed tablets in the confectionery and pharmaceutical industries.
4. Avoidance of colour staining or bleeding where colour migration is a problem, such as in fruit or yogurt, striped confectionery, chewing gum, frozen desserts and gelatin desserts.
5. Colouring powder drinks, desserts, soups and spice blends where dry appearance is important.
6. Reduction of colour fading in light, compared to the corresponding water-soluble colours.
7. Increasing heat stability, in some cases, compared to the corresponding water-soluble colours.
8. Colouring of plastic packaging materials, inks and internal lacquers for metal cans, which are subject to food contact.

Lake colours should not be used in strong acid or alkaline conditions as these destroy the colour–alumina bond resulting in colour bleeding. Stability is satisfactory in the 3·5 to 9·5 pH range.

Lake colours are available in a wide variety of shades and as dispersions in various carriers, including sugar syrups, edible oils, glycerine and propylene glycol, for ease of incorporation into products.

STABILITY PROPERTIES OF FOOD COLOURS

The stability of synthetic food colours towards the conditions prevailing in food processing depends upon a number of factors. These include the medium in which the colour is used, the concentration of the colour and of the various food additives used and the temperature and time of exposure. Changes that occur as a result of these factors vary for each colour used so that all of the components of a blend of food colours will not fade at the same rate. The resulting shade may, therefore, be entirely unlike that of the original blend.

Action of Light
Strong sunlight and particularly ultra-violet light are capable of bringing about a photochemical change in food colours resulting in total decolorisation. The most stable of the commonly used synthetic organic colours for food are Red 2G, Tartrazine and Yellow 2G. Carmoisine, Amaranth, Allura Red AC, Brown FK, Chocolate Brown HT, and Brilliant Blue FCF also show good light fastness. Green S, Erythrosine and Indigo Carmine are the least stable. Light has a destructive effect on all of the colours so it is important to protect the coloured foodstuff, where possible, from direct exposure. Infra-red rays may also cause some colour fading, and the increase in temperature they cause accelerates the deterioration.

Affect of Food Processing Temperatures
Temperatures used in cooking can be detrimental to food colours. The most stable of the commonly used synthetic food colours to average boiling and baking temperatures of 100 °C and 200 °C, respectively, are Ponceau 4R, Allura Red AC, Sunset Yellow FCF, Tartrazine, Brown FK, Chocolate Brown HT, Green S and Brilliant Blue FCF. Indigo Carmine is not stable to processing heat. At very high temperatures some carbonisation may occur which will cause colour loss or change of shade. All colours should be added at the lowest possible temperature, and as late as possible in the food manufacturing process, usually at the same time as the flavour, when little further heating will take place.

Action of Alkalis and Acids
Stabilities to alkalis and acids vary considerably, the Azo class of food colours showing the best resistance. Indigo Carmine fades rapidly in acid media, while Erythrosine is precipitated from the soluble sodium salt as the insoluble free acid at a pH less than 4. Carmoisine, Ponceau 4R, Allura Red

AC, Sunset Yellow FCF, Tartrazine and Brilliant Blue FCF are the most stable under acidic conditions. Under alkaline conditions Red 2G and Brilliant Blue FCF are the most stable, while Carmoisine, Allura Red AC, Sunset Yellow FCF, Tartrazine, Brown FK, Chocolate Brown HT, Black PN and Patent Blue V also show good stability to alkali. Indigo Carmine fades rapidly in alkaline media. Fading of all colours in acid or alkaline media is accelerated by contact with metals particularly at higher temperatures.

Action of Food Preservatives
The synthetic organic colours are stable to the levels of benzoic acid and sodium benzoate generally used as preservatives in foodstuffs, apart from Patent Blue V, Quinoline Yellow and Indigo Carmine. Erythrosine is precipitated from solution in the presence of benzoic acid.

The addition of sulphur dioxide or sulphurous acid as a preservative in fruit-based products causes colour deterioration in any added food colour. Red 2G, Tartrazine, Fast Green FCF, Brilliant Blue FCF, Erythrosine and Quinoline Yellow are the most stable food colours. At levels of sulphur dioxide below 25 ppm, Carmoisine, Amaranth, Allura Red AC, Brown FK, Chocolate Brown HT and Green S are also stable. Patent Blue V and Indigo Carmine are decolorised rapidly by sulphur dioxide.

Action of Ascorbic Acid
Vitamins and antioxidants are added to a wide range of processed food and vitamin C, in the form of ascorbic acid, is frequently used to perform both functions. It is a strong reducing agent and careful studies must be made of colour stability in its presence. Sunset Yellow FCF, Tartrazine, Fast Green FCF and Brilliant Blue FCF are moderately stable to levels of ascorbic acid up to about 160 ppm, while Amaranth is stable in the presence of levels of ascorbic acid less than 70 ppm.

Action of Reducing and Oxidising Agents
All of the commonly used food colours are affected by reducing agents and in most cases complete colour loss occurs eventually. This is common in canned goods where metals, particularly iron, tin, zinc and copper, react with the acid content to liberate hydrogen, with subsequent colour loss. Indigo Carmine may be considered the most stable of the food colours under these reducing conditions as, although it is readily reduced, it is rapidly re-oxidised in the presence of air to its original shade. Erythrosine

remains relatively stable in the presence of sulphur dioxide once it has been precipitated from solution by the action of acid. Some sugars also have a reducing action on food colours. This is especially true of invert sugar, formed by the hydrolysis of cane sugar with citric acid or invertase. Amaranth fades rapidly in products in which invert sugar is present.

Where micro-organisms occur, in the form of bacteria, moulds or yeast, they will have a biochemical reducing action on the food colours causing partial or, in certain instances, total colour loss. Spoilage with subsequent loss of colour is especially common in non-carbonated soft drinks during hot weather.

Colour loss from synthetic organic dyes also takes place in the presence of oxidising agents. In general the Azo class of colours and Erythrosine possess better stability than the other food colours.

Action of Proteins

When subjected to higher processing temperatures, particularly at above atmospheric pressure while retorting, colour loss can occur as a result of reaction with proteins. This applies particularly in fish and meat processing but may also occur in processed milk products. In view of the varying protein contents of each product, it is important to carry out small-scale tests on each type of raw material to be used. Amaranth is the most susceptible food colour to this type of action, while Erythrosine is the most stable.

STORAGE OF FOOD COLOURS

Synthetic organic colours are commercially sterile when manufactured, and they will be stable for an indefinite period while remaining in sealed containers and stored under cool, dry conditions. The food colours are hygroscopic and once opened their containers should be re-sealed after each off-take to prevent excessive moisture absorption.

The food processor will usually make up a stock colour solution. This should be used within 24 h and always be kept under sterile conditions. If it is necessary to keep a stock solution for a longer period, a preservative, such as 0·1 % sodium benzoate, 25 % glycerine or 25 % propylene glycol, may be added. Glass, plastic or stainless steel containers are preferred for colour stock solutions to minimise contact with metals that may cause electrochemical reducing reactions.

SOLUBILITY OF FOOD COLOURS

A knowledge of the solubility of colours is essential in their application in food products. Apart from the lake colours, all of the important food colours, permitted for general use in food in the EEC and the USA, are soluble in water and insoluble in oils and fats. They are sufficiently soluble in glycerine, sorbitol and propylene glycol to allow the preparation of non-aqueous solutions or pastes, for use when the addition of water is undesirable. Solubilities of the food colours in ethanol and isopropanol differ substantially and the Triarylmethane dyes and Erythrosine are the most soluble.

Dilute strength food colours are not suitable for preparing concentrated stock solutions as their diluent content, usually sodium chloride or sodium sulphate, has a depressant effect on solubility. Ideally, distilled water should be used to make up aqueous food colour solutions. Failing this, softened water, with maximum total hardness of 100 ppm, can be used, although some small amount of turbidity can be expected at this hardness level. At a total hardness of 400 ppm in the water, cloudy solutions may result due to the precipitation of colour. It is a useful precaution to filter stock solutions before use to eliminate traces of insoluble material that may arise from the food colour or from its interactions with hard water.

Food colours should be taken into solution by making up the required weight of colour into a thin paste with cold water or solvent and then dissolving to the correct concentration by adding boiling water or warm solvent with continuous stirring. When all of the solvent has been added, the solution is stirred for 30 min, while warming, or until a clear solution is obtained.

APPLICATIONS OF FOOD COLOURS

The amount of food consumed in the UK containing added colour is approximately 0·5 kg per head per day, representing nearly half of the total diet. The average colour content of the coloured food is less than 50 ppm and the average total of synthetic food colours consumed is less than 10 g per head per year. The yellow colours, Tartrazine and Sunset Yellow FCF, and the red colours, Carmoisine, Ponceau 4R and Amaranth, or Allura Red AC, where permitted, make up the bulk of the colour consumed. The FACC have estimated that Chocolate Brown HT is the major colour additive consumed in an average diet,[6] but these findings are not substantiated by colour production figures.

Synthetic food colours are used in a very wide range of processed products and they must be carefully selected to remain stable during processing and storage.

Soft Drinks and Non-Alcoholic Beverages

Soft drinks require colours having good light fastness as well as stability in acidic media and to preservatives and flavouring compounds. Fruit acids, including citric and malic acids, are the most common acidulants but phosphoric acid is used in cola drinks. The preservatives used are benzoic acid or, in the presence of fruit juice, sulphur dioxide. In canned drinks, light stability is not important, but the colour must not accelerate corrosion of the metal can. Carmoisine, Amaranth, Allura Red AC, Sunset Yellow FCF and Tartrazine are frequently used synthetic colours, while Ponceau 4R (in the absence of sulphur dioxide), Chocolate Brown HT, Brilliant Blue FCF, Green S, Quinoline Yellow and Indigo Carmine are also used in soft drinks.

Examples of the colours used with average levels of application are:

Soft drinks		mg/kg
Orange	Sunset Yellow FCF	40
Lemon and lime	Tartrazine	30
Cherry	Ponceau 4R	50
Blackcurrant	Amaranth	100
Strawberry	Carmoisine + Sunset Yellow FCF	50
Raspberry	Carmoisine + Ponceau 4R	60
Grape	Amaranth + Brilliant Blue FCF	100
Caramel	Sunset Yellow FCF + Amaranth + Green S + Tartrazine	40
Chocolate	Chocolate Brown HT + Green S + Tartrazine	80

Sugar Confectionery

Sugar confectionery products require the widest possible range of colour shades. In addition, good heat stability at the temperatures of sugar boilings (150 °C) and stability to flavouring components and the usual concentrations of sulphur dioxide present in cane sugar and glucose syrups are essential. Carmoisine, Ponceau 4R, Amaranth, Allura Red AC, Sunset Yellow FCF and Tartrazine are the most frequently used synthetic colours, while Chocolate Brown HT, Black PN, Brilliant Blue FCF, Green S, Patent Blue V, Erythrosine and Indigo Carmine are also in general use in confectionery.

Examples of the colours used with average levels of application are:

Sugar confectionery		mg/kg
Orange	Sunset Yellow FCF	80
Lemon	Tartrazine	60
Blackcurrant	Amaranth	120
Strawberry	Ponceau 4R	60
Raspberry	Carmoisine	100
Chocolate	Chocolate Brown HT	120
Caramel	Sunset Yellow FCF + Amaranth +	
	Green S + Tartrazine	80
Liquorice	Carmoisine + Tartrazine + Green S	120

The best results are obtained by adding the colour as late as possible in the manufacturing process, usually at the same time as the flavour. Therefore the food colour must have good solubility in the sugar syrups. The rate of application will vary depending upon whether clear pastel shades are required or deep richer shades. These can be obtained by using 50 to 100 mg/kg for the former and 100 to 300 mg/kg for the latter. Excessive use of colour will result in unattractive dull shades.

Desserts, Icings and Frozen Confectionery

A very wide range of shades is required to colour desserts, sugar icings, ice-cream, sorbets and ice-lollies. The colour should have good light fastness properties. Processing conditions are generally not severe and the whole range of approved synthetic food colours may be used but Carmoisine, Ponceau 4R, Amaranth, Allura Red AC, Sunset Yellow FCF, Tartrazine, Chocolate Brown HT, Brilliant Blue FCF and Green S are most frequently used. Black PN and Patent Blue V are occasionally used in ice-cream.

Examples of the colours used with average levels of application are:

Desserts		mg/kg
Strawberry	Ponceau 4R	40
Raspberry	Carmoisine	80
Blackcurrant	Amaranth	100
Orange	Sunset Yellow FCF	80
Lemon	Tartrazine	50
Chocolate	Chocolate Brown HT	100
Caramel	Sunset Yellow FCF + Amaranth +	
	Green S + Tartrazine	60

Preserves and Table Jellies

Jams, marmalades and preserves require colours having good stability to heat (120 °C), to fruit acids and preservatives, including sulphur dioxide and benzoic acid. The colour is best added in aqueous solution at the end of the boil after the temperature has begun to fall and the sulphur dioxide content has reached its minimum. A high colour solubility is therefore desirable. Bright colours are preferable to counteract the dull shade of the fruit pulp. Carmoisine, Ponceau 4R (in the absence of sulphur dioxide), Amaranth, Allura Red AC, Tartrazine and Erythrosine are the most frequently used synthetic colours, while Red 2G, Sunset Yellow FCF, Chocolate Brown HT, Black PN, Green S and Indigo Carmine are also in general use in preserves.

Examples of the colours used with average levels of application are:

Jams		mg/kg
Strawberry	Ponceau 4R	50
Raspberry	Carmoisine	80
Blackcurrant	Red 2G	120
Plum	Ponceau 4R	60
Cherry	Amaranth	60

Marmalades		
Orange	Sunset Yellow FCF	50
Lime	Tartrazine	50

Lemon curd is best coloured with Tartrazine, at about 80 mg/kg, and shaded with Sunset Yellow FCF if required. Table jellies require colour fastness to heat, flavours, gelatin and sulphur dioxide, and most of the synthetic food colours are found to be suitable.

Examples of the colours used with average levels of application are:

Table jellies		mg/kg
Orange	Sunset Yellow FCF	40
Lemon	Tartrazine	20
Lime	Tartrazine	30
Strawberry	Ponceau 4R	50
Raspberry	Carmoisine	50
Blackcurrant	Amaranth	50

Baked Goods

Cakes, biscuits, wafers and cereals require colour stability under the prolonged high temperatures (250 °C) encountered in baking, as well as to the action of carbon dioxide and, in some cases, alkaline baking powders. Ponceau 4R, Allura Red AC, Sunset Yellow FCF, Tartrazine and Chocolate Brown HT are the most frequently used synthetic colours. Examples of the colours used with average levels of application are:

Baked goods		mg/kg
Madeira cake	Tartrazine + Sunset Yellow FCF	40
Chocolate cake	Chocolate Brown HT	200
Wafers	Ponceau 4R	60
Breakfast cereal	Tartrazine	70

Canned Fruit, Vegetables and Soups
Canned foods must withstand the high temperatures (140°C) of sterilisation and cooking and the action of any fruit acids present. Any acidic components in the canned food may attack the metal container giving reducing conditions which can affect the colour. The use of internally lacquered cans usually minimises this metal corrosion as does absence of oxygen. Carmoisine (in the absence of ascorbic acid), Ponceau 4R, Amaranth, Allura Red AC and Sunset Yellow FCF are the most frequently used synthetic colours, while Red 2G and Indigo Carmine are also used in canned fruits. Erythrosine is readily precipitated by acids as its free acid where it maintains its original shade. It is, therefore, particularly suitable for colouring canned cherries, where no bleeding is essential. Examples of the colours used with average levels of application are:

Canned fruit		mg/kg
Strawberry	Ponceau 4R + Sunset Yellow FCF	100
Raspberry	Carmoisine	150
Blackcurrant	Amaranth	150
Rhubarb	Ponceau 4R	100
Cherry	Erythrosine	100
Blackberry	Red 2G + Indigo Carmine	150

In canned vegetables and soups the principal colours used are Sunset Yellow FCF, Tartrazine, Yellow 2G, and Green S. Level staining to the vegetable is important while leaving the liquor practically free from colour. Examples of the colours used with average levels of application are:

Canned vegetables		mg/kg
Broad beans	Sunset Yellow FCF	10
Green beans	Yellow 2G + Green S	70
Processed peas	Tartrazine + Green S	50
Garden peas	Tartrazine + Green S	60

Canned soups

Mushroom	Tartrazine + Carmoisine	20
Vegetable	Sunset Yellow FCF + Green S	100
Tomato	Sunset Yellow FCF + Amaranth	200
Beef	Sunset Yellow FCF + Amaranth +	
	Green S	100

Meat and Fish Products and Analogues

Colours added to sausage meat or vegetable protein, as a supplement to meat, must be stable to sulphur dioxide, added as a preservative, usually in the form of bisulphite or metabisulphite. Carmoisine, Ponceau 4R, Red 2G, Allura Red AC, Tartrazine and Erythrosine are the most suitable colours for this purpose.

Meat and fish pastes require colours having stability under the sterilisation temperatures used. The uncoloured pastes are frequently dull in shade and require bright colours to produce an attractive product. Red 2G, Sunset Yellow FCF, Chocolate Brown HT and Green S are the most suitable colours to use, while Erythrosine may be acceptable if the product is not packed in glass. All colours in meat pastes, and particularly in fish pastes, are fugitive to a large extent to light, and generally glass containers are not wholly suitable for extended storage periods.

The colouring of cured herring (kippers) and white fish fillets in the brine bath prior to their smoking requires colours that are soluble in brine, have an affinity for fish flesh and colour it evenly, without leaching out or fading during cooking. Brown FK is particularly suited to this application and can be shaded with Carmoisine or Tartrazine if required. Sunset Yellow FCF or blends of Carmoisine, Tartrazine and, in some cases, Brilliant Blue FCF or Indigo Carmine can be used in countries where Brown FK is not permitted but rainbow effects may be observed in some cases.

Examples of the colours used with average levels of application are:

Meat and fish products		mg/kg
Sausages	Red 2G	10
Meat pastes	Erythrosine	20
Fish-pastes	Red 2G	30
Kipper fillets	Brown FK	30
Haddock fillets	Tartrazine	40

Dry–Premix Convenience Foods

Dry powder drinks, desserts, custard powder, soups, sauces, toppings and gravies require a wide range of colour shades of high aqueous solubility which have good light fastness, show no colour speckiness in solution and are stable to the mild heat of processing. Carmoisine, Ponceau 4R, Amaranth, Allura Red AC, Sunset Yellow FCF and Tartrazine are the most frequently used synthetic colours, while Chocolate Brown HT, Green S, Erythrosine and Indigo Carmine are also in use in dry convenience foods. A finely ground powder may provide an acceptable shade to both the dry powder and the final hydrated product; alternatively the use of lake colours can also be an advantage to impart a satisfactory shade to the dry powder mix.

Examples of the colours used with average levels of application are:

Dry–premix food		mg/kg
Orange drink	Sunset Yellow FCF	60
Strawberry drink	Ponceau 4R	60
Custard powder	Tartrazine	80
Blancmange powder	Carmoisine	80
Gravy mix	Chocolate Brown HT	150

Milk Products

Milk-based products may require colours having heat stability for short pasteurisation periods and usually require good light stability. Carmoisine, Ponceau 4R, Amaranth, Allura Red AC, Sunset Yellow FCF, Tartrazine, Erythrosine and Indigo Carmine are the most widely used synthetic colours in milk products.

Examples of the colours used with average levels of application are:

Milk products		mg/kg
Strawberry yogurt	Ponceau 4R	40
Banana milk shake	Tartrazine + Sunset Yellow FCF	20
Chocolate milk drink	Sunset Yellow FCF + Amaranth + Indigo Carmine	100
Crème caramel	Sunset Yellow FCF + Carmoisine + Indigo Carmine	60

Snack Foods

Potato crisps and extruded snack foods require colours with good stability to high processing temperatures and good light fastness. Tartrazine, at usage levels from 50 to 300 mg/kg, is predominantly used and may be shaded with Sunset Yellow FCF or Erythrosine.

Pickles, Sauces and Ketchups

Pickles, sauces and ketchups require colours having good light fastness as well as stability to processing temperatures and frequently an acetic acid medium. Tartrazine, Yellow 2G and Green S are used in salad cream, mayonnaise, piccalilli and various other pickles. When caramel shades are required they may be blended from Sunset Yellow FCF, Amaranth, Green S and Tartrazine. Ponceau 4R is blended with Sunset Yellow FCF or Tartrazine to colour tomato ketchup.

Pet Foods

Dry pet foods can be coloured with any of the permitted synthetic colours by mixing with the dough. Processing temperatures are generally low and light stability is rarely important. The most commonly used colours are Amaranth, Sunset Yellow FCF and Tartrazine.

Canned pet foods require colours which are stable to the temperatures of retorting and to the proteins used in the food. Brown shades are the most important and can be provided by blends from Tartrazine, Chocolate Brown HT, Brilliant Blue FCF and Erythrosine.

Pharmaceutical and Cosmetic Products

Pharmaceutical and cosmetic products require a very wide range of colours to enhance appearance, and, in many cases, to provide a means of identification. All of the food colours and permitted drug or cosmetic colours may be used. Compressed tablets are coloured at the dry mixing stage prior to their compaction and provide few colour problems for the processor. Sugar-coated tablets, however, must be pan coated with a large number of applications of coloured syrup. The lake colours, dispersed in the coating syrup, are preferred because their opaque character allows fewer coloured coats to be applied, taking less time to build up a satisfactory surface shade, compared to the water-soluble colours.

Toothpastes can be coloured with a wide range of water-soluble colours as heat and light stability are not required. If colour staining during use or colour bleeding in striped products is a problem, then any of the lake colours may be used.

POLYMERIC DYES

Attachment of a functional additive, including a food colour, to an appropriate polymer molecule can result in an entity of molecular size large enough to be no longer absorbed through the intestinal lining. Such a molecule would not enter the bloodstream nor be metabolised but would pass through the gastrointestinal tract and be excreted provided it is stable to the conditions prevalent including gut microflora, enzymes and pH. The polymer must also be stable during food processing and storage to prevent breakdown and release of smaller, absorbable, and potentially toxic fragments as well as to preserve functionality. The risk of toxicity of such a non-absorbable polymer is greatly reduced and only local effects, such as irritation, need be studied. This concept is currently being applied[9] to food colour additives.

Further details of this interesting development are given in Chapter 4.

REFERENCES

1. Francis, F. J., *Proc. Third International Congress of Food Science and Technology*, Washington DC, 1970, 415.
2. EEC Council Directive of 23.10.1962, *Official Journal of the European Communities* L115, 11.11.1962, 2645.
   EEC Council Directive of 25.10.1965. First Amendment to EEC Colours Directive, No 65/469/EEC.
   EEC Council Directive of 24.10.1967. Second Amendment to EEC Colours Directive, No 67/653/EEC.
   EEC Council Directive of 20.12.1968. Third Amendment to EEC Colours Directive, No 68/419/EEC.
   EEC Council Directive of 13.7.1970. Fourth Amendment to EEC Colours Directive, No 70/358/EEC.
3. Parent, R. A., *J. Sci. Dyers Colourists*, 1976, **92**, 368.
4. Parish, G. J., *Rev. Prog. Coloration*, 1976, **7**, 55.
5. The Colouring Matter in Food Regulations 1973, Ministry of Agriculture, Fisheries and Food, HMSO, London, SI 1973, No 1340.
6. Interim Report on the Review of the Colouring Matter in Food Regulations 1973, FAC/REP/29, by the Food Additives and Contaminants Committee, Ministry of Agriculture, Fisheries and Food, HMSO, London, 1979.
7. Knox, J. H. and Laird, G. R., *J. Chromatography*, 1976, **122**, 17.
8. *Federal Register*, 1979, **44**(122), 36411.
9. US Patent 3 940 503, 24.2.1976.

SYNTHETIC ORGANIC COLOURS PERMITTED IN THE EEC AND THE USA FOR USE IN FOOD (1979)

Colour	Class	Synonym	CI (1971) Food No	CI (1971) No	EEC No	FD and C No	Structure
1. WATER SOLUBLE							
1.1 Azo							
Carmoisine	M	Azorubine	Red 3	14720	E122	—	
Ponceau 4R	M	Cochineal Red A Brilliant Scarlet 4R New Coccine	Red 7	16255	E124	—	
Amaranth	M	Bordeaux S Naphthol Red S	Red 9	16185	E123 (Red No 2)		
Red 2G	M	Azo Geranine	Red 10	18050	—	—	

Colour	Class	Synonym	CI (1971) Food No	CI (1971) No	EEC No	FD and C No	Structure
Allura Red AC	M	—	Red 17	16035	—	Red No 40	
Sunset Yellow FCF	M	Orange Yellow S	Yellow 3	15985	110	Yellow No 6	
Tartrazine	M, P	—	Yellow 4	19140	102	Yellow No 5	
Yellow 2G	M, P	—	Yellow 5	18965	—	—	
Brown FK	M, D, T	—	Brown 1	—	—	—	Essentially a mixture of:

Name	Structure	Class	Synonyms	Colour	C.I. No.	E No.
Chocolate Brown HT		D	—	Brown 3	20 285	—
Black PN		D	Brilliant Black BN Brilliant Black 1743	Black 1	28 440	E151
1.2 *Triarylmethane* Fast Green FCF		TAM	—	Green 3	42 053	— Green No 3
Food Green S		TAM	Brilliant Acid Green BS LISSAMINE Green B Wool Green S	Green 4	44 090	E142
Patent Blue V		TAM	—	Blue 5	42 051	E131

Colour	Class	Synonym	CI (1971) Food No	CI (1971) No	EEC No	FD and C No	Structure
Brilliant Blue FCF	TAM	—	Blue 2	42 090	—	Blue No 1	
1.3 *Xanthene* Erythrosine	X	Erythrosine BS Erythrosine J	Red 14	45 430	E127	Red No 3	
1.4 *Quinoline* Quinoline Yellow	Q	Quinoline Yellow Water Soluble	Yellow 13	47 005	E104	—	Essentially a mixture of 2 compounds
1.5 *Indigoid* Indigo Carmine	I	Indigotine	Blue 1	73 015	E132	Blue No 2	

2 SURFACE MARKING COLOURS
2.1 Azo

Lithol Rubine BK M Pigment Rubine, Lithol Rubine BN, Rubine Pigment — Pigment Red 57 — 15850 — E180 —

Citrus Red No 2 M — — 12156 — Citrus Red No 2

2.2 *Triarylmethane*

Methyl Violet TAM Methyl Violet 2B, Methyl Violet B — 42535 —

and

APPENDIX 2
SYNTHETIC ORGANIC COLOURS PERMITTED FOR FOOD USE OUTSIDE THE EEC AND THE USA AND THE IMPORTANT FORMERLY PERMITTED COLOURS

Colour	Class	Synonym	CI (1971) Food No	CI (1971) No	EEC No	FD and C No	Structure
1 WATER SOLUBLE							
1.1 Nitro							
Naphthol Yellow S	N	—	Yellow 1	10 316	—	(Yellow No 1–Na salt) (Yellow No 2–K salt)	
1.2 Azo							
Ponceau SX	M	—	Red 1	14 700	—	(Red No 4)	
Scarlet GN	M	—	Red 2	14 815	(E125) —		
Fast Red E	M	Naphthol Red Fast Red S Fast Red	Red 4	16 045	—		

Name		Synonyms	Red No.	C.I. No.		
Ponceau MX	M	Ponceau 2R Ponceau G Ponceau RR Ponceau R	Red 5	16 150	—	—
Ponceau 3R	M	Ponceau N3R	Red 6	16 155	—	(Red No 1)
Ponceau 6R	M	Scarlet 6R	Red 8	16 290	(E 126)	—
Red 10B	M	Fast Acid Magenta B	Red 12	17 200	—	—
Red 6B	M	LISSAMINE Red 6B Amido Naphthol Red 6B Acid Red 6B	Red 11	18 055	—	—
Red FB	M	—	Red 13	14 780	—	—

APPENDIX 2—contd.

Colour	Class	Synonym	CI (1971) Food No	CI (1971) No	EEC No	FD and C No	Structure
Orange I	M	Naphthol Orange	—	14 600	—	(Orange No 1)	
Orange RN	M	Croceine Orange	Orange 1	15 970	—	—	
Orange GGN	M	Orange GGP	Orange 2	15 980	(E111)	—	
Orange G	M	Orange GG	Orange 4	16 230	—	—	
Yellow RFS	M	Acid Yellow FWA	Yellow 6	13 010	—	—	
Fast Yellow AB	M	Acid Yellow G Fast Yellow Acid Yellow	Yellow 2	13 015	(E105)	—	

Name	Type	Alt. names	C. name	C.I.	E-number	Other
Yellow 27175N	M	—	Yellow 7	13 445	—	—
Chrysoin S	M	Chrysoin / Resorcinol Yellow / Chrysoine Yellow	Yellow 8	14 270	(E103)	—
Yellow RY	D	Yellow 11 651	Yellow 9	20 281	—	—
Chocolate Brown FB	D	—	Brown 2	—	—	—
Black 7984	D	—	Black 2	27 755	(E152)	—
1.3 *Triarylmethane* Guinea Green B	TAM	—	Green 1	42 085	—	(Green No 1)

APPENDIX 2—contd.

Colour	Class	Synonym	CI (1971) Food No	CI (1971) No	EEC No	FD and C No	Structure
Light Green SF Yellowish	TAM	Light Green Light Green SF Acid Brilliant Green ASF	Green 2	42 095	—	(Green No 2)	
Blue VRS	TAM	Blue 1085	Blue 3	42 045	—	—	
Violet BNP	TAM	—	Violet 3	42 580	—	—	
Violet 6B	TAM	Wool Violet Benzyl Violet 4B Acid Violet 6B	Violet 2	42 640	—	(Violet No 1)	

	TAM/X/A/M		Colour Index	C.I. No.		
Violet 5BN	TAM	Violet 1942 Acid Violet 5BN	Violet 1	42 650	—	—
1.4 *Xanthene* Rhodamine 6G	X	—	—	45 160	—	—
Rhodamine B	X	Rhodamine B Extra	Red 15	45 170	—	—
2 *INSOLUBLE (PIGMENT)* 2.1 *Anthraquinone* Indanthrene Blue	A	Indanthrone Indanthrene Blue RS Anthraquinone Blue Anthragen Blue Solanthrene Blue RS Indanthrene GZ	Blue 4	69 800	(E130)	—
3 *OIL SOLUBLE* 3.1 *Azo* Oil Red XO	M	Sudan II Oil Orange XX	—	12 140	—	(Red No 32)

APPENDIX 2—contd.

Colour	Class	Synonym	CI (1971) Food No	CI (1971) No	EEC No	FD and C No	Structure
Orange SS	M	—	—	12 100	—	(Orange No 2)	
Yellow AB	M	Oil Yellow AB	Yellow 10	11 380	—	(Yellow No 3)	
Yellow OB	M	Oil Yellow OB	Yellow 4	11 390	—	(Yellow No 4)	
Oil Yellow GG	M	Sudan G Oil Yellow G	Orange 3	11 920	—	—	
Oil Yellow XP	M. P	Oil Yellow SEG	Yellow 12	12 740	—	—	

NB Figures in brackets are the allocated numbers before the colours were delisted by the respective authority.

Key to Classes in Appendices 1 and 2:

N = Nitro.   P = Pyrazolone.   T = Trisazo,   X = Xanthene.   I = Indigoid.
M = Monoazo,   D = Disazo.   TAM = Triarylmethane,   Q = Quinoline.   A = Anthraquinone.

Chapter 4

NOVEL SYNTHETIC COLOURS FOR FOOD

J. Walford

Organics Division, Imperial Chemical Industries Ltd, Blackley, Manchester, UK

SUMMARY

Recent withdrawals of some synthetic food colours have resulted in technical deficiencies in the available range, especially in the USA following delisting of FD and C Red No 2 (Amaranth) for food use. The development of FD and C Red No 40 (Allura Red AC) and novel methods of using the technically deficient FD and C Red No 3 (Erythrosine) as alternatives to Red No 2 are noted.

The major initiative in the synthetic field is the polymeric colour concept developed by the Dynapol Corporation in the USA. In this approach, it is argued that adverse toxicological effects from food additives can only arise if the additive or breakdown product is absorbed into the body from the gastrointestinal tract. When a chromophore is fixed on to a polymer such that the molecular weight of the resultant colour is high enough to prevent its absorption, potential toxic effects are substantially reduced if not entirely eliminated.

Towards the end of the nineteenth century when synthetic colours were first adopted for food use on a large scale, they were hailed as a significant technological breakthrough. The term 'synthetic' was associated with the idea of 'progress' and the synthetic colours were actually considered safer in food than the naturals, in that they were tinctorially much stronger and hence needed a smaller quantity to achieve a specified coloured effect.

Certain colours began to attract suspicion from the safety-in-use angle
however, and as alternative colours were substituted, a small nucleus of
acceptable colours was gradually adopted.

In recent times the safety-in-use of synthetic colours has come under
increasing scrutiny and the number of delistings has greatly outweighed the
number of listings. This has caused real problems from the technical
performance viewpoint when attempting to substitute alternative colours.

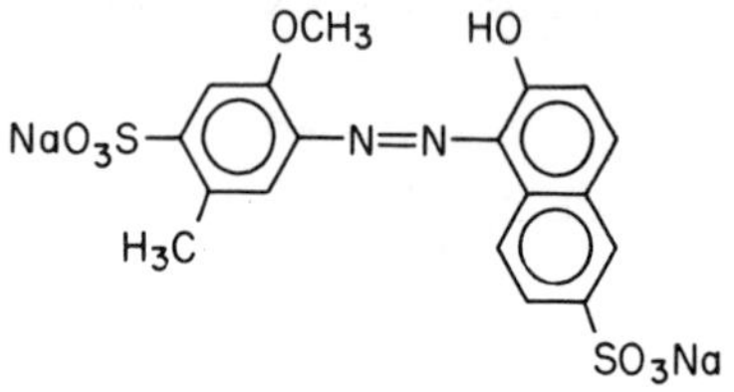

FIG. 1.   Allura Red AC. CI Food Red 17. CI 16035 FD and C Red No 40.

In the UK for example, delisting Orange G and Orange RN has affected the
soft drinks trade significantly. Alternatives based on Sunset Yellow FCF
give excellent shade matches but comparable colour fastness performance
may be retained only by altering the processing conditions or the stage at
which the colour is added. Withdrawal of FD and C Red No 2 (Amaranth)
in the USA in 1976 caused similar problems for the bluish red shades in all
branches of the food industry. This situation has led to greatly increased
activity in the field of research into new food colours, although because of
the cost of development and toxicological testing of new colours, together
with the prevailing climate of opinion on traditional synthetic colours, the
number of initiatives in the synthetic area over the last few years has been
small. The one major exception is that of FD and C Red No 40 (Allura Red
AC) first listed for food use in the USA in 1971.[1] Red No 40 (Fig. 1) was the
first completely new colour to be proposed for general use in food in the
USA since 1938.[2]

Red No 40 was developed to fill the colour gap existing due to lack of an
approved bright red of a similar shade to that of FD and C Red No 4
(Ponceau SX) at that time approved for use in maraschino cherries only; it
has since been delisted. After the withdrawal of Red No 2 (Amaranth), Red
No 40 is the only synthetic red technically suitable as a general purpose
colour and in fact in 1978 had the largest certification volume of any on the
FDA certifiable colour list. Red No 40 is approved only in isolated

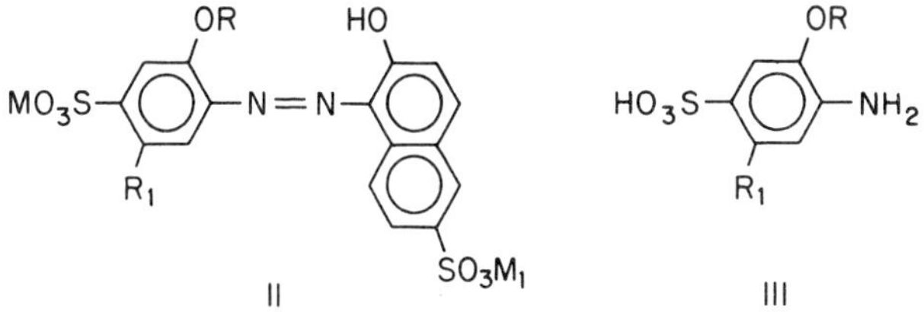

FIG. 2. Allura Red AC type structures. R and R_1 = 1–6 carbon alkyl; M and M_1 = H or a cation.

countries outside the FDA orbit and does not have either UK or EEC approval due to lack of both demonstrated need and available toxicological evidence with which to judge its safety-in-use.[3]

A recently disclosed Dutch patent application[4] by Allied Chemical Corporation, however, describes the Allura Red AC types. The structure is disclosed as a 1-(2-alkoxy)-4-(sulpho-5-alkyl phenyl)-2-hydroxy-naphthalene-6-sulphonic acid of general formula shown in Fig. 2. Structures represented by II are prepared by diazotisation of a compound of formula III and coupling the diazonium salt obtained with an alkali metal salt of 2-hydroxynaphthalene-6-sulphonic acid.

The properties are similar to other azo-based reds, claiming low toxicity and high water solubility. The colours are resistant to sulphur dioxide in aqueous solutions and also to hydrogen ions in aqueous solution of pH $\geq$ 3. Baking fastness is good, and at 50–100 ppm ascorbic acid resistance is also good. Excellent light fastness and a high preserving activity are claimed.

Work on azo-based colours has also been carried out in the UK; two recent patents deal with red azo colours.[5,6] The work was prompted by the need to find an alternative to Structure IV, which is the existing colour Red 10B (Colour Index Food Red 12, CI 17200), see Fig. 3.

This colour had regulatory approval and was frequently used for soft drink coloration, but it exhibited an undesirable feature in that it is known to produce an increase in Heinz bodies in the bloodstream when

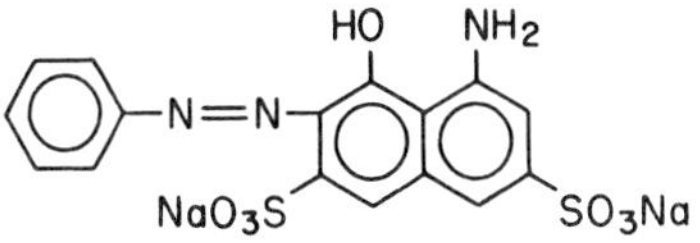

IV

FIG. 3. Red 10B.

administered in high concentrations in the diets of test animals. These are the bodies which appear in ageing red cells of blood. One of the patents[5] discloses a red colouring matter, Red SA, which has been shown not to produce Heinz bodies. The colour has the Structure V given in Fig. 4.

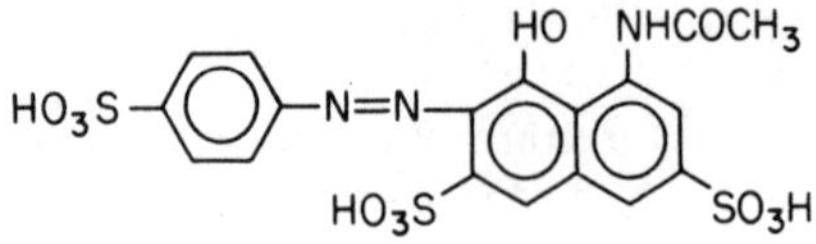

V

FIG. 4. Red SA.

The colour is particularly recommended for sausage meats in that it has excellent resistance to sulphur dioxide preservative. Under acid conditions however, such as encountered in soft drinks (pH 3·0–3·5), the acetamido group hydrolyses to a colour of Structure VI (Fig. 5) which was named Red AB and is the subject of the second patent.[6]

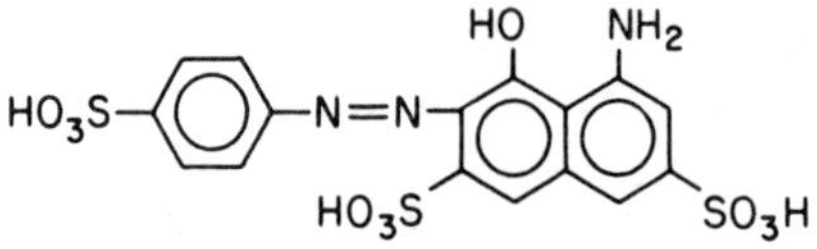

VI

FIG. 5. Red AB.

This colour, although disclosed in earlier British Patent BP 858 183 as a dyestuff for textile materials, had not been incorporated as a colouring matter in foodstuffs or cosmetics. Its advantages over Red 10B include higher tinctorial power, hence greater safety-in-use as lower quantities are sufficient for a given shade, good acid stability and the fact that it does not produce Heinz bodies in the blood.

Red AB is suitable as an all purpose red colouring matter, particularly useful for those shades associated with dark-coloured fruits such as blackcurrant, black cherry, blackberry and blueberry. Preferred amounts of Red AB for use in syrups and cordials are 75–300 ppm and in ready to drink beverages, 25–50 ppm. An example of the use of Red AB in blackcurrant syrup is quoted below.[6]

Blackcurrant Syrup

Blackcurrant juice	40 % v/v
Sugar	60 % v/v
Sulphur dioxide (preservative)	300 mg/kg
Colouring: Red AB	125 mg/kg
Tartrazine	23 mg/kg
Green S	2·7 mg/kg

Quantities of colouring matter required to produce the same colouring effect for a blackcurrant syrup using:
(1) Red 10B and (2) Red AB are as follows:

(1) *Red 10B*		(2) *Red AB*	
Red 10B	133 ppm	Red AB	125 ppm
Tartrazine	23 ppm	Tartrazine	23 ppm
Green S	2·7 ppm	Green S	2·7 ppm
Total	158·7 ppm	Total	150·7 ppm

The patent was published on 5 May 1976. To date the colour has not been approved for food use by any authority and, as far as is known, no extensive programme of toxicological work has been carried out or is planned.

An alternative tactic to carrying out research into new colouring matters is to attempt to improve the technical performance of existing colours so that they may be considered for use in areas where they were previously unsatisfactory. One example is the case of FD and C Red No 3 (Erythrosine). As noted earlier, when approval for the uses of Red No 2 (Amaranth) was withdrawn in the USA in 1976, a large gap emerged in the synthetic red spectrum. To a large extent, Red No 40 (Allura Red AC) can be substituted for virtually all shades when in admixture with suitable other permitted colours. Red No 40 itself was and still is not completely in the clear until further test work has been reported however, and the prospect of its possible delisting gave impetus to research on Red No 3 (Erythrosine) the only other approved traditional synthetic red in the USA (see Fig. 6).

Red No 3 has several drawbacks including high cost and low light fastness in pale depths. The major problem however is its complete instability at low pH (i.e. < 4·5) when it reduces to the acid form which is water insoluble.

Clearly this factor prevents its use in soft drink and gelatin dessert outlets, both major areas of colour usage.

Recent work by the General Foods Corporation[8] involved improving the stability of Red No 3 by two methods,

1. Dispersing and fixing the colour on a stabilising support such as gelatin.[7]
2. Mixing with water and polyoxyethylene sorbitan ester.[5]

In the gelatin method, the colour is dispersed in a solvent of pH > 4.5 in which a major part of the dye is dissolved. The colour is then fixed with a

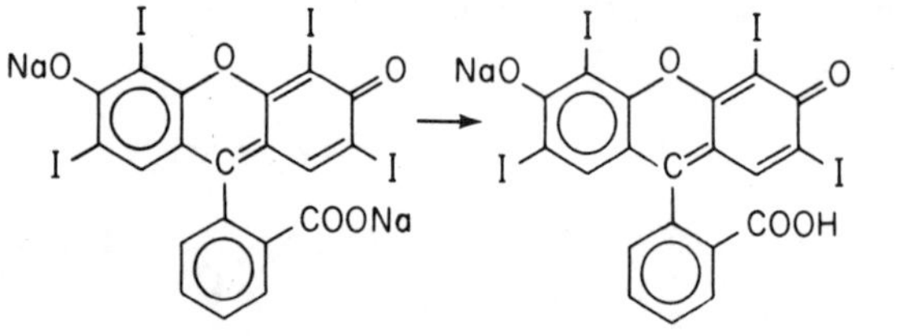

VII   VIII
CI Food Red 14   CI Solvent Red 140
CI 45430   CI 45430:2
Water-soluble sodium salt   Water-insoluble acid form

FIG. 6.   FD and C Red No 3 (Erythrosine).

support, followed by solubilisation in an aqueous solution in the presence of gelatin for a sufficient time to give an aqueous solution free of cloudiness and precipitate when the pH is adjusted to below 4.5. A dry composition of the colour, which when dissolved at below pH 4.5 gives a solution as above, comprises the colour fixed on a support plus a stabilising amount of gelatin. The colour is used in food and, as stabilised above is applicable for use in jelly desserts, sauces, decorations and drinks. It is claimed that the process overcomes the inherent stability of the colour below pH 4.5 and results in satisfactory solutions.

In the second method, the colour is rendered soluble and stable in an aqueous food substance of pH <4.5 by mixing in aqueous medium with a hydrophilic surfactant selected from polyoxyethylene (20) sorbitan monostearate, tristearate or mono-oleate, or mixtures of these. The components are combined under shear conditions effective to make the dye soluble in the food substance for more than 24 h at 4–7 °C. The ratio of aqueous medium to surfactant is sufficient to produce a colloidal system. The optimum ratio of colour to surfactant is 1:9. The solubilised colour is combined with a carrier in aqueous medium and the mixture is dehydrated either by freeze- or vacuum-drum-drying. The ratio of the aqueous medium to the hydrophilic surfactant is between 1–5:1. It is claimed that a red food colouring is provided which can be added to an aqueous food system or used in the formulation of a dry mix to give a haze-free solution, also free of precipitate under acid conditions.

A further attempt at stabilisation of Red No 3 as well as several other colours is disclosed in a recent USA patent assigned to the Sterling Drug Co.[9] Edible acidic materials are coloured red by adding a stabilised solid solution of 0·1–40 weight percentage Red No 3 (or FD and C Blues Nos 1 and 2 or Yellows Nos 5 and 6) and 60–99·9 % weight percentage edible gelatin. The solid solution itself is produced by dissolving the gelatin in water, dissolving the colour(s) in the aqueous gelatin solution, evaporating the water from the solution and comminuting the residual solid to the desired particle size. The formulation is used in mixtures of pH ≤ 4·2 (e.g. gelatin desserts and either carbonated or non-carbonated fruit flavoured beverages) where it exhibits strong tinctorial power of great stability.

The above methods of colour utilisation are particularly designed to enable wider application of Red No 3 (Erythrosine). The same techniques could also be used to modify the characteristics of other permitted food colours in an effort to widen their scope.

POLYDYE CONCEPT (DYNAPOL)

The most interesting and significant development in the synthetic colour field in recent years has been the 'Polydye' concept. The company behind the move is the Dynapol Corporation of Palo Alto, California, set up as a subsidiary of the Alza Corporation in 1972 with the remit to exploit the idea of non-absorbable food additives.

The argument is that adverse toxicological effects from food additives can only arise if the additive or breakdown product is absorbed into the body from the gastrointestinal tract. If an additive were designed to be physiologically inert and not to migrate, it would be excreted unchanged and hence should be above suspicion from the toxicological angle. Out of this idea grew the concept of fixing a chromophore onto a polymer such that the molecular weight of the resultant colour is high enough to prevent its migration across the mucosa from the gastrointestinal tract. It was suggested that with this approach, any potential toxic effects would be substantially reduced if not entirely eliminated.

Several basic patents have been published in the USA, all assigned to the Dynapol Corporation.[10–14] Emphasis is placed on the fact that the means for chemically attaching a chromophore to a large carrier molecule must give a final colour meeting stringent criteria.

1. Freedom from potentially absorbable impurities such as oligomers, unreacted monomers, catalysts and solvents. (Dialysis techniques in fact can be used to create a final product of the correct molecular characteristics.)
2. Very high resistance to hydrolysis, degradation or metabolic effects at either the food processing or storage stage, or under the conditions encountered in the gastrointestinal tract.
3. Non interference by the carrier molecules with either the optical properties of the chromophores or their technical performance in food coloration.

Two basic approaches are disclosed in the patent literature. The first[10] deals mainly with chromophores typical of those now permitted by the FDA as certifiable food colours e.g. FD and C Yellow No 5 (Tartrazine), FD and C Red No 2 (Amaranth), FD and C Blue No 2 (Indigo Carmine) and FD and C Green No 3 (Brilliant Green FCF). Other chromophores such as Malachite Green (CI Basic Green, CI 42000), Sudan Blue (CI Solvent Blue 11, CI 61525), and Uranine (Fluorescein CI Acid Yellow 73, CI 45350) are mentioned however. The choice of a high stability bond leashing the chromophore to the carrier, a high molecular weight polymer, is the sulphonamido link (see Fig. 7).

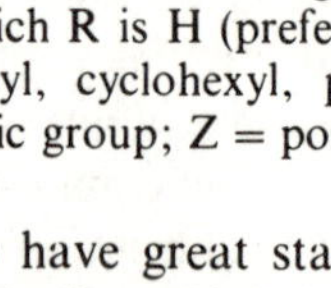

IX

Fig. 7. Sulphonamido linkage. M = non-degradable backbone, NR—SO$_2$ = sulphonamido linkage in which R is H (preferred) or a hydrocarbon up to 6 carbons, e.g. methyl, isopropyl, cyclohexyl, phenyl or xylyl; K = optically chromophoric group; Z = positive integer.

The linkage is claimed to have great stability under food processing conditions and during metabolism. If R is above 6 carbon atoms, the evidence suggests that the size of the attached group begins to interfere with the positioning of the chromophoric groups causing distortion of the configuration and hence unpredictability of the final shade. In the schematic diagram (Fig. 8) of the modes of attachment, both examples are possible but X is preferable since it allows the —SO_2— portion to be part of the chromophore, thus simplifying preparation. The polymer backbone to which the dye molecule is attached has an optimum molecular weight of 20 000–1 000 000, giving a final product molecular weight of 20 000–2 000 000. Linear organic polymers are preferred, e.g. polyacrylic acid, polyvinylamine and polyvinyl alcohol but branches such as polyethyleneimine and substituents may be present.

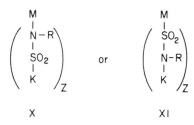

$$X \qquad \qquad XI$$

FIG. 8. Sulphonamido linkage.

Naturally occurring polymers such as cellulose and dextran and the 2-amino derivatives of these polymers have been employed. Adequate water solubility is achieved when 10% or greater of the backbone or chromophore carbons carry a hydrophilic polar group, such as ether, hydroxyl, carboxyl or sulphonate for example. It is also possible to provide oil or fat solubility by adding non-polar oleophilic groups such as hydrocarbon chains to the backbone, at the same time ensuring that less than 10% of the carbons contain polar groups.

The backbones can be prepared by several methods. When chromophoric groups are to be constructed on a pre-existing amine-containing polymer, the polymer is treated with N-acetyl sulphanilyl chloride, 4-acetamido-1-naphthalene sulphonyl chloride or any other aromatic sulphonyl chloride bearing a protected amino group. The resultant sulphonamido polymer is hydrolysed in either acid or base to free the aromatic amino group which may be subsequently diazotised and coupled to a great variety of coupling agents. These agents may be any aromatic compound, carbocyclic or heterocyclic bearing a hydroxy, alkoxy, amino, monoalkylamino or dialkylamino group on an aromatic ring. Usually the agent is a phenol, aniline, naphthol, naphthylamine or pyrazolone derivative. Most often the coupling agent is naphthol either sulphonated or unsulphonated, or a pyrazolone. Alternatively, an N-vinyl-N-alkyl sulphonamido group can be constructed on an aromatic amine which is then polymerised and diazotised-coupled in either order.

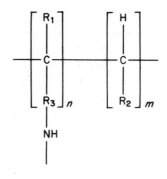

XII

FIG. 9. Amino linkage. R_1 = H (preferred) or lower saturated alkyl up to 4 carbon atoms, i.e. methyl, ethyl, propyl, butyl; R_2 = H (preferred) or a lower saturated alkyl of up to 4 carbon atoms (see R_1) or phenyl; R_3 = A simple covalent bond or 1–4 carbon atom saturated alkyl bridge or a phenyl bridge; N = A positive integer > 1; m = At least n such that not more than half the backbone carbons carry an amino group; NH = Amino linkage.

In a second patent,[11] an alternative to the sulphonamido linkage for binding the chromophore to the polymeric backbone is disclosed, namely the amino linkage. Further groups of chromophores, based on the anthraquinone structure, are disclosed and claimed to be more stable than the azo structures described earlier.

Here again the olefinically saturated hydrocarbon backbones are essentially linear with no appreciable long chain branching. Structurally they are represented by XII (Fig. 9).

Another possible structure is where R_3 is a methylene bridge which joins together with an adjacent R_3 into a repeating unit, i.e. a cyclodiallylamine arrangement where R_1 and R_2 are preferred to be —H or —CH$_3$ (Fig. 10).

Suitable preferred backbones are the homopolymers polyvinylamine,

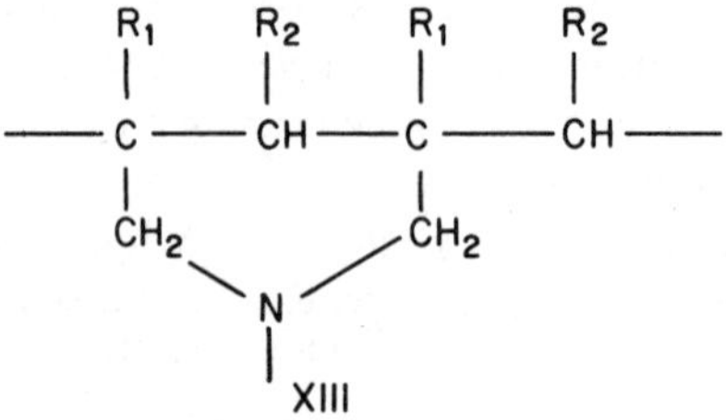

FIG. 10. Cyclodiallylamine linking bond.

TABLE 1
ANTHRAQUINONE-BASED CHROMOPHORES FOR POLYMERIC DYES, AMINO
LINKAGE TO POLYMER

1. Structure: Amino anthraquinone
    Colours: Purplish, greenish or navy blue

R_1 = hydrogen *or* lower saturated alkyl of up to 4 carbon atoms.

R_2 = hydrogen *or* lower saturated alkyl of up to 4 carbon atoms *or* an aryl or alkaryl of from 6 to 8 carbons.

2. Structure: Anthrapyridone
    Colours: Reds

R_1 = hydrogen *or* a lower saturated alkyl of from 1 to 4 carbon atoms *or* an aryl group of about 6 carbons.

R_2 = a 1 to 4 carbon lower saturated alkyl *or* a 1 to 4 carbon lower saturated alkoxy *or* an aryl grouping of about 6 carbon atoms.

R_3 = hydrogen *or* a 1 to 4 carbon lower saturated alkyl.

R_1 = hydrogen *or* methyl.

R_2 = hydrogen *or* 1 to 4 carbon lower alkyl.

R_3 = hydrogen *or* a halogen (i.e. —Br or —Cl), cyano (i.e. —CN), —NO_2 *or* a lower alkyl of 1 to 4 carbon atoms.

3. Structure: Anthrapyridines
    Colours: Yellows, reds and browns

R_1 = a 1 to 4 carbon lower alkyl group *or* aryl grouping of about 6 carbons.

R_2 = hydrogen *or* 1 to 4 carbon lower alkyl.

R_3 = a 1 to 4 carbon alkyl group *or* aryl grouping of about 6 carbons.

TABLE 1—*contd.*

4. Structure: Pyridino anthrone
    Colours: Yellows and reds

R = hydrogen *or* a 1 to 4 carbon
saturated alkyl.

5. Structure: Anthrapyrimidine
    Colours: Yellows and reds

R = hydrogen *or* a 6 carbon aryl *or*
a 1 to 4 carbon saturated alkyl
or a halogen.

6. Structure: Anthrapyridones
    Colour: Violet

poly *N*-methylvinylamine and poly α-methylvinylamine. The length of the backbone is clearly of great importance to the technical performance of the colour. The optimum value for *n*, the number of amino groups on a polymer chain is found to be between 100 and 1500. In molecular weight terms, backbones meeting this criterion include polyvinylamine of molecular weight 4300 to 64 500 and poly *N*-methylvinylamine or poly α-methylvinylamine of molecular weight 5900 to 88 500. The amino linkages serving to attach covalently the chromophoric and water-solubilising

$$\begin{matrix} | & & | \\ NH & & NR \\ | & & | \\ XIV & & XV \end{matrix}$$

FIG. 11. Amino linkage. R = methyl, ethyl, propyl or butyl.

groups to the backbone may be secondary (XIV) or tertiary (XV), but the secondary is preferred (see Fig. 11).

The linkage is via a nitrogen–carbon covalent bond both to the hydrocarbon backbone and to the chromophoric or water-solubilising groups. The preferred chromophoric groups are water-insoluble types. From the viewpoints of stability and shade range it is claimed the most

TABLE 2

CHROMOPHORES FOR POLYMERIC DYES, SULPHONIC LINKAGE TO POLYMER

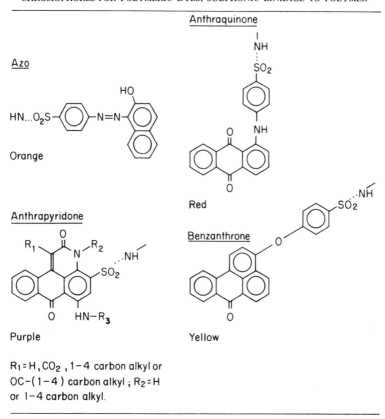

$R_1 = H, CO_2$, 1–4 carbon alkyl or
$OC-(1-4)$ carbon alkyl ; $R_2 = H$
or 1–4 carbon alkyl.

suitable are anthraquinone-based molecules having a 'leaving' group allowing easy attachment to the backbone by the known technique wherein copper is used to catalyse the leaving group's displacement by amines. The catalyst is not required in many cases however. Examples of suitable 'leaving' groups are —Cl, —Br, —I, —SO_3Na, —NO_2 attached to the aromatic ring.

Examples of suitable anthraquinone-based chromophores are shown in Table 1.[11]

Further chromophores, in this case featuring the sulphonamido linkage, are also disclosed, based on the azo, anthraquinone, anthrapyridone and benzanthrone structures, see Table 2.

These chromophores have monomeric forms containing a sulphonyl chloride group, enabling easy·attachment to the amine backbone via the Schotten–Baumann reaction.

SOLUBILISING GROUPS

Since most edible substrates contain water, it is highly desirable that polymeric food colours should be water soluble. Several methods of achieving solubility are possible. In one method the solubilising groups are incorporated in the backbone. A major disadvantage here however is the need to prepare a new backbone each time a change in solubility is required. Also, the presence of solubilising groups in the backbone may cause the polymer to break down under certain conditions. In a second method in which soluble chromophores only are used, the resultant limitation of choice precludes the use of some potentially highly stable structures. A third method, where solubilising groups are attached to the chromophores themselves leads to undesired modification of the structure and hence unpredictability of the final colour.

The best approach seems to be the attachment of water soluble and colour groups directly and separately, and is the one preferred in the patent.[11] One of the advantages claimed is that the resulting simple hydrocarbon backbone has great stability under the conditions of processing, storage and metabolism, and does not interfere with the colour properties of the attached chromophore. Secondly, the degree of solubilisation is independent of the shade and, thirdly, the amine linkage is very stable and hence there is essentially no risk of loss of solubility by detachment of solubilising groups. The preferred groups are:

$$-SO_3^-, \qquad -R-SO_3^- \qquad \text{and} \qquad -SO_2-R-O-SO_3^-$$

where R = a 2 to 4 carbon alkyl, or:

$$-SO_2-R-SO_3^-$$

where R = a 2 carbon alkyl.

Examples of the resulting structure after attachment of the solubilising groups is given in Fig. 12.

$$\begin{array}{cc}
-CH_2-CH- & -CH_2-CH- \\
| & | \\
NH & NH \\
| & | \\
SO_3^- & R-SO_3^- \\
\\
XVI & XVII
\end{array}$$

FIG. 12.   Solubilising group structure on backbone.

The $-SO_3^-$ groups are attached by treating the polymer with stabilised sulphur trioxide. The $-R-SO_3^-$ groups may be introduced by reaction with an amine alkylating sulphonate, e.g. propane sultone or butane sultone, or by nucleophilic displacement reactions with β substituted ethane sulphonic acid salts such as:

$$X-CH_2-CH_2SO_3Na$$

where X = $-Br$, $-Cl$, $-I$, $-OMe$ or $-SO_3^-$.

The $-SO_2-R-SO_3^-$ and $-SO_2-R-O-SO_3^-$ groups may be attached by reacting the polymer with compounds such as carbyl sulphate.

The patent[11] states that the invention claimed may be represented by the general structural formula in Fig. 13.

Normally amino groups are carried by at least one-eighth, but not more than one-half the backbone atoms. A portion (n) of these amines carries chromophores while a portion (m) carries solubilisers. The values of n are about 0·4 to 2 times those of m. If n is less than about 0·2 times m, the colour strength of the polymeric dye is too low. If n is greater than about 4 times m, the resulting product will often have reduced solubility in water. Similarly,

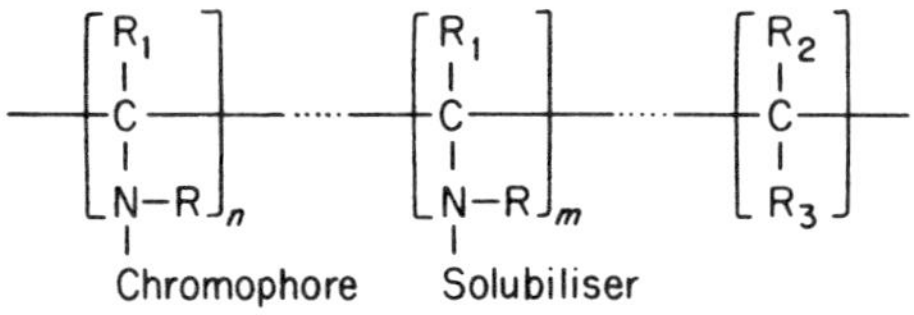

$$-\left[\begin{array}{c} R_1 \\ | \\ C \\ | \\ N-R \end{array}\right]_n \cdots \cdots \left[\begin{array}{c} R_1 \\ | \\ C \\ | \\ N-R \end{array}\right]_m \cdots \cdots \left[\begin{array}{c} R_2 \\ | \\ C \\ | \\ R_3 \end{array}\right]-$$

Chromophore   Solubiliser

FIG. 13.   Polymeric colourant: general structural formula.[11]

if less than about one-eighth the carbon backbones carry amine groups, the colour will be too weak, i.e. too much of the polymeric molecule will be non-chromophoric. If greater than one-half the backbone carbons carry an amine group, there is too great a tendency for reaction among the attached chromophoric and solubilising groups.

An outline of the preparation of the polymeric colours lists several methods.[11]

1. An *N*-vinylamine substituted chromophore (or precursor) can be polymerised with an *N*-vinylamine substituted solubiliser group under free radical conditions to yield the desired solubilised product. If a precursor is used, further processing is necessary.
2. A preformed backbone can be treated to attach solubilisers and then to attach chromophores.
3. A preformed backbone can be treated to attach chromophoric precursors and then to attach solubilisers and finally to convert precursors to chromophores.
4. A preformed backbone can be treated to add chromophores and thereafter treated to attach solubilisers.

Experience has shown that the first method does not permit close control of molecular size. The second method gives excellent results when the amines of the uncombined backbone are secondary amines, since it is only possible for a solubiliser or a chromophore, and not both, to be attached to a single amine. When a primary amine-containing backbone is employed, it is likely that there will be a mixture of single and double attachment to a single amine. If the colour of the chromophore is dependent upon the double versus single attachment, there may be problems with the predictability of the resulting shade. The third method eliminates this difficulty and is an effective route to polymeric colours. The fourth route is preferred because of the increased degree of selectivity which can be obtained when attaching solubilisation groups. The patent[11] discloses full preparation details of numerous examples.

USE OF POLYMERIC COLOURS IN FOOD

The novel effects of the use of polymeric colours in food coloration are outlined in three patents, one describing their general use,[12] while the others mention specific novel effects.[13,14]

During development of the concept of polymeric colours, it was discovered that when they are used as colourants for translucent substrates such as beverages, cordials, soft drinks, jellies, boiled sweets and cough syrups etc., they exhibit greater colouring power weight for weight than do monomeric colours.[13] The amount of polymeric colour required ranges from 0·4–0·9 times the amount of monomeric dye required to produce the same colouring effects. As a general guide, polymeric dyes containing relatively larger proportions of non-chromophoric material, e.g. 50:50 chromophore:non-chromophore, show less advantage than those polymeric colours containing a smaller proportion of non-chromophoric material.

A further patent[14] makes use of the non-migrating characteristics of the polymeric colours. When semi-solid visco-elastic foodstuffs such as gelatin desserts, pies, and fruit parfaits etc. are coloured with conventional dyes, colour migration occurs to a greater or lesser extent. This is desirable for uniform effects, but it is a disadvantage where varicoloured products are required. To counteract this effect, the insolubilised 'Lake' forms of permitted water-soluble colours have been used and although migration is cut down appreciably, the colours tend to give cloudy appearances. When polymeric colours are used however, the cloudiness is eliminated, and a stable clear varicoloured effect is obtained. It is claimed that the colours work well in aqueous protein gels such as gelatin, as well as polysaccharide gels such as pectin, both of which are widely used in the food industry. Other substrates such as partially hydrolysed collagen glues, casein and egg albumin have been successfully coloured also. Generally, the preferred substrates contain from 60 % to 98 % by weight of water.

The coloration method involves dissolving the polymeric dye in the substrate material in a fluid state, then allowing the mass to revert to its semi-solid state. The multizoned effect is achieved by next adding a differently coloured, semi-liquid substrate and allowing that, in turn, to solidify. In this manner, for example, two- or three-layered fruit parfaits can be produced having excellent stability under refrigerated conditions. Another method describes how two or three or more different coloured substrates may be lightly mixed in semi-liquid state to achieve a 'swirling' effect suitable for novelty puddings or children's confectionery as examples. Coloration levels of 25–200 ppm are reported to give excellent effects.

SELECTION OF POLYMERIC DYES FOR FOOD COLORATION

The polymeric dye concept, as an alternative to the current synthetic colours, is being developed with a view to establishing a food additive toxicology which is 'beyond criticism'. Work is also being carried out on devising a similar system for sweeteners and antioxidants.

A basic range of colours has been selected for development based on its technical performance and ability to match known food industry target shades.[15]

Poly Y-607	Yellow
Poly D	Orange
Poly R-481	Red
Poly R-478	Red–violet
Poly B	Blue

'Poly' is the registered trade-mark of the Dynapol Corporation work carried out using ^{14}C radiolabelled polymeric colours which indicates no absorption for practical purposes during feeding tests compared with considerable absorption of current FD and C certified colours under similar circumstances. The selected colours have also been proven negative in the Ames-type mutagenicity tests, both before and after subjecting to the action of heat and light:[15] manufacturing reaction by-products have also proved negative. Other toxicological tests planned or in progress are acute oral toxicity, 90-day toxicity, lifetime carcinogenicity, three-generation reproduction and teratology, and one-year toxicity. The tests are being carried out on rats, mice, dogs and rabbits and should take $2\frac{1}{2}$–3 years. The findings are expected to prove uneventful.

The polymeric colours are interchangeable with FD and C certified colours in food processing operations and in comparison with the insolubilised 'Lake' colours show improved technical performance in that higher strength colours of much improved fastness to bleeding are possible.[15] In practice excellent fastness performance to light, heat, acids and preservatives has been demonstrated in all major food colour applications, in many cases superior to the fastness performance of the traditional synthetic colours. The fact that the colours do not migrate, while being an advantage in some applications,[14] does mean that they cannot be used in some traditional outlets such as in maraschino and glacé cherries (at least by conventional methods) and they may also be unsuitable in canned fruits and vegetables.

Strength relationships with FD and C certifiable colours, i.e. relative total dye weights to match most 'food' shades, are stated to vary between 1:1 and 25:1, averaging 2:1. These ratios are expected to result in up to a sixfold increase in cost compared with the certifiable colours, although even at this level, the increased cost of say a kilogram of dessert powder or a gallon of soft drink would be negligible.

In the event of the banning of currently approved food colours a range of polymeric colours such as described above with regulatory clearance could prove invaluable in retaining the accepted shade characteristics of processed food. Even where polymeric dyes are listed alongside the current certified range, a number of food manufacturers and some major chain stores might consider it worth while to pay the premium for what is perceived as enhanced safety-in-use.

REFERENCES

1. US Patents 3 519 617 (7 July 1970) and 3 640 733 (8 February 1972) both assigned to Allied Chemical Corporation, New York, USA.
2. McCormick, R. D., 'Allura Red—New Food Colour Offers Greater Brilliance and Stability', Food Product Development, February–March, 1971.
3. Ministry of Agriculture Fisheries and Food, Food Additives and Contaminants Committee Interim Report on the Review of The Colouring Matter in Food Regulations, 1973. FAC/REP/29 1979.
4. Dutch Patent NL 159 131. (15 January 1979) assigned to Allied Chemical Corporation, New York, USA.
5. UK Patent 1 270 656 (12 April 1972) assigned to Unilever Limited, Port Sunlight, UK.
6. UK Patent 1 434 526 (5 May 1976) assigned to the Beecham Group, London.
7. Belgian Patent BE 870 061 (18 December 1978) assigned to General Foods Corporation New York, USA.
8. US Patent 4 133 900 (9 January 1979) assigned to General Foods Corporation, New York, USA.
9. US Patent 4 139 645 (13 February 1979) assigned to the Sterling Drug Co, USA.
10. US Patent 3 920 855 (18 November 1975) assigned to the Dynapol Corporation, Palo Alto, California, USA.
11. US Patent 4 000 118 (28 December 1976) assigned to the Dynapol Corporation, Palo Alto, California, USA.
12. US Patents 4 051 138 (27 September 1977) and 4 144 252 (13 March 1979) assigned to the Dynapol Corporation, Palo Alto, California, USA.
13. US Patent 3 940 503 (24 February 1976) assigned to the Dynapol Corporation, Palo Alto, California, USA.
14. US Patent 3 937 851 (10 February 1976) assigned to the Dynapol Corporation, Palo Alto, California, USA.
15. Furia, T. E., 'Nonabsorbable Polymeric Food Colours', Food Technology, 31 May 1977, p. 34.

Chapter 5

ANTHOCYANINS

COLIN F. TIMBERLAKE and PETER BRIDLE

Long Ashton Research Station, Bristol, UK

SUMMARY

The types of anthocyanins which occur naturally are described and their distribution in edible plant material is documented. Recent work on structural transformations of pure pigments induced by pH changes shows the existence of four chemical species; their equilibria and kinetic effects are discussed. In natural products, additional physico-chemical effects influence colour, e.g. 'self-association', co-pigmentation, metal complexing and intramolecular interactions which stabilise certain acylated anthocyanins. In a review of reactions of anthocyanins in food systems, particular emphasis is given to the 'amphoteric' nature of the anthocyanin cation and the bleaching action of sulphur dioxide. The bulk of the chapter deals with the development of anthocyanins as food colour additives, viz. requirements, sources, economics, extraction, purification, formulation, stability, applications and analysis. Some problems remain, but these may well be overcome by greater understanding of anthocyanin chemistry.

INTRODUCTION

Among the pleasures of life the appreciation of good food and drink must surely rank high. Colour plays an important role in our enjoyment of foodstuffs and in our assessment of their quality. Such is the bond or association between the flavours of fruits and their colours that, if it is not realised, the consumer is psychologically upset or confused. Colour is liked for its own sake—thus much of the charm of red wine lies in its colour and its subtle variations during ageing which are reflected in corresponding changes in aroma and flavour. Among the natural pigments, the anthocyanins are the largest water-soluble group responsible for the attractive colours ranging from strawberry to blue, of most fruits, juices, flowers and leaves. Anthocyanins have been on earth presumably since the appearance of the flowering plants some hundred million years ago, but Man has investigated them in detail only since the turn of this century. Thanks to the researches of Willstätter, Robinson, Hayashi and Harborne among others, we now know a great deal of their chemistry and properties. But there are many features, particularly those relating to the physico-chemical basis of fruit and flower colour, which require further work to enable a fuller understanding of the factors affecting colour to be made. This review will emphasise current work in this field as well as describing the types of anthocyanins, their occurrence and distribution in edible plants, structural transformations, reactions in model and food systems and the development work being devoted to extraction, purification, evaluation and analysis of anthocyanin extracts as potential food colours.

TYPES OF ANTHOCYANINS

The anthocyanins are flavylium or 2-phenylbenzopyrylium salts. They are part of the C15 group of compounds known collectively as flavonoids and are glycosides of anthocyanidins (or aglycones). The major anthocyanidins and the numbering of their carbon atoms are illustrated in Fig. 1; rarer ones include the recently discovered 5-O-methyl cyanidin[1] and others documented previously.[2,3] Anthocyanin sugars comprise:

(a) monosides, principally glucose, galactose, rhamnose and arabinose;
(b) biosides derived from combinations of these four monosides and xylose, e.g. rutinose, sambubiose, lathyrose, sophorose, gentiobiose, neohesperidose, laminariobiose and robinobiose among others; and
(c) triosides containing combination of the above sugars in linear or branched-chain arrangements.

Position 3 of the molecule is always occupied by a sugar. Position 5 may contain glucose or rarely rhamnose.[4-6] To lesser extents, positions 7, 3',5' and possibly 4' can also be substituted, usually with glucose. Many of the sugars are acylated, usually with phenolic acids such as p-coumaric, caffeic, ferulic and sinapic acids, and, more rarely p-hydrobenzoic,

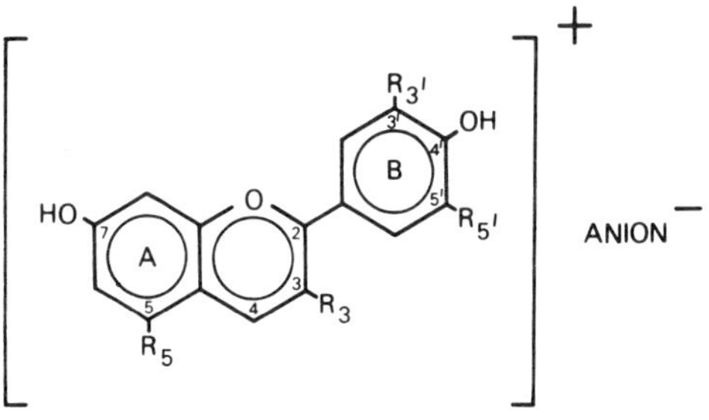

ANTHOCYANIDINS : R_3 = OH , R_5 = OH

		R_3'	R_5'
PELARGONIDIN	(Pg)	H	H
CYANIDIN·	(Cy)	OH	H
PEONIDIN	(Pn)	OCH_3	H
DELPHINIDIN	(Dp)	OH	OH
PETUNIDIN	(Pt)	OCH_3	OH
MALVIDIN	(Mv)	OCH_3	OCH_3

ANTHOCYANINS : Pg, Cy, Pn, Dp, Pt, Mv with

R_3 = O - sugar or O - acylated sugar

R_5 = OH or O - glucose

FIG. 1.   The common anthocyanidins and anthocyanins.

malonic and acetic acids. The acylating groups are usually attached to the 6-hydroxyl group of glucose (that glucose residue adjacent to the anthocyanidin if the anthocyanin is a 3-diglucoside) and the 4-hydroxyl group of rhamnose. In all acylated anthocyanins so far characterised completely, the acyl group is attached only to the sugar in position 3 of the molecule. However, recently discovered anthocyanins, such as delphinidin 3-rutinoside-5,3',5'-triglucoside (incidentally the first pentaglycoside reported in *Nature*) contain four moles of phenolic acid[7] some of which may be attached to glucose in positions other than 3. Glycosidation in position 3 confers solubility and stability on the aglycone. The natures of the individual sugars have little general effect but their positions in the molecule have a pronounced effect on the occurrence and reactivity of their various chemical forms.

OCCURRENCE AND DISTRIBUTION

Table 1 lists anthocyanins identified in edible plant material[8] and mentioned in *Chemical Abstracts* to the end of 1978. Data have been

TABLE 1
ANTHOCYANINS IN EDIBLE PLANTS

Common name	Botanical name	Organ/cv.	Anthocyanins present	Reference
APPLE	Malus pumila	(Skin)	Cy 3-glucoside, 3-galactoside, 3-xyloside, 3- and 7-arabinosides free and acylated	9–13
ARTICHOKE (globe)	Cynara scolymus		Cy 3-caffeylglucoside, 3-caffeylsophoroside and 3-dicaffeylsophoroside	14
ASPARAGUS	Asparagus officinalis	(Shoot)	Cy and Pn 3-rhamnosylglucosides. 3-rhamnosyl diglucosides. Cy 3-glucoside and 3,5-diglucoside	15, 16
AUBERGINE	Solanum melongena	(Skin)	Dp 3-glucoside, 3-rutinoside, 3-p-coumaryl-rutinoside-5-glucoside, 3,5-diglucoside, 3-p-coumarylglucoside-5-glucoside, 3-p-coumaryl-rutinoside, 3-caffeyldiglucoside-5-glucoside, 3-diglucoside-5-glucoside and 3-rutinoside-5-glucoside	17–22
BANANA	Musa sapientum	(Fruit)	3-deoxyanthocyanidins	23
BARBERRY	Berberis buxifolia		Dp and Mv 3-glucosides and rutinosides, Pn and Pt 3-rutinoside-5-glucosides and 3-glucosides, Pt 3-rutinoside and 3-gentiobioside	24
	B. thunbergii		Pg and Cy 3-glucosides	25
BEAN (bush)	Phaseolus vulgaris	(Seed coat)	Pg and Cy 3,5-diglucosides and Pg, Cy and Dp 3-glucosides	26, 27
BEAN (French)	P. vulgaris		Pg, Cy and Dp 3,5-diglucosides and Pg, Cy, Dp, Pt and Mv 3-glucosides	2, 28
		(Hypocotyl)	Mv, 3,5-diglucoside	29
BEAN (mung)	P. aureus	(Hypocotyl)	Dp 3-glucoside	29
		(Cotyledon)	Dp 3,5-diglucoside free and p-coumaryl ester	30
BEAN (runner)	P. multiflorus	(Pod)	Mv 3,5-diglucoside	2
BEAN 'AZUKI'	Phaseolus sp.	(Seed coat)	Dp 3-glucoside	31

BLACKBERRY	*Rubus fruticosus*	cvs.	Cy 3-rutinoside and 3-glucoside	32
			Cy 3-glucoside (acylated), Mv biosides and Cy glycosides	33
BLUEBERRY (lowbush)	*Vaccinium angustifolium*		Cy, Pn, Dp, Pt and Mv 3-glucosides, 3-galactosides and 3-arabinosides	34
BLUEBERRY (highbush)	*V. corymbosum*		Cy, Pn, Dp, Pt and Mv 3-glucosides and galactosides and Pn, Dp, Pt and Mv 3-arabinosides	35, 36
		cv. 'Wolcott'	Cy, Pn, Dp, Pt and Mv 3-glucosides, 3-galactosides and 3-arabinosides	37
BOYSENBERRY	*Rubus* sp.		Cy 3-rutinoside-5-glucoside, 3,5-diglucoside, 3-rutinoside, 3-glucoside, 3-glucosylrutinoside and 3-sophoroside	38–40
CABBAGE (red)	*Brassica oleracea*	(Leaf)	Cy 3-malonylisophoroside-5-glucoside, 3-*p*-coumarylsophoroside-5-glucoside, 3-di-*p*-coumarylsophoroside-5-glucoside, 3-ferulylisophoroside-5-glucoside, 3-di-ferulylsophoroside-5-glucoside, 3-sinapyl-sophoroside-5-glucoside, 3-disinapylsophoro-side-5-glucoside and free 3-sophoroside-5-glucoside and 3,5-diglucoside	2, 41–43
CARROT (black)	*Daucus carota* ssp. *sativa*	(Root)	Cy 3-xylosylglucosylgalactoside ferulyl ester and free, and 3-xylosylgalactoside	44
CELERY	*Apium graveolens*	(Stem)	Cy 3-xylosylglucosylgalactoside, ferulyl, sinapyl and *p*-coumaryl esters	44
CHERRY (sweet)	*Prunus avium*	var. 'Bing' and cvs.	Cy 3-rutinoside and 3-glucoside	32, 45
			Cy and Pn 3-rutinosides and 3-glucosides	46, 47
CHERRY (sour)	*P. cerasus*	'Montmorency'	Cy 3-glucosylrutinoside, 3-sophoroside, 3-rutinoside and 3-glucoside	32, 47–49
			Cy 3-xylosylrutinoside, 3-glucosylrutinoside, 3-sophoroside, 3-rutinoside, 3-glucoside and Pn 3-rutinoside	50–52
		vars.	Cy 3-gentiobioside, 3-glycoside, 3-rutinoside and 3-glucoside	53, 54

TABLE 1—*contd*

Common name	Botanical name	Organ/cv.	Anthocyanins present	Reference
CHERRY	*Prunus* spp.		Cy 3-diglucoside (acylated), 3-glucoside and Pn 3-diglucoside	33
			Cy 3-rutinoside and 3-glucoside	55
			Cy 3,5-diglucoside and 3-rutinoside	56
			Cy 3-sophoroside, 3-rutinoside, 3-glucoside and Pn 3-rutinoside	57
COCOA	*Theobroma cacao*	(Pod)	Cy 3-arabinoside and 3-galactoside	58
COWBERRY	*Vaccinium vitis-idaea*		Cy 3-xylosylglucoside and Mv 3,5-diglycoside	59
CRANBERRY	*Vaccinium macrocarpon*		Cy and Pn 3-arabinosides and 3-galactosides	34, 60, 61
			Cy and Pn 3-glucosides, 3-arabinosides and 3-galactosides	62–64
CURRANT (red)	*Ribes rubrum*		Cy 3-xylosylrutinoside, 3-glucosylrutinoside, 3-sambubioside, 3-sophoroside, 3-rutinoside and 3-glucoside	32
CURRANT (black)	*R. nigrum*		Cy and Dp 3-rutinosides and 3-glucosides	32, 48, 65
			Cy 3-glucoside and diglucoside and Dp 3-diglucoside and 3-glucoside (both acylated)	33
DURRA or EGYPTIAN RICE CORN	*Sorghum durra*	(Grain)	Pg and Cy glycosides	66
		(Glume)	Ap and Lt glycosides	67
ELDERBERRY	*Sambucus nigra*		Cy 3-sambubioside-5-glucoside, 3-sambubioside and 3-glucoside	68
FENNEL	*Foeniculum vulgare*	(Stem)	Cy 3-xylosylglucosylgalactoside ferulyl and sinapyl esters	44
FIG	*Ficus carica*	(Skin)	Cy 3-glucoside	69
			Pg 3-rutinoside and Cy 3,5-diglucoside, 3-rutinoside and 3-glucoside	70
GARLIC	*Allium sativa*		Cy 3-glucoside and acyl derivative	71
GOOSEBERRY	*Ribes grossularia*		Cy 3-rutinoside and 3-glucoside	32

GRAPE (red)

Vitis vinifera		Cy, Pn, Dp, Pt and Mv 3-*p*-coumarylglucosides, 3-caffeylglucosides, 3-acetylglucosides, 3-glucosides and Pn, Dp, Pt and Mv 3-di-*p*-coumarylglucosides	72–80
	'Trousseau'	Cy, Pn, Pt and Mv 3-glucosides	81
	'Barbera'	Pn, Dp, Pt and Mv 3-glucosides, Cy 3-caffeylglucoside and 3-*p*-coumarylglucoside, Mv 3-*p*-coumarylglucoside also acylated Pn and Mv 3-glucosides	82
	'Tinta Cao'	Cy, Pn, Pt and Mv 3-glucosides, Mv and Pn 3-*p*-coumarylglucosides and Cy, Pt and Mv 3-caffeylglucosides	83
V. labrusca	'Concord'	Cy, Pn, Dp, Pt and Mv 3-*p*-coumarylglucosides-5-glucosides, 3,5-diglucosides, 3-*p*-coumarylglucosides and 3-glucosides	84, 85
V. cinerea		Cy, Pn, Dp, Pt and Mv 3-*p*-coumarylglucosides, 3-caffeylglucosides and 3-glucosides	86
V. flexuosa		Dp, Pt and Mv 3-glucosides and Mv 3,5-diglucoside and 3-sophoroside-5-glucoside also 5 other pigments	87
V. rotundifolia		Cy, Pn, Dp, Pt and Mv 3,5-diglucosides	88
Vitis spp.		Pn, Dp, Pt and Mv 3,5-diglucosides and 3-glucosides also Cy 3-glucoside, acyl derivatives and mixed diglucosides	89–94
		Cy, Pn, Dp, Pt and Mv mono- and diglucosides, free and acylated	95
Vitis vars./hybrids	'Rubired'	Pn, Dp, Pt and Mv 3,5-diglucosides and 3-glucosides, Mv 3-*p*-coumarylglucoside and 3-*p*-coumarylglucoside-5-glucoside and Pn 3-*p*-coumarylglucoside	96
	'Mavrud' 'Pamid' 'Saperavi'	Pn, Dp, Pt and Mv 3-glucosides	97, 98
	'Campbell Early'	Cy, Pn and Dp 3,5-diglucosides and 3-glucosides	99

TABLE 1—contd

Common name	Botanical name	Organ/cv.	Anthocyanins present	Reference
		'Seibel 9549'	Cy, Pn, Dp, Pt and Mv 3,5-diglucosides	100
		'Seibel 13053'	Pn, Dp, Pt and Mv 3,5-diglucosides and 3-glucosides	101
		'Royalty'	Cy, Pn, Dp, Pt and Mv 3-glucosides Pn, Pt and Mv 3,5-diglucosides, Pn and Mv 3-p-coumarylglucosides and 3-p-coumarylglucoside-5-glucosides and Mv 3-caffeylglucoside-5-glucoside	102
WINES		Hybrid grape wine (151 grape vars.)	Cy, Pn, Dp, Pt and Mv 3-glucosides, and 3,5-diglucosides	103
HUCKLEBERRY	Solanum nigrum		Cy, Pn, Dp and Mv acyl derivatives	104
		Var. guineense	Pt 3-rutinoside-5-glucoside and p-coumaryl ester Pt 3-rutinoside-5-glucoside-di-p-coumaryl ester and Mv 3-(p-coumarylrutinoside)-5-glucoside	105
LITCHI	Litchi chinensis		Pg 3,5-diglucoside and 3-glucoside and Cy 3-galactoside and 3-glucoside	106
LOGANBERRY	Rubus loganobaccus		Cy 3-glucosylrutinoside, 3-sophoroside, 3-rutinoside and 3-glucoside	48
MAIZE (Indian corn)	Zea mays	(Aleurone)	Pg and Cy 3-glucosides and acyl derivatives	107
		(Tissue)	Lt, Pg, Cy and Pn + 5 unidentified pigments	108
		(Kernel and cob)	Pg, Cy and Pn 3-glucosides	109
(Bolivian purple corn)			Pn 3-galactoside	110
MANGO	Mangifera indica	(Rind)	Cy 3-sophoroside and 3-glucoside	111
MANGOSTEEN	Garcinia mangostana		Ap, Lt and Cy glycosides	112–114
MILLET	Sorghum vulgare	(Seed)	Cy and Dp 3-galactosides, 3-arabinosides and 3-glucosides	115
MIRACLE FRUIT	Synsepalum dulcificum	(Skin)		
MULBERRY	Morus nigra		Cy 3-glucoside	2,116
	M. alba		Cy 3,5-diglucoside and 3-glucoside and Dp 3-glucoside	117
			Cy 3-rutinoside and 3-glucoside	118

OLIVE	*Olea europaea*		Cy triosides, 3-rutinoside and 3-glucoside	119
	Olea sp.		Cy 3-caffeylrhamnosyldiglucoside, 3-caffeyl-rutinoside, 3-glucoside, Cy and Pn 3-*p*-coumarylglucosides and Pn 3-rhamnosyldiglucoside	120
	Olea sp.		Cy 3-glucosylrutinoside-caffeyl ester, Cy 3-glucosylrutinoside linear and branched, 3-rutinoside free and caffeyl ester and 3-glucoside	121
ONION	*Allium cepa*		Pn 3-arabinoside	122
			Cy 3-diglucoside and Cy and Pn 3-glucosides	123
			Cy 3-laminariobioside	124
ORANGE	*Citrus sinensis*	'Blood orange'	Cy and Dp 3-glucosides	125
		'Moro orange'	Cy 3-glucoside	126
			Cy 3,5-diglucoside and Cy, Dp and Pt 3-glucosides and Pn 5-glucoside also 2 unidentified pigments	127
PASSION FRUIT	*Passiflora edulis*	(Flesh)	Dp 3-glucoside	2
PEA	*Pisum sativa*	(Rind)	Pg 3-glucosylglucoside	2
		(Pod)	Cy 3-sambubioside-5-glucoside and 3-sophoroside-5-glucoside	2
PEACH	*Prunus persica*		Cy and Dp 3-sophoroside-5-glucosides and 3-sambubioside-5-glucosides	128
			Cy 3-glucoside	76, 118, 129–131
PEAR	*Pyrus communis*		Cy 3-rutinoside, 3-glucoside, 3-galactoside and 3-arabinoside	2, 12, 132
PEPPER (Japanese)	*Zanthoxylum piperitum*		Cy 3-rutinoside	118
PLUM (cherry)	*Prunus cerasifera*		Cy and Pn 3-rutinosides and 3-glucosides	133
PLUM (Japanese)	*P. salicina*		Cy 3-rutinoside and 3-glucoside	118
PLUM	*P. domestica*	'Santa Rosa'	Cy and Pn 3-rutinosides and 3-glucosides	2, 48, 134
			Cy 3-xylosylglucoside and 3-glucoside	135
POMEGRANATE	*Punica granatum*		Pg, Cy and Dp 3,5-diglucosides and 3-glucosides	2, 136, 137

TABLE 1—contd

Common name	Botanical name	Organ/cv.	Anthocyanins present	Reference
POTATO	Solanum tuberosum		Pg, Pn, Pt and Mv 3-rutinoside-5-glucoside-p-coumaryl esters and Pg, Cy, Dp and Pt 3-rutinosides and Pn 3-ferulylrutinoside-5-glucoside	138–140
POTATO (sweet)	Ipomoea batatas	(Tuber)	Cy 3-sophoroside-5-glucoside-caffeyl ester	2
		(Stem)	Cy and Pn 3-diglucoside-5-glucoside-dicaffeyl esters	141
QUINCE	Cydonia oblonga	(Fruit)	Cy 3,5-diglucoside and 3-glucoside	142
RADISH	Raphanus sativus	(Root)	Pg and Cy 3-sophoroside-5-glucoside-p-coumaryl and ferulyl esters	143, 144
	R. caudatus		Mv 3,5-diglucoside	145
	Raphanus		Pg 3-glucoside	146
RASPBERRY (red)	Rubus idaeus	3 cvs.	Cy 3-glucosylrutinoside, 3-sophoroside, 3-rutinoside and 3-glucoside	32, 134, 147, 148
			Pg and Cy 3-glucosides and Cy 3-glucosyl-rutinoside, 3-sophoroside and 3-rutinoside	48, 149
			Cy 3-glucosylrutinoside, 3-sophoroside, 3-rutinoside and 3-glucoside, free and acylated	150
		cv. Willamette	Cy 3,5-diglucoside. 3-sophoroside and 3-glucoside and Pg glycoside	40
		cv. Meeker	Cy 3-glucosylrutinoside, 3-sophoroside, 3-rutinoside and 3-glucoside and Pg glycoside	40
			Cy 3-diglucosylrhamnoside, 3-diglucoside, 3-rutinoside and 3-glucoside	151
			Pg and Cy 3-glucosylrutinosides, 3-sophorosides, 3-rutinosides and 3-glucosides and Cy 3,5-diglucoside	152

Common name	Latin name	Part	Anthocyanins	Ref.
RASPBERRY (black)	Rubus occidentalis		Cy 3-xylosylrutinoside, 3-sambubioside, 3-rutinoside and 3-glucoside	32, 39
			Cy 3-rutinoside-5-glucoside, 3-diglucoside, 3,5-diglucoside and 3-glucoside	153, 154
RHUBARB	Rheum rhaponticum		Cy 3-rutinoside and 3-glucoside	155–158
RYE	Secale cereale	(Seed)	Cy and Pn 3-rutinosides and 3-glucosides, free and acylated and Dp 3-rutinoside	159, 160
SALMONBERRY	Rubus spectabilis		Cy 3-glucosylrutinoside, 3,5-diglucoside, 3-sophoroside, 3-rutinoside and 3-glucoside	40
SAMPHIRE	Crithmum maritimum	(Leaf)	Cy 3-xylosylglucosylgalactoside sinapyl ester	44
SLOE	Prunus spinosa		Cy and Pn 3-rutinosides and 3-glucosides	32
SOYBEAN	Glycine maxima	(Seed coat)	Cy 3-glucoside	161
			Cy and Dp 3-glucosides	162
STRAWBERRY	Fragaria x ananmasa		Pg and Cy 3-glucosides	48, 118, 144, 149, 163–166
	F. vesca		Pg and Cy 3-glucosides	48, 167
SUGAR CANE	Saccharum sp.	(Peel)	Pn 3-galactoside	168
TAMARILLO	Cyphomandra betaceae	(Fruit)	Pg, Cy and Dp 3-rutinosides and 3-glucosides	169
TARO	Colocasia antiquorum		Pg and Cy 3-glucosides and Cy 3-rhamnoside	170
THIMBLEBERRY	Rubus parviflorus		Pg and Cy 3-rutinosides and 3-glucosides	40
WHEAT	Triticum aestivum	(Pericarp)	Cy and Pn 3-rutinosides and free and acylated 3-glucosides	160
WHORTLEBERRY	Vaccinium myrtillus		Dp 3-rutinoside, 5-glucoside and 3-glucoside	59
YAM	Dioscorea alata	(Fruit)	Cy 3,5-diglucoside	171
			Cy 3-ferulylgentiobioside and two ferulylglycosides	172
	D. tryphida	(Tuber)	Pn and Mv 3,5-diglucosides and Mv 3,5-diglucoside ferulyl ester	173
	D. batatas		p-coumaryl esters of Cy 3-gentiobioside, Mv 3-gentiobioside-5-rhamnoside and 3-gentiobioside-5-glucoside	5

Key to abbreviations: Ap = Apigeninidin, Lt = Luteolinidin, Pg = Pelargonidin, Cy = Cyanidin, Pn = Peonidin, Dp = Delphinidin, Pt = Petunidin and Mv = Malvidin.

confined largely to the edible portions with additional information on other organs or species where it is thought helpful to indicate the type of pigments present. For example, the edible barberry is *Berberis vulgaris*, but its pigments do not appear to have been identified. Related species have been included however to indicate the anthocyanins occurring in the genus. For brevity we have recorded all identifications without listing authors' individual findings.

Table 1 does not include several sources suggested for commercial exploitation (e.g. calyces of Roselle, leaves of cherry plum) which might not normally be considered edible. Extensive lists of pigments identified in other plant material have been documented previously.[2,3] There may be many rich sources but these would need careful purification before their safety-in-use could be established by consideration of chemical and toxicological data.

STRUCTURAL TRANSFORMATIONS

An intriguing feature of the anthocyanins is the way in which their colours vary according to pH. In acid solutions they are red but the intensity of colour decreases with rise in pH. Freshly made neutral or alkaline solutions are violet or blue but their colours fade slowly. The nature of the chemical structures which the anthocyanins can adopt has been clarified recently.[174-176] Protonation of the blue quinoidal base (A) gives the red flavylium cation (AH$^+$), which hydrates to a colourless carbinol pseudo-base (B), itself existing in tautomeric equilibrium with its chalcone (C) also colourless, according to the following scheme:

$$A \xrightleftharpoons[]{H^+} AH^+ \xrightleftharpoons[H^+]{H_2O} B \xrightleftharpoons[]{} C$$

proton transfer hydration tautomeric equilibrium

and illustrated in Fig. 2 for malvidin 3-glucoside. The stabilities of these four structures as a function of pH when equilibrium conditions have been attained is shown in Fig. 3(a). In very acid solutions (pH < 0·5) the red cation AH$^+$ is the sole structure. With increasing pH its concentration decreases as hydration to the colourless carbinol base (B) occurs, the equilibrium being characterised by a pK value—in this case 2·6—when equal amounts of both forms exist. Already at this pH, small amounts of the colourless chalcone (C) and the blue quinoidal base (A) are also present and

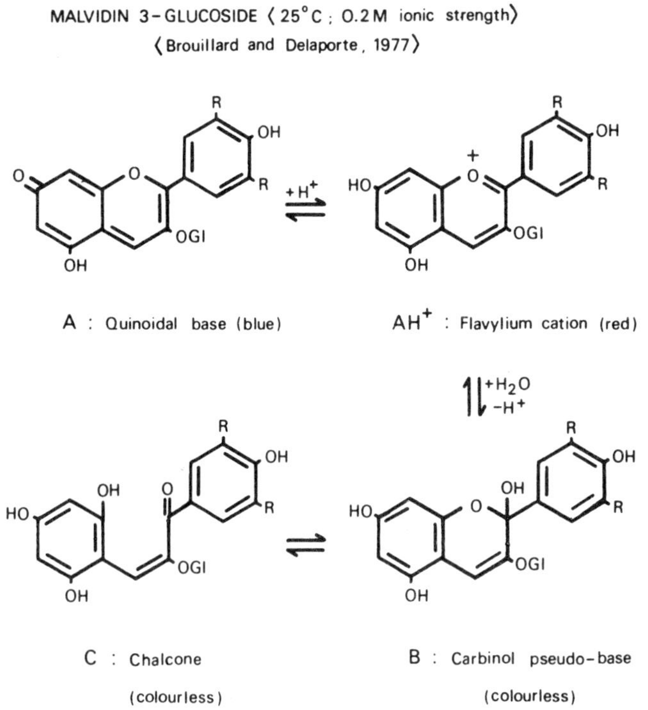

MALVIDIN – GLUCOSIDE ⟨ 25°C ; 0.2 M ionic strength⟩
⟨Brouillard and Delaporte, 1977⟩

A : Quinoidal base (blue)   AH⁺ : Flavylium cation (red)

FIG. 2.   Anthocyanin structural transformations with pH.

the proportions of these and the carbinol base increase with increasing pH at the expense of the red cationic form (AH^+) up to about pH 4·5. Between pH 4 and 5·5 very little colour remains in the anthocyanin since the amounts of both coloured forms, viz. the cation and quinoidal base are very small. The equilibrium between these is also characterised by a pK value 4·25, when the solution is violet. Between pH 5 and 6, a very small amount of the quinoidal base is the only coloured form present. The diagram thus indicates the most disadvantageous feature of anthocyanins when considered as food colours, viz. the lack of colour in weakly acid and near neutral solutions.

Anthocyanin 3,5-diglycosides exhibit even less colour than the 3-glycosides, because the pK value for the equilibrium between the cationic form and the carbinol base of a diglycoside is approximately one pH unit lower than that of the 3-glycoside,[177] as shown in Fig. 3(b). There is much less colour over the whole pH range and solutions are practically colourless

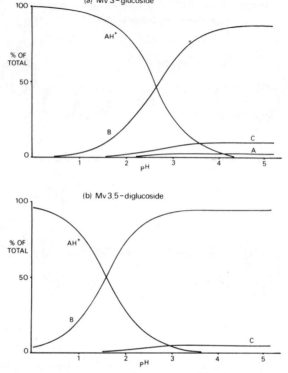

FIG. 3.   Distribution of structures with pH (25 °C).

between pH 4 and 6 since the percentage of quinoidal base is now so small as to be almost negligible.

The colour changes induced by pH and temperature variations have been explained by kinetic studies;[174-176] they indicate that the rate of deprotonation of the cation (to form the quinoidal base A) is significantly faster than its rate of hydration (to form the carbinol base B). Ring opening of (B) to form chalcone (C) is significantly slower again. However, because the magnitude of the hydration equilibrium constant is much greater than that of the proton transfer equilibrium, the quinoidal base is unstable and rearranges (through AH^+) into the carbinol base and chalcone.

From left to right in the scheme, all the reactions are endothermic so that heating shifts all equilibria to the right, i.e. towards the chalcone. On cooling and acidification, which is the usual method of investigating so-called thermal degradation of anthocyanins, the quinoidal base (A) and the carbinol base (B) very quickly transform to the cationic form (AH^+), but the change of the chalcone (C) is very slow. Thus, sufficient time for re-equilibration should be allowed; this has been rarely done in previous investigations of thermal degradation.

STABILISATION AND AUGMENTATION BY PHYSICO-CHEMICAL EFFECTS

From considerations of pH the anthocyanins appear unsuitable and wasteful compounds as far as colour is concerned since they exist largely in colourless forms over a wide pH range. How then can we explain the many vivid colours of fruits, fruit juices, wines, flower petals and leaves? Several mechanisms are suggested, although far from explained, by which the coloured forms can be stabilised and augmented so that considerable colour results even at unfavourable pH values.

The first of these mechanisms is the ion-association or 'self-association' of the cationic form. In colorimetric analysis, the colour of most solutions increases linearly with concentration in accordance with Beer's Law, until at sufficiently high concentrations colour increases less than pro-portionately. Indeed this situation pertains in acid solutions (pH < 1) of red wine anthocyanins which have to be very dilute to obey Beer's Law.[178] But at higher pH values (3-4) the opposite situation prevails; colour increases more than proportionally to its concentration, an effect attributed to 'self-association' of the anthocyanin molecules. Thus at pH 3·16 a 100-fold increase in concentration (from 10^{-4} to 10^{-2} M of cyanidin, 3,5-diglucoside), resulted in a 300-fold increase in absorbance.[179] Two points need emphasising: (a) strongly coloured anthocyanin solutions should be measured without dilution using short path-length cells if necessary and, (b) it is vital to prevent even a small pigment loss in a foodstuff, since this can result in proportionately greater loss in colour.

The second effect producing colour augmentation is the co-pigmentation of anthocyanins with other flavonoids and related compounds, notably flavonols (quercetin and rutin), aureusidin (an aurone) and particularly C-glycosyl flavones such as swertisin.[178] Co-pigmentation causes batho-chromic wavelength shifts (i.e. towards blue) with both flavylium cation and quinoidal base but the colour increase appears due only to stabilisation of the latter. The effect increases with increasing anthocyanin concentration and the ratio of co-pigment to anthocyanin. By suitable combinations of anthocyanins and co-pigments at appropriate concentrations and pH values it is possible to reproduce the spectra of intact flower petal cells.[180,181] Such considerations help us to explain the striking colours of many flowers, when at the pH of cell-sap, viz. 3·5–5·5, they may be expected to have little colour. In particular the occurrence of blue flowers can be attributed largely to stabilisation of the quinoidal base by co-pigmentation.[182]

The third mechanism, metal-complexing, can also cause blueness in cornflower (iron, aluminium or magnesium) and flowers of *Commelina communis*[183] (magnesium). The latter pigment 'commelinin' can be synthesised from its component parts,[184] as can similar blue pigments with the magnesium replaced by other metals.[185]

The fourth mechanism of colour stabilisation is believed to be an intramolecular interaction between the acyl groups of an acylated anthocyanin and the phenolic groups in the B ring of the anthocyanin. Such a mechanism has been postulated to account for the great stability of several blue flower pigments recently isolated which contain neither co-pigments nor metals.[7,186–189] Hydrophobic interactions have been proposed to explain the stability of 'commelinin'.[190]

Let us consider these findings in relation to the food situation. Most of the pigments in Table 1 are 3-glycosides but some sources, notably hybrid grapes, red cabbage, elderberry and aubergine contain 3,5-diglycosides. It is appropriate to enquire whether these give more or less colour per unit weight or mole than the more common 3-glycosides. As already stated, the pure 3,5-diglycosides in isolation exhibit much less colour than their corresponding 3-glycosides. The red colour of both types is augmented by self-association of their cationic forms but it is not clear as yet whether they are augmented to differing extents and how much this might vary according to pH. In beverages and foodstuffs, anthocyanins do not occur in isolation but with many other components which might act as co-pigments. Co-pigmentation produces a much greater effect with the 3,5-diglycosides than the 3-glycosides. Thus in studies of the effect of rutin on several malvidin glucosides at pH 3·2, the colour of the 3,5-diglucoside increased 10 times but that of the 3-glucoside only 1·5 times under comparable conditions (10^{-5} M anthocyanin, $1·2 \times 10^{-2}$ M rutin).[191] But this larger *relative* colour increase of the 3,5-diglucoside was insufficient to counteract its low initial colour, so that the *actual* absorption of the co-pigmented 3,5-diglucoside remained lower than that of the co-pigmented 3-glucoside over the pH range (1–7) studied.[192] This is surprising, for it is surely not without significance that all the blue flower pigments so far isolated are based on 3,5-diglycosides and not 3-glycosides. Thus glucose in position 5 must surely play a special role, as yet unexplained, in stabilisation of the quinoidal base. During this work on co-pigmentation, increasing anthocyanin concentrations caused increasing self-association of the cationic form. The anthocyanins so associated were then not available for co-pigmentation with rutin, so that its relative effect was diminished.[191] It is evident that the two mechanisms can act in opposition and that both should be considered in any anthocyanin solution containing other components. Co-pigmentation is thought to be due to intermolecular hydrogen bonding between the quinoidal keto and hydroxyl groups of adjacent anthocyanin molecules and is reduced by ethanol. Thus, the effects are less pronounced in alcoholic than in non-alcoholic beverages.

Effect of Acylation
Co-pigmentation of malvidin-3-(p-coumaryl glucoside)-5-glucoside with rutin at pH 3·2 was very similar to that observed with malvidin 3,5-diglucoside except that the percentage colour increase was halved. In contrast, the effect of rutin was relatively greater (3–4 times) with malvidin 3-p-coumaryl glucoside than with malvidin 3-glucoside.[191]

As already mentioned (mechanism four), the most intriguing recent findings are those of the Japanese workers indicating that if the anthocyanin is of suitable constitution, i.e. containing sufficient moles of phenolic acids and a glucose molecule in position 5, its blue quinoidal base is stabilised by intramolecular hydrogen bonding to a remarkable extent, without a requirement for co-pigments. It remains to be seen how stable are the red cationic forms of such compounds and if there will be application to the colouring of foodstuffs.

REACTIONS OF ANTHOCYANINS IN MODEL AND FOOD SYSTEMS

Although anthocyanins can be degraded through mediation of enzymes,[3] it is the non-enzymic degradation or fading of attractive colour, sometimes accompanied by undesirable browning which is of most concern during processing of food products. Studies have been made in model systems using pure pigments and also in foodstuffs. In complex systems many components can interact. Isolation of the main factors concerned is attempted as follows:

1. Nature of the anthocyanidin—stability increases with methoxyl substitution but decreases with hydroxylation[193,194]—Fig. 1. The

nature of the sugar appears less important although galactosides are reported more stable than glucosides.[195]

2. Position of sugars and acylation—anthocyanidin 3,5-diglucosides (in wines) are more heat and light stable than corresponding 3-glucosides but brown more; acylated 3,5-diglucosides are most light stable;[91] 3-glucosides react faster than 3,5-diglucosides with acetaldehyde, without and with flavan 3-ols.[196,197] Coumarin derivatives can be formed from 3,5-diglucosides (and acylated) but not from 3-glucosides.[198,199] Some of these differences can be interpreted as follows:

3. The 'amphoteric' nature of the anthocyanin cation—although the anthocyanin cation is usually depicted as an oxonium ion (e.g. AH^+—Fig. 2), the charge is delocalised over the whole structure (Fig. 1). Because of the charge distribution, the cation form can react with nucleophilic reagents (hydroxyl, phenolics) at positions 2 and 4, and with electrophiles such as aldehydes at positions 6 or 8. Conditions which expedite one reaction have the reverse effect on the other type. Thus, one cause of browning of anthocyanins in red wines[200] and strawberry juice[201] is the condensation of anthocyanins with flavan 3-ols such as the catechins and pro-anthocyanidins. This is believed to occur at the electrophilic C4 position of the anthocyanin, in view of the production of xanthylium salts[196] and increased resistance to bleaching by sulphur dioxide, known to be a characteristic of 4-substituted flavylium salts. Since anthocyanidin 3,5-diglucosides brown faster than 3-glucosides, the glucose in position 5 appears, by a mechanism not yet fully understood, to increase the electrophilic character of C4. At the same time the nucleophilic activities of C8 and C6 are reduced so that reaction with aldehydes is slower.

4. Hydrolysis of the aglycone–sugar bond (position 3)—this can occur at 100 °C (pH 2–4). Both unreacted anthocyanin and the aglycone produced are transformed into their corresponding chalcones, that from the aglycone (cyanidin) further forming an α-diketone. Both chalcone glycoside and α-diketone are degraded into brown products in air.[202] All previous quantitative work on so-called thermal degradation of anthocyanins, particularly related to the relative stabilities of the various structural forms, needs reappraisal following the recent work of Brouillard and his collaborators.[175]

5. Food components—metal ions (aluminium, tin, iron, etc.) can form complexes with anthocyanins containing *o*-diphenolic groups. Metals may enhance and stabilise anthocyanins in fruit products[203-205] with reduced browning. But they can also cause fading and discoloration,[206,207] not surprising considering the known ability of metals, such as copper and iron to function as redox catalysts, so that the net result is not beneficial.[208] Stabilisation of strawberry colour is most promising—by tin[209] and iron[206] salts. Ascorbic acid and anthocyanins are mutually destructive in the presence of oxygen.[195,210-212] Losses are inhibited by flavonols but are accelerated by copper[203,212] probably because of oxidation by hydrogen peroxide produced in the ascorbic acid–copper system. In acid solutions, hydrogen peroxide can oxidise acylated 3,5-diglucosides directly to acylated *o*-benzoylphenylacetic acid esters.[199] In the absence of metals, ascorbic acid may condense with anthocyanins at their electrophilic C4 positions.[213] Sugars and sugar derivatives such as furfural and 5-hydroxymethylfurfural can also cause anthocyanin discoloration. Reactive carbonyls can be formed by photochemically-induced decomposition of organic acids in the presence of iron salts, and may be factors in the light instability of anthocyanins. Likewise acetaldehyde can cause fading of crude extracts of plant material but when allowed to interact with pure anthocyanins and flavan 3-ols, such as catechins and procyanidins, considerable colour augmentation can occur, up to seven times under certain conditions (Fig. 4). This is believed to be due to the formation of highly coloured compounds in which anthocyanin and flavan 3-ol are linked by CH_3CH bridges. Other aldehydes behave similarly. When these reactions are applied to a crude mixture of elderberry anthocyanins, the newly formed pigments are much more coloured between pH 4–6 than the unchanged pigments, and should be more effective food colorants.[214]

6. Sulphur dioxide—a further disadvantage of anthocyanins is that they are readily bleached by sulphur dioxide widely used in the food industry. A simple calculation utilising measured formation constants[215] indicates that at pH 3·2 and 20 °C a solution of malvidin 3-glucoside is half-decolorised when the equilibrium concentration of free SO_2 is only 4 ppm. The total amount of SO_2 to produce this effect depends upon the amount of anthocyanin

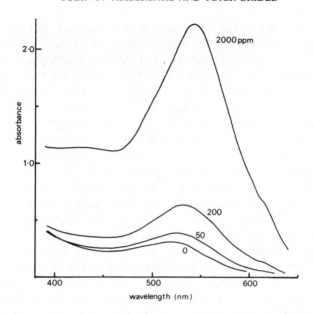

FIG. 4.   Effect of acetaldehyde concentration (ppm) on Mv 3,5-diglucoside and catechin (after 46 days at 20 °C in darkness).

present. Thus a typical red juice or young red wine (say 0·025 % anthocyanin) would be half-decolorised by an amount of SO_2 totalling about 20 ppm. Sulphur dioxide appears to react at position 4 since in flavylium salts where this position is occupied— particularly with a large group such as phenyl—SO_2 becomes ineffective.[216] Fortunately for the prospects of anthocyanin compounds as potential food colours, the anthocyanins behave similarly. As already mentioned this occurs naturally in red wines and probably many fruit juices and liquid anthocyanin extracts by condensation with flavan 3-ols. The quinoidal bases of these condensation products are also stabilised so that there is the added advantage of increased colour over a wider pH range.

The only bisulphite-resistant anthocyanin so far found in fresh plant material is purpurinidin fructo-glucoside extracted from willow bark.[217] This intriguing orange pigment is unique in containing fructose which is readily removed by cold acid to form a red glucoside. The aglycone is violet. It is significant that the NMR spectrum of the orange pigment does not show the low field singlet attributed to the C4 hydrogen of other anthocyanins[218] and anthocyanidins,[219] indicating that, as expected, it contains a substituent in this position. To try to find a more accessible and productive source of this pigment, anthocyanin extracts from 190 plant sources, representing 56 families were screened by the simple expedient of adding bisulphite to the chromatographic solvents. Although some pelargonidin glycosides appeared slightly more resistant to SO_2 than all others examined by the same technique, no pigment as resistant as purpurinidin fructo-glucoside was found. Even in the Salicaceae it was found in only 2 of 29 cultivars of *S. purpurea*, this species being only one of 14 examined; it thus remains an anomaly among plant anthocyanins. Shortage of material has hampered its complete characterisation, but even if this were known the pigment would require synthesis for commercial development—an uneconomic proposition. More economic would be the readily synthesised 3-deoxyanthocyanidins[220,221] and simple flavylium salts similar to the anthocyanins but with H only in position 3.[222] The latter when possessing a substituent in position 4 are bleached less by SO_2 and are more coloured because their quinoidal bases are stabilised. They are more stable to light, ascorbic acid and iron than many synthetic food colours.[223] Unfortunately they have solubility problems and would still require toxicological clearance for use as food colours.

ANTHOCYANINS AS FOOD COLOURS

The last decade or so has seen the introduction of increasingly severe restrictions on the legal use of artificial colorants for foods. The colours under criticism are mainly coal tar derived azo-type dyes, and it would seem that pigments responsible for the production of colours in the red region of the spectrum have been particularly hard hit.[224] However, since the consumer's desire for coloured foods is strong, the replacement of the de-listed colours by more acceptably derived pigments has been seriously investigated. If synthetics can be replaced by colorants of natural origin—from an edible plant source, then the prospects are good.[225] Since most of the orange, red and blue colours found in the plant kingdom are due to anthocyanins, these compounds are an obvious choice as a source of tinctorial additives over this colour range.

Anthocyanins are produced by numerous species of plants, but their usefulness as potential colorants must be balanced against the limitations imposed by availability and general economic considerations.[226] Factors of this nature reduce the feasible sources to only a few plant species. Thus, of the sources examined, the greatest weight of anthocyanins for food usage is obtainable from black grapes—the total grape crop constitutes one-quarter of the world's fruit production.[227] The extraction of grape skin pigment into juice or wine is not an efficient process, and large amounts of extractable anthocyanins are available in grape pomaces and wastes. Anthocyanin extracts have been produced from these sources by numerous workers;[227-232] liquids and powders are commercially available and sources have been compared.[233] Pure grape pigments have been tested and are successfully used commercially for colouring canned fruit, fruit syrups, yogurt and other products. Enocyanin, a grape pomace extract of Italian origin is used mainly to intensify red wine colour.

The need for performance comparable to that of the coal tar reds is important to the processor. Anthocyanins thrive in a low pH environment and their successful application also requires minimal levels of dissolved oxygen, trace metals and sulphur dioxide. Other factors are known to contribute to anthocyanin loss, e.g. ascorbic acid and the sugar breakdown product hydroxymethylfurfural, while more recent work[201] indicates that other reactive phenolics play a major role in anthocyanin colour loss by promoting polymerisation reactions, with browning as a consequence. The anthocyanins have fair heat stability, and resistance to fading in daylight is good compared with some other natural reds (e.g. betalains and cochineal) and, in this respect, the anthocyanins are better than certain synthetic reds.[233]

For economic feasibility, the anthocyanin source should best be a waste or by-product of another process or an inexpensive crop, e.g. red cabbage[234] or elderberries,[235] since growing a more expensive crop for pigment content alone is not viable. By-production of anthocyanins from wastes other than that from grapes has been achieved using cranberry press-cake[236] and miracle fruit-skins.[237] The former contains up to 40 % of the original fruit anthocyanins, even after double pressing to extract the juice,[238] while the miracle fruit is a source of a novel non-nutritive sweetener. However, this aspect of the miracle fruit is itself undergoing toxicological investigations, and so the future extraction prospects for the strong orange–red skin colour are uncertain. These and other plant materials examined for possible colorant use are tabulated (Table 2).

Extraction and Purification
For practical purposes, it is important that extraction and clean-up processes should not be too involved or time-consuming. The classical method of extracting anthocyanins from plant material involves mace-

TABLE 2
ANTHOCYANIN SOURCES USED FOR FOOD COLOURS

Source	Major anthocyanins	Colour imparted
Grape skin (*Vitis vinifera*)	Cy, Pn, Dp, Pt and Mv monoglycosides, free and acylated	Purple–Red
Grape skin (Hybrid)	Cy, Pn, Dp, Pt and Mv mono- and diglycosides, free and acylated	Purple–Red
Cranberry fruit	Cy and Pn monoglycosides	Pink–red
Red cabbage	Cy glycosides, free and acylated	Purple–red
Cherry plum leaves	Cy and Pn mono- and biosides	Red
Roselle calyces	Cy and Dp mono- and biosides	Red
Miracle fruit	Cy and Dp monoglycosides	Orange–red
Purple corn	Pg, Cy and Pn monoglycosides	Red
Clitorea ternatea	Dp glycosides	Blue
Blueberry	Cy, Pn, Dp, Pt and Mv monoglycosides	Red

ration or soaking in methanol or ethanol containing a small amount of mineral acid (e.g. $< 1\%$ HCl). Thus, the leaves of the cherry plum (*Prunus cerasifera*) were extracted using an ethanol–HCl mixture (85 ml ethanol + 15 ml 1·5 M HCl).[239,240] However, when the presence of acylated anthocyanins is suspected, the use of mineral acid is not advised,[86] particularly if identification work is to be carried out, since the acyl linkage is labile and easily hydrolysed.

When sufficient extraction of colour is achieved, the acidified alcoholic solution is concentrated by removal of solvent, for example on a rotary vacuum evaporator, at low temperature ($< 30\,^{\circ}$C) to prevent anthocyanin degradation and hydrolysis. The concentrate can then be purified, if required, by techniques such as column or paper chromatography.[109]

This theme has been pursued for a cranberry pomace anthocyanin recovery system.[236,238] The pigment in the residue from the cranberry juice cocktail process was extracted using methanol containing 0·03% HCl. This solvent gave optimum recovery, although others were tested, including acetone, ethylene glycol, propylene glycol, methyl ethyl ketone, isopropanol and water. However, these latter solvents were discarded for reasons including anthocyanin degradation (acetone) and the extraction of extraneous materials, e.g. water also extracts pectin. For this application, HCl was notably better than acetic acid; maximal colour extraction was with 0·03 % HCl. Ion exchange was used to purify the concentrate obtained after rotary evaporation. The cation exchange resin requires a mainly aqueous extract (< 30 % methanol content) for efficient absorption of anthocyanins, and resins typically used include Amberlite CG–50 and Dowex 50W X 4. The crude concentrate was applied at the top of a resin column, the anthocyanins absorbed and impurities washed off by water elution. The anthocyanins were eluted using methanol with a minimum content of HCl compatible with anthocyanin stability—0·0001 % is recommended. It is usually difficult to obtain complete recovery of all the anthocyanin absorbed by the resin whether using strongly acid (Dowex 50) or weakly acid (Amberlite CG–50) resins. The absorption efficiency is dependent on resin particle size and the smaller mesh sizes give better release of pigment but also cause physical problems of column efficiency. Thus it appears that Amberlite CG–50 (100–200 mesh) is optimum, giving 95 % recovery. Overall loss of pigment originally extracted amounted to 26 % (13 % during solvent evaporation, 8 % during ion exchange and 5 % during freeze-drying to give a solid product). A similar extraction and clean-up approach has been applied also to blueberry and red cabbage extracts,[241] and to make miracle fruit anthocyanins.[237]

Extraction of anthocyanins from two sources was achieved using ethanol acidified with citric acid (0·01 %) instead of HCl.[242] Citric acid is less corrosive than HCl, chelates metals and still maintains a low pH. The level chosen gave a final extract pH of 3·0–3·2 after 10:1 concentration. Further, citric acid was thought to have an added protective effect throughout the processing, which included a final spray-drying treatment. Philip[229] describes another acidified methanol solvent for extracting grape pomace and centrifuge wastes from Beauty Seedless grape juice. Tartaric acid was used to acidify the methanol, and grape wastes dried to < 10 % water content were packed into a column and extracted three times with methanol containing 0·1–1·0 % tartaric acid. Excess tartaric acid was precipitated using 40 % KOH in such quantity that only 10–15 % of the original tartaric acid was left in solution. Concentration and removal of further tartrate precipitate left an aqueous anthocyanin extract which was acceptable when added to a colourless artificial grape drink.

The use of SO_2 in the extracting medium has been patented.[228] Fruit pomace was soaked in sulphur dioxide (200–2000 ppm) in aqueous or alcoholic solution. The best result for grape pomace pigment extraction was obtained using SO_2 (1000 ppm) in ethanol. After separation and concentration to remove solvent and SO_2 a juice concentrate rich in natural colour and flavour was obtained. Extraction using ethanol alone produced a concentrate having only half the colour and desirable flavour intensity. Palamidis and Markakis[227] compared extraction using aqueous SO_2 solution with hot water extraction of Napa-Gamay grape wine pomace. A level of 500 ppm SO_2 was most suitable, and was preferred to hot water treatment—which leached out other substances besides anthocyanins. Two extractions with SO_2 gave a crude mixture containing 94 % of the available anthocyanins. This technique has been applied to blueberries and red cabbage using 350 ppm SO_2 solvent, and compared with a methanol–HCl ion exchange treatment.[241] It was concluded that SO_2 extraction of anthocyanins was less selective than the ion exchange process, which gave a purer and more potent final concentrate.

Hot water alone was used to leach the anthocyanins from the calyces of roselle (*Hibiscus sabdariffa*), and the frozen concentrate had excellent long-term storage properties.[243,244] Again, water has been used to extract the dried flowers of *Clitorea ternatea*, and the blue solution of delphinidin glycosides strained off and used without further treatment to colour rice cakes.[245] Other means of pigment preparation include a preliminary treatment of purple corn (*Maiz morado*) with amylase and protease and subsequent spray-drying of the filtered mixture,[246] while a crude methanolic–HCl extract of Bolivian purple corn was subjected to various methods of purification—including ion exchange, polyamide, Sephadex LH20, cellulose column and paper chromatography.[109] The use of cranberry juice concentrate has been proposed as a colorant for pie fillings.[247] The concentrate reduced the pH of the pie fillings from 3·4 to 3·2, due to its citric acid content, but this extra acidity was acceptable, and produced a more tart and pleasing taste.

Further Processing of Extracts
Anthocyanin extracts in acid aqueous solution may be used as such, or frozen; concentrates keep well, and undergo little or no change at $-20\,°C$ over two years.[244] Alternatively, the concentrate may be converted to a powder by a drying process. For example, freeze-drying yields a powder,[227,234,238,241,244] which keeps satisfactorily in hermetically sealed containers, with long-term storage stability at room temperature.[244] The powder from this process is often hygroscopic and must be handled with this property in mind.

More recently, spray-drying of anthocyanin concentrates has been used.[242,246] In this process a carbohydrate carrier is added to give c. 30 % total solids mixture and enables the pigment to be produced in encapsulated form. The mechanics of the process involves feeding the liquid concentrate in an atomised form via a centrifugal nozzle (40 000 rev min^{-1}), into a cylindrical drying chamber. Heated air (175–220 °C) is fed in, and the small droplets, which offer a large surface area for evaporation to take place, yield a powder which is separated in a collection trap. Outlet temperatures higher than 100 °C are not recommended, since the pigment degrades under these conditions. Spray-drying is considered more economical and practical than freeze-drying for producing large quantities of powdered material.[242]

Stability of Anthocyanin Additives

Fundamental requirements for any potential food colour derived from plant material are chemical stability, good water solubility and freedom from unwanted flavours or odours[248] of the source material. From the chemical standpoint, it is clear that anthocyanin-type additives are vulnerable to the same factors which may adversely affect any anthocyanins already present in a product. Thus in order to minimise degradation, colours should be added at a late stage in processing, so that any subsequent colour loss is less apparent to the eye. On the other hand, it has been noted that almost 50 % of the total anthocyanin content of beverage mixes coloured with grape anthocyanin can degrade before the change becomes visually apparent, and often dark coloured degradation products are acceptable up to a point, in the eyes of the consumer.[232]

Anthocyanin extracts are used mainly in acidic-type products, excepting *Clitorea ternatea* anthocyanins used to colour rice cakes.[245] This flower pigment is based on delphinidin—the least stable and most easily oxidised of the common anthocyanins. The unexpected stability in use was attributed to adsorption of pigment on to the starch gel—effectively keeping the anthocyanins out of solution, although in an aqueous medium.

Carbonated beverages coloured with roselle pigment concentrate were stable only in short-term storage,[224] but cooler storage temperatures extended their shelf-life.[227,237] It is claimed, however, that reduction in residual oxygen content, achieved by carbonation, gives better pigment retention than in non-carbonated liquids.[231] Thus oxygen removal is critical for anthocyanin stability, especially if ascorbic acid is present, since oxidation products of ascorbic acid degrade anthocyanins.[195,212]

When anthocyanin powders were used in soft drink mixes, it was found that when SO_2 was used in the initial extracting process, both anthocyanin and ascorbic acid were more stable in the reconstituted coloured drinks.[241]

Stability of anthocyanin additives is affected by other liquid system components including organic acids; tartaric acid causes least degradation, malic acid the most.[237] Sugar degradation products can be tolerated at moderate levels (100 ppm)[231] although certain sugars themselves appear to have a protective effect on anthocyanin colour in preserves and concentrates.[211] When *Vaccinium myrtillus* anthocyanins were used in pharmaceutical formulations, they were stable if residual moisture was less than 3 % and neutral or acidic excipients were used.[249] Other anthocyanin extracts have also been tested for suitability in pharmaceuticals.[250]

Anthocyanin products used as food colours are likely to be of varying quality, some perhaps containing pigments partly degraded, condensed or polymerised with other substances. They may contain other components simultaneously extracted, such as tannins. Some of these may act as co-pigments and enhance colours; others may be undesirable from the point of view of taste, stability and toxicology. They present problems of (a) identification—the types of pigments, simple or complex, and (b) quantitative measurement.

ANALYSIS

The anthocyanins are not the easiest compounds to measure for several reasons:

(i)   Suitable, simple, pure standard compounds are not easily available and even if they were, they may not be very similar to the complex type of pigment which might be present in the extract.

(ii)   Anthocyanins are difficult to measure independently of other flavonoids since they react also with the usual reagents used for phenolic analysis such as Folin-Ciocalteau, vanillin, etc.

(iii)   Methods based on colour are possible, such as:

(a)   Differential methods—relying on differences in colour produced by pH change,[251] bleaching by sulphur dioxide[252] or hydrogen peroxide.[253] It must be assumed that the reagents SO_2 and peroxide have no effect on other components (e.g. background brown colour).

(b)   Conversion of all chemical forms to the red flavylium cation by adding normal acid.[254] This is suitable for the simple monomeric anthocyanins but condensed or polymerised pigments can give low colour response.

(iv) The best method would be to separate and measure the individual components by chromatography—low pressure liquid gel filtration on Sephadex or, better still, high pressure liquid chromatography. Such methods are being developed.[255-257]

However, even if one could measure accurately the amount of pigment present, this may bear little relation to the amount of colour perceived at the product pH because of operation of the effects which have been discussed already.

CONCLUSIONS

In their Report on the Review of the Colouring Matter in Food Regulations, 1973, the Committee on the Toxicity of Chemicals in Food, Consumer Products and the Environment placed the natural food colours into four categories.[258]

Most of the anthocyanin extracts discussed in this chapter fall into category (i), i.e. those derived from natural foods by physical processes. Even though toxicological data might be lacking, the Committee considered it unrealistic to recommend that colours in category (i) should not be added to food, provided overall intake was in keeping with available toxicological data. This is entirely reasonable since a great deal of anthocyanins have been consumed by the human race throughout the ages. It can be estimated that approximately 10 000 tonnes of anthocyanin pigments are consumed annually from black grapes alone. Additional quantities derive from soft and stone fruits and some vegetables. Thus, while appropriate toxicological data are lacking because of the extreme difficulty of preparing and characterising large amounts of pure anthocyanins for this purpose, there is little indication that these pigments are harmful.

A few of the extracts are derived from natural sources that are not natural foods and hence fall into category (ii) of those listed by the Committee on Toxicity. It is proper that these should be allowed in food only after consideration of appropriate chemical and/or toxicological data.

Unfortunately, the anthocyanin extracts (as Anthocyanins E 163) have been omitted from any revised list of permitted colouring matters which may be recommended.[258] This present review has outlined some of the disadvantages of anthocyanin pigments as food colours but has also indicated that these are problems which may well be overcome in the future through greater understanding of anthocyanin chemistry. It would be a great pity if future permission to use these was to be withheld by default—by lack of sufficient representation on the part of users or food manufacturers, as the food industry would be the poorer for lack of these very useful products.

REFERENCES

1. Momose, T., Abe, K. and Yoshitama, K., *Phytochemistry*, 1977, **16**, 1321.
2. Harborne, J. B., *Comparative Biochemistry of the Flavonoids*, 1967, Academic Press, London and New York.
3. Timberlake, C. F. and Bridle, P., in *The Flavonoids*, Ed. J. B. Harborne, T. J. Mabry and H. Mabry, 1975, pp. 214–266. Chapman and Hall, London.
4. Crowden, R. K. and Jarman, S. J., *Phytochemistry*, 1974, **13**, 1947.
5. Tsukui, A., Kuwano, K., Toshio, M. and Wahachiro, T., *Chem. Abstr.*, 1977, **87**, 180667.
6. Ishikura, N. and Minekishi, K., *Bot. Mag. Tokyo*, 1978, **91**, 181.
7. Yoshitama, K., *Phytochemistry*, 1977, **16**, 1857.
8. Harrison, S. G., Masefield, G. B., Wallis, M. and Nicholson, B. E., *The Oxford Book of Food Plants*, 1969, Oxford University Press.
9. Sando, C. E., *J. biol. Chem.*, 1937, **117**, 45.
10. Pais, I. and Gombkötö, G., *Kertész. szolész. Föisk. Kemiai Tanszeke*, 1967, **31**, 73.
11. Sun, B. H. and Francis, F. J., *J. Food Sci.*, 1967, **32**, 647.
12. Timberlake, C. F. and Bridle, P., *J. Sci. Fd Agric.*, 1971, **22**, 509.
13. Bazarova, V. I. and Samorodova-Bianki, G. B., *Chem. Abstr.*, 1972, **76**, 44780.
14. Pifferi, P. G. and Vaccari, A., *Industria conserv.*, 1978, **53**, 107.
15. Wann, E. V. and Thompson, A. E., *Proc. Am. Soc. hort. Sci.*, 1965, **87**, 270.
16. Francis, F. J., *J. Food Sci.*, 1967, **32**, 430.
17. Nagashima, Y. and Taira, Y., *Chem. Abstr.*, 1965, **64**, 10086.
18. Watanabe, S., Sakamura, S. and Obata, Y., *Agric. and Biol. Chem. (Jap.)*, 1966, **30**, 420.
19. Tigchelaar, E. C., Janick, J. and Erickson, H. T., *Genetics*, 1968, **60**, 475.
20. Casoli, U. and Dall'Aglio, G., *Industria conserv.*, 1969, **44**, 18.
21. Pifferi, P. G. and Zamorani, A., *Ind. Agric.* (Florence), 1969, **7**, 51.
22. Tanchev, S. S., Ruskov, P. J. and Timberlake, C. F., *Phytochemistry*, 1970, **9**, 1681.
23. Singh, N. S., *Phytochemistry*, 1972, **11**, 163.
24. Pomilio, A. B., *Phytochemistry*, 1973, **12**, 218.
25. Du, C. T. and Francis, F. J., *Hortscience*, 1974, **9**, 40.
26. Stanton, W. R. and Francis, B. J., *Nature, Lond.*, 1966, **211**, 970.
27. Yoshikura, K. and Hamaguchi, Y., *J. Jap. Soc. Fd Nutr.*, 1971, **24**, 275.
28. Okita, C., Suwa, K., Yoshikura, K. and Hamaguchi, Y., *Chem. Abstr.*, 1972, **77**, 137394.

29. Nozzolillo, C., *Phytochemistry*, 1971, **10**, 2552.
30. Proctor, J. T. A., *Diss. Abstr. Int. B.*, 1970, **31**, 10.
31. Sasanuma, S., Takeda, K. and Hayashi, K., *Bot. Mag. Tokyo*, 1966, **79**, 807.
32. Harborne, J. B. and Hall, E., *Phytochemistry*, 1964, **3**, 453.
33. Casoli, U., Cultrera, R. and Gherardi, S., *Industria conserv.*, 1967, **42**, 255.
34. Francis, F. J., Harborne, J. B. and Barker, W. G., *J. Food Sci.*, 1966, **31**, 583.
35. Ballinger, W. E., Maness, E. P. and Kushman, L. J., *J. Am. Soc. hort. Sci.*, 1970, **95**, 283.
36. Ballinger, W. E., Maness, E. P., Galletta, G. J., and Kushman, L. J., *J. Am. Soc. hort. Sci.*, 1972, **97**, 381.
37. Makus, D. J. and Ballinger, W. E., *J. Am. Soc. hort. Sci.*, 1973, **98**, 99.
38. Luh, B. S., Stachowicz, K. and Hsia, C. L., *J. Food Sci.*, 1965, **30**, 300.
39. Nybom, N., *J. Chromat.*, 1968, **38**, 382.
40. Barritt, B. H. and Torre, L. C., *J. Chromat.*, 1973, **75**, 151.
41. Tanchev, S. S. and Timberlake, C. F., *Phytochemistry*, 1969, **8**, 1825.
42. Lanzarini, G. and Morselli, L., *Industria conserv.*, 1974, **49**, 16.
43. Hrazdina, G., Iredale, H. and Mattick, L. R., *Phytochemistry*, 1977, **16**, 297.
44. Harborne, J. B., *Biochem. Syst. and Ecol.*, 1976, **4**, 31.
45. Ryugo, K., *Proc. Am. Soc. hort. Sci.*, 1966, **88**, 160.
46. Lynn, D. Y. C. and Luh, B. S., *J. Food Sci.*, 1964, **29**, 735.
47. Olden, E. J. and Nybom, N., *Hereditas*, 1968, **59**, 327.
48. Blundstone, H. A. W. and Crean, D. E. C., *The Pigments of Red Fruits*, 1966, Fruit and Veg. Pres. Res. Assoc., Chipping Campden, Glos.
49. Tanchev, S., Vasilev, V. and Ioncheva, N., *Chem. Abstr.*, 1972, **77**, 60286.
50. Dekazos, E. D., *J. Food Sci.*, 1970, **35**, 237.
51. Fischer, R. R. and von Elbe, J. H., *J. Milk Fd Technol.*, 1970, **33**, 481.
52. Shrikhande, A. J. and Francis, F. J., *J. Food Sci.*, 1973, **38**, 649.
53. Schaller, D. R. and von Elbe, J. H., *J. Food Sci.*, 1968, **33**, 442.
54. von Elbe, J. H., Bixby, D. G. and Moore, J. D., *J. Food Sci.*, 1969, **34**, 113.
55. Kazmierczak, T., *Chem. Abstr.*, 1969, **71**, 11818.
56. Sobolevskaya, K. A. and Demina, T. G., *Chem. Abstr.*, 1971, **75**, 59777.
57. Tanchev, S., Ioncheva, N., Vasilev, V. and Tanev, T., *Chem. Abstr.* 1973, **79**, 63533.
58. Forsyth, W. G. C. and Quesnel, V. C., *Biochem. J.*, 1957, **65**, 177.
59. Troyan, A. V. and Borukh, I. F., *Chem. Abstr.*, 1970, **73**, 119394.
60. Suomalainen, H. and Keranen, A. J. A., *Nature, Lond.*, 1961, **191**, 498.
61. Sakamura, S. and Francis, F. J., *Fd. Res.*, 1961, **26**, 318.
62. Zapsalis, C. and Francis, F. J., *J. Food. Sci.*, 1965, **30**, 396.
63. Fuleki, T. and Francis, F. J., *Phytochemistry*, 1967, **6**, 1705.
64. Fang-Yang, A. F. and Kuznetsova, N. A., *Chem. Abstr.*, 1972, **77**, 123792.
65. Demina, T. G., *Rast. Resur.*, 1968, **4**, 88.
66. Olifson, L. E., Nechaev, A. P., Osadchaya, N. D. and Mikhailova, L. F., *Chem. Abstr.*, 1971, **75**, 22922.
67. Misra, K. and Seshadri, T. R., *Indian J. Chem.*, 1967, **5**, 409.
68. Reichel, L. and Reichwald, W., *Naturwissenschaften*, 1960, **47**, 41.
69. Duro, F. and Condorelli, P., *Quad. Merceol.*, 1977, **16**, 37.
70. Puech, A. A., Rebeiz, C. A., Catlin, P. B. and Crane, J. C., *J. Food Sci.*, 1975, **40**, 775.

71. Du, C. T. and Francis, F. J., *J. Food Sci.*, 1975, **40**, 1101.
72. Koeppen, B. H. and Basson, D. S., *Phytochemistry*, 1966, **5**, 183.
73. Somers, T. C., *J. Sci. Fd Agric.*, 1966, **17**, 215.
74. Sivtsev, M. V. and Tyutyunnik, V. I., *Chem. Abstr.*, 1968, **69**, 103819 and 1969, **70**, 886.
75. Conradie, J. D. and Neethling, L. P., *J. Chromat.*, 1968, **34**, 419.
76. Ueno, N., Takemura, E. and Hayashi, K., *Bot. Mag. Tokyo*, 1969, **82**, 155.
77. Anderson, D. W., Gueffroy, D. E., Webb, A. D. and Kepner, R. E., *Phytochemistry*, 1970, **9**, 1579.
78. Fong, R. A., Kepner, R. E. and Webb, A. D., *Am. J. Enol. Vitic.*, 1971, **22**, 150.
79. Gueffroy, D. E., Kepner, R. E. and Webb, A. D., *Phytochemistry*, 1971, **10**, 813.
80. Philip, T., *J. Food Sci.*, 1974, **39**, 449.
81. Carreno-Diaz, R. and Luh, B. S., *J. Food Sci.*, 1969, **34**, 415.
82. Sakellariades, H. C. and Luh, B. S., *J. Food Sci.*, 1974, **39**, 329.
83. Liao, F. W. and Luh, B. S., *J. Food Sci.*, 1970, **35**, 41.
84. Shewfelt, A. L., 1966, South Carolina Agric. Exp. Sta. Tech. Bull. No 1025.
85. Hrazdina, G., *Lebensm.-Wissen. Technol.*, 1975, **8**, 111.
86. Anderson, D. W., Julian, E. A., Kepner, R. E. and Webb, A. D., *Phytochemistry*, 1970, **9**, 1569.
87. Ishikura, N. and Ito, S., *Kumamoto J. Sci. Biol.*, 1976, **13**, 7.
88. Ballinger, W. E., Maness, E. P., Nesbitt, W. B. and Carroll, D. E., *J. Food Sci.*, 1973, **38**, 909.
89. Cano-Marotta, C. R., Grois, G. and Pons, J. A., *Chem. Abstr.*, 1966, **64**, 5449.
90. Getov, G., *Chem. Abstr.*, 1967, **66**, 27831.
91. Robinson, W. B., Weirs, L. D., Bertino, J. J. and Mattick, L. R., *Am. J. Enol. Vitic.*, 1966, **17**, 178.
92. Schmidt-Hebbel, H., Michelson, W., Masson, L., and Stelzer, H., *Z. Lebensmittelunters. u.-Forsch.*, 1968, **146**, 198.
93. Bokuchava, M. A., Valuiko, G. G. and Filippov, A. M., *Chem. Abstr.*, 1971, **75**, 95420.
94. Maglitto, C., *Riv. Vitic. Enol.*, 1971, **24**, 389.
95. Ribereau-Gayon, P., 'The Chemistry of red wine colour', in *Chemistry of Winemaking*, Ed. A. D. Webb, 1974. Advances in Chemistry Series 137. American Chem. Soc. Washington D.C.
96. Smith, R. M. and Luh, B. S., *J. Food Sci.*, 1965, **30**, 995.
97. Valuiko, G. G. and Germanova, L. M., *Appl. Biochem. and Microbiol.*, 1969, **5**, 460.
98. Tanchev, S. S. and Stanchev, P., *Lozar Vinar*, 1970, **19**, 39 and 44.
99. Lee, Y. B. and Ahn, S., *Chem. Abstr.*, 1970, **72**, 120211.
100. Hrazdina, G., *J. agric. Fd Chem.*, 1970, **18**, 243.
101. Akuta, S., Ohta, H., Sakane, Y. and Osajima, Y., *J. Jap. Soc. Fd. Sci. Technol.*, 1977, **24**, 631.
102. Chen, L. F. and Luh, B. S., *J. Food Sci.*, 1967, **32**, 66.
103. Van Buren, J. P., Bertino, J. J., Einset, J., Remaily, G. W. and Robinson, W. B., *Am. J. Enol. Vitic.*, 1970, **21**, 117.
104. Francis, F. J. and Harborne, J. B., *J. Food Sci.*, 1966, **31**, 524.

105. Saito, N., Hotta, R., Imai, K. and Hayashi, K., *Proc. Japan. Acad.*, 1965, **41**, 593.
106. Prasad, U.S. and Jha, O. P., *Plant Biochem. J.*, 1978, **5**, 44.
107. Harborne, J. B. and Gavazzi, G., *Phytochemistry*, 1969, **8**, 999.
108. Styles, E. D. and Ceska, O., *Phytochemistry*, 1972, **11**, 3019.
109. Nakatini, N., Fukuda, H. and Fuwa, H., *Abstracts 5th. Int. Congress Fd Sci. Technol.*, Kyoto, 1978, 5e, 218.
110. Proctor, J. T. A. and Creasy, L. L., *Phytochemistry*, 1969, **8**, 2108.
111. Du, C. T. and Francis, F. J., *J. Food Sci.*, 1977, **42**, 1667.
112. Stafford, H. A., *Pl. Physiol.*, 1968, **43**, 318.
113. Nip, W. K. and Burns, E. E., *Cereal Chem.*, 1969, **46**, 490.
114. Nip, W. K. and Burns, E. E., *Cereal Chem.*, 1971, **48**, 74.
115. Buckmire, R. M. and Francis, F. J., *J. Food Sci.*, 1975, **41**, 1363.
116. Toscano, M. A. and Lamonica, G., *Chem. Abstr.*, 1975, **83**, 55669.
117. Maki, Z. and Inamoto, H., *Chem. Abstr.*, 1973, **78**, 82073.
118. Ishikura, N., *Bot. Mag. Tokyo*, 1975, **88**, 41.
119. Vazquez, R. A. and Maestro, D. R., *Grassas aceit.*, 1970, **21**, 208.
120. Luh, B. S. and Mahecha, G., *Chem. Abstr.*, 1972, **77**, 60298.
121. Maestro, D. R. and Vazquez, R. A., *Grasas aceit.*, 1976, **27**, 237.
122. Brandwein, B. J., *Fd Res.*, 1965, **30**, 680.
123. Fuleki, T., *J. Food Sci.*, 1971, **36**, 101.
124. Du, C. T., Wang, P. L. and Francis, F. J., *Food Sci.*, 1974, **39**, 1265.
125. Chandler, B. V., *Nature, Lond.*, 1958, **182**, 933.
126. Porretta, A., Casoli, U. and Dall'Aglio, G., *Industria conserv.*, 1966, **41**, 175.
127. Licastro, F. and Bellomo, A., *Rass. chim.*, 1973, **25**, 306.
128. Statham, C. M., Crowden, R. K. and Harborne, J. B., *Phytochemistry*, 1972, **11**, 1083.
129. Hsia, C. L., Luh, B. S. and Chichester, C. O., *J. Food Sci.*, 1965, **30**, 5.
130. Van Blaricom, L. O. and Senn, T. L., *Proc. Am. Soc. hort. Sci.*, 1967, **90**, 541.
131. Chung, J. I. and Luh, B. S., *Confructa*, 1972, **17**, 8.
132. Francis, F. J., *Hortscience*, 1970, **5**, 42.
133. Tanchev, S. S. and Vasilev, V. N., *Gradinar. Lozar. Nauka*, 1973, **10**, 23.
134. Popov, K., *Chem. Abstr.*, 1969, **71**, 10290.
135. Ahn, S-Y., *Chem. Abstr.*, 1974, **80**, 94348.
136. Markh, A. T. and Lysogor, T. A., *Chem. Abstr.*, 1973, **79**, 41100.
137. Du, C. T., Wang, P. L. and Francis, F. J., *J. Food Sci.*, 1975, **40**, 417.
138. Harborne, J. B., *Biochem. J.*, 1960, **74**, 262.
139. Howard, H. W., Kukimura, H. and Whitmore, E. T., *Potato Res.*, 1970, **13**, 142.
140. Sachse, L., *Z. Lebensmittelunters. u.-Forsch.*, 1973, **153**, 294.
141. Imbert, M. P., Seaforth, C. E. and Williams, D. B., *Proc. Am. Soc. hort. Sci.*, 1966, **88**, 481.
142. Markh, A. T. and Kozenko, S. I., *Chem. Abstr.*, 1966, **64**, 1014.
143. Harborne, J. B., *Phytochemistry*, 1964, **3**, 151.
144. Fuleki, T., *J. Food Sci.*, 1969, **34**, 365.
145. Lele, S. S., *J. Sci. Indian Res.*, 1959, **18b**, 243.
146. Sovos'kin, I. P. and Demina, T. G., *Genetika*, 1971, **7**, 21.
147. Francis, F. J., *Hortscience*, 1972, **7**, 398.

148. Misic, P. D., *Hort. Res.*, 1973, **13**, 45.
149. Blundstone, H. A. W., *Quantitative Survey of Anthocyanins of Red Fruits, Fruit and Veg. Pres. Res. Assoc.*, Chipping Campden, Glos. Tech. Bull. No. 17. 1969.
150. Gombkötö, G. and Pais, I., *Chem. Abstr.*, 1970, **73**, 22132.
151. Duclos, J., Dupuy, P. and Lantin, B., *Annls Amél. Pl.*, 1971, **21**, 287.
152. Barritt, B. H. and Torre, L. C., *J. Am. Soc. hort. Sci.*, 1975, **100**, 98.
153. Daravingas, G. and Cain, R. F., *J. Food Sci.*, 1966, **31**, 927.
154. Daravingas, G. and Cain, R. F., *J. Food Sci.*, 1968, **33**, 138.
155. Gallop, R. A., *Variety, Composition and Colour in Canned Fruits, particularly Rhubarb*, Fruit and Veg. Canning Res. Assoc., Chipping Campden, Glos. 1965.
156. Wrolstad, R. E. and Heatherbell, D. A., *J. Food Sci.*, 1968, **33**, 592.
157. Hetmanski, W. and Nybom, N., *Fruchtsaft Ind.*, 1968, **13**, 256.
158. Wrolstad, R. E. and Struthers, B. J., *J. Chromat.*, 1971, **55**, 405.
159. Dedio, W., Kaltsikes, P. J. and Larter, E. N., *Phytochemistry*, 1969, **8**, 2351.
160. Dedio, W., Hill, R. D. and Evans, L. E., *Can. J. Pl. Sci.*, 1972, **52**, 977 and 981.
161. Kuroda, C. and Wada, M., *Proc. imp. Acad.* Japan, 1935, **11**, 189.
162. Yoshikura, K. and Hamaguchi, Y., *J. Jap. Soc. Fd Nutr.*, 1969, **22**, 367.
163. Popov, K., *Chem. Abstr.*, 1967, **67**, 41030.
164. Co, H. and Markakis, P., *J. Food Sci.*, 1968, **33**, 281.
165. Wrolstad, R. E. and Putnam, T. B., *J. Food Sci.*, 1969, **34**, 154.
166. Wrolstad, R. E., Hildrum, K. I. and Amos, J. F., *J. Chromat.*, 1970, **50**, 311.
167. Sondheimer, E. and Karash, C. B., *Nature*, Lond., 1956, **178**, 648.
168. Misra, K. and Dubey, R. C., *Curr. Sci.*, 1974, **43**, 544.
169. Wrolstad, R. E. and Heatherbell, D. A., *J. Sci. Fd Agric.*, 1974, **35**, 1221.
170. Chan, H. T., Kao-Jao, T. H-C. and Nakayamo, T. O. M., *J. Food Sci.*, 1977, **42**, 19.
171. Rasper, V. and Coursey, D. G., *Experientia*, 1967, **23**, 611.
172. Imbert, M. P. and Seaforth, C., *Experientia*, 1968, **24**, 445.
173. Carreno-Diaz, R. and Grau, N., *J. Food Sci.*, 1977, **42**, 615.
174. Brouillard, R. and Dubois, J. E., *J. Am. chem. Soc.*, 1977, **99**. 1359.
175. Brouillard, R. and Delaporte, B., *J. Am. chem. Soc.*, 1977, **99**, 8461.
176. Brouillard, R. and Delaporte, B., *Protons and Ions involved in Fast Dynamic Phenomena*, 1978, 403, Elsevier, Amsterdam.
177. Timberlake, C. F. and Bridle, P., *J. Sci. Fd Agric.*, 1967, **18**, 473.
178. Somers, T. C. and Evans, M. E., *J. Sci. Fd Agric.*, 1977, **28**, 279.
179. Asen, S., Stewart, R. N. and Norris, K. H., *Phytochemistry*, 1972, **11**, 1139.
180. Asen, S., Norris, K. H. and Stewart, R. N., *J. Am. Soc. hort. Sci.*, 1971, **96**, 770.
181. Asen, S., Stewart, R. N. and Norris, K. H., *Phytochemistry*, 1971, **10**, 171.
182. Asen, S., Stewart, R. N., Norris, K. H. and Massie, D. R., *Phytochemistry*, 1970, **9**, 619.
183. Hayashi, K. and Takeda, K., *Proc. Japan. Acad.*, 1970, **46**, 535.
184. Takeda, K. and Hayashi, K., *Proc. Japan. Acad.*, 1977, **53**, Ser B p. 1.
185. Takeda, K., *Proc. Japan. Acad.*, 1977, **53**, Ser B p. 257.
186. Saito, N., Osawa, Y. and Hayashi, K., *Bot. Mag. Tokyo*, 1972, **85**, 105.
187. Yoshitama, K. and Hayashi, K., *Bot. Mag. Tokyo*, 1972, **87**, 33.

148   COLIN F. TIMBERLAKE AND PETER BRIDLE

188. Asen, S., Stewart, R. N. and Norris, K. H., *Phytochemistry*, 1977, **16**, 1118.
189. Yoshitama, K., *Bot. Mag. Tokyo*, 1978, **91**, 207.
190. Goto, T., Hoshino, T. and Takase, S., 20th Symposium on the Chemistry of Natural Products Preprint, 1976, 59–66.
191. Scheffeldt, P. and Hrazdina, G., *J. Food Sci.*, 1978, **43**, 517.
192. Williams, M. and Hrazdina, G., *J. Food Sci.*, 1979, **44**, 66.
193. Hrazdina, G., Borzell, A. J. and Robinson, W. B., *Am. J. Enol. Vitic.*, 1970, **21**, 201.
194. Flora, L. F., *J. Food Sci.*, 1978, **43**, 1819.
195. Starr, M. S. and Francis, F. J., *Fd Technol.*, Champaign. 1968, **22**, 1293.
196. Timberlake, C. F. and Bridle, P., *Am. J. Enol. Vitic.*, 1976, **27**, 97.
197. Timberlake, C. F. and Bridle, P., *J. Sci. Fd Agric.*, 1977, **28**, 539.
198. Hrazdina, G., *Phytochemistry*, 1971, **10**, 1125.
199. Hrazdina, G. and Franzese, A. J., *Phytochemistry*, 1974, **13**, 231.
200. Somers, T. C., *Phytochemistry*, 1971, **10**, 2175.
201. Abers, J. E. and Wrolstad, R. E., *J. Food Sci.*, 1979, **44**, 75 and 81.
202. Adams, J. B., *J. Sci. Fd Agric.*, 1973, **24**, 747.
203. Starr, M. S. and Francis, F. J., *J. Food Sci.*, 1973, **38**, 1043.
204. Andreotti, R., Tomasicchio, M. and Macchiavelli, L., *Industria conserv.*, 1976, **51**, 193.
205. Segal, B. and Oranescu, E., *Flussiges Obst.*, 1978, **45**, 132.
206. Pyysalo, H. and Kuusi, T., *Z. Lebensmittelunters. u.-Forsch.*, 1973, **153**, 224.
207. Kuusi, T., Pyysalo, H. and Pippuri, A., *Z. Lebensmittelunters. u.-Forsch.*, 1977, **163**, 196.
208. Francis, F. J., in *Current Aspects of Food Colorants*, Ed. T. E. Furia, 1977, pp. 19–27. CRC Press, Ohio.
209. Wrolstad, R. E. and Erlandson, J. A., *J. Food Sci.*, 1973, **38**, 460.
210. Lewicki, P. P., *Chem. Abstr.*, 1974, **80**, 133733.
211. Rosa, J., *Chem. Abstr.*, 1975, **82**, 2902.
212. Shrikhande, A. J. and Francis, F. J., *J. Food Sci.*, 1974, **39**, 904.
213. Jurd, L., in 'Structural and functional aspects of phytochemistry', *Recent Advances in Phytochemistry*, Eds. V. C. Runeckles and T. C. Tso, 1972, Vol. 5, pp. 135–64. Academic Press, London and New York.
214. Timberlake, C. F. and Bridle, P., Annual Rept. Long Ashton Research Station. 1977, p. 128.
215. Timberlake, C. F. and Bridle, P., *J. Sci. Fd Agric.*, 1967, **18**, 479.
216. Timberlake, C. F. and Bridle, P., *Chemy Ind.*, 1968, p. 1489.
217. Bridle, P., Stott, K. G. and Timberlake, C. F., *Phytochemistry*, 1973, **12**, 1103.
218. Goto, T., Takase, S. and Kondo, T., *Tetrahedron Lett.*, 1978, No. 27, 2413.
219. Nilsson, E., *Chem. Scripta*, 1973, **4**, 49.
220. Sweeny, J. G. and Iacobucci, G. A., *Tetrahedron*, 1977, **33**, 2927.
221. Iacobucci, G. and Sweeny, J. G., *Verfahren zur Herstellung von 3-Deoxyanthocyanidinen*, Ger. Offen. 1977, 2 708 845 Cl. C07D 311/60.
222. Jurd, L., Methods of using Flavylium Compounds for Food Colouring, U.S. Patent, 1966, No. 3 266 903.
223. Timberlake, C. F., Improvements Relating to the Colouring of Foodstuffs, U.K. Patent, 1968, No. 5477/68.
224. Walford, J., *Intern. Flavours and Food Additives*, 1978, **9**, 215.
225. Coulson, J., *Intern. Flavours and Food Additives*, 1978, **9**, 207.

226. McClelland, C. W., in *Current Aspects of Food Colorants*, Ed. T. E. Furia, 1977, pp. 67–76. CRC Press, Ohio.
227. Palamidis, N. and Markakis, P., *J. Food Sci.*, 1975, **40**, 1047.
228. Peterson, R. G. and Jaffe, E. B., Berry and Fruit Treating Process, U.S. Patent, 1969, No. 3 484 254.
229. Philip, T., *J. Food Sci.* 1974, **39**, 859.
230. Nakamura, M., Hosokawa, M., Yajima, I. and Hayashi, K., *Chem. Abstr.*, 1975, **83**, 176995.
231. Calvi, J. P. and Francis, F. J., *J. Food Sci.*, 1978, **43**, 1448.
232. Clydesdale, F. M., Main, J. H., Francis, F. J. and Damon, R. A., *J. Food Sci.*, 1978, **43**, 1687.
233. Wallin, B. K. and Smith, B. J., *Intern. Flavours and Food Additives*, 1977, **8**,102.
234. Shewfelt, R. L. and Ahmed, E. M., *Food Prod. Dev.*, 1977, **11**, 52, 57, 62.
235. Chkheidze, Z. K., Belov, N. I., Yarovenko, V. V., Medzmariashvili, F. V. and Kobaladze, O. R., *Chem. Abstr.*, 1974, **81**, 90009.
236. Chiriboga, C. and Francis, F. J., *J. Am. Soc. hort. Sci.*, 1970, **95**, 233.
237. Buckmire, R. E. and Francis, F. J., *J. Food Sci.*, 1978, **43**, 908.
238. Chiriboga, C. D. and Francis, F. J., *J. Food Sci.*, 1973, **38**, 464.
239. Baker, C. H., Johnston, M. R. and Barber, W. W., *Food Prod. Dev.*, 1974, **8**, 65,68,70.
240. Baker, C. H., Johnston, M. R. and Barber, W. D., *Food Prod. Dev.*, 1974, **8**, 83, 86.
241. Shewfelt, R. L. and Ahmed, E. M., *J. Food Sci.*, 1978, **43**, 435.
242. Main, J. H., Clydesdale, F. M. and Francis, F. J., *J. Food Sci.*, 1978, **43**, 1693.
243. Esselen, W. B. and Sammy, G. M., *Food Prod. Dev.*, 1973, **7**, 80.
244. Esselen, W. B. and Sammy, G. M., *Food Prod. Dev.*, 1975, **9**, 37.
245. Lowry, J. B. and Chew, L., *Econ. Bot.*, 1974, **28**, 61.
246. Kikuchi, K., Chiba, A., Miyake, K., Nakai, T. and Tokuda, M., Anthocyanin food colouring agent from purple corn. Japan, Kokai. 1977, No. 77, 130824 via *Chem. Abstr.*, 1978, **88**, 150953.
247. Volpe, T., *Food Prod. Dev.* 1976, **10**, 13.
248. Soukup, R. J. and Il-Young Maing, in *Current Aspects of Food Colorants*, Ed. T. E. Furia, 1977, pp. 77–84. CRC Press, Ohio.
249. Bonati, A. and Crippa, F., *Fitoterapia*, 1978, **49**, 10.
250. Auslander, D. E., Goldberg, M., Hill, J. A. and Weiss, A. L., *Drug Cosmet. Ind.*, 1977, **121**, 55.
251. Lees, D. H. and Francis, F. J., *Hortscience*, 1972, **7**, 83.
252. Ribereau-Gayon, P. and Stonestreet, R., *Bull. Soc. Chim. Fr.*, 1965(9) 2649.
253. Swain, T. and Hillis, W. E., *J. Sci. Fd Agric.*, 1959, **10**, 63.
254. Niketić-Aleksić, G. K. and Hrazdina, G., *Lebensm.-Wiss. Technol.*, 1972, **5**, 163.
255. Wilkinson, M., Sweeny, J. G. and Iacobucci, G. A., *J. Chromat.*, 1977, **132**, 349.
256. Wulf, L. W. and Nagel, C. W., *Am. J. Enol. Vitic.*, 1978, **29**, 42.
257. Williams, M., Hrazdina, G., Wilkinson, M. M., Sweeny, J. G. and Iacobucci, G. A., *J. Chromat.*, 1978, **155**, 389.
258. Food Additives and Contaminants Committee. Interim report on the review of the colouring matter in food regulations, 1973, FAC/REP/29, HMSO, London.

Chapter 6

SOME SYNTHETIC CAROTENOIDS AS FOOD COLOURS

J. N. COUNSELL

Roche Products Ltd, Chemicals Division, Dunstable, UK

SUMMARY

The carotenoids are an especially widely distributed group of plant pigments. They are responsible either directly, alone or in combination with other colours, or in the form of complexes for many of nature's colours. Some of the carotenoids are now available commercially as a result of highly-developed, industrial chemistry. The pure substances are converted to specialised application forms which successfully overcome solubility and stability problems. A very extensive technology has been built up enabling the potential user to colour products with ease and success. After briefly discussing these points, the chapter deals in detail with many of these applications.

OCCURRENCE

The primary objective intended for this chapter is that of providing a fairly practical guide to the use of synthetic carotenoids in the food industry. The scope is very considerable and the progress which has been made since the first commercial product appeared in 1954 is wide ranging. Not only have many applications been investigated but also other carotenoids have been added to the palette of the technologist. There is no doubt that further progress will be made in both directions and the pace may be expected to increase as the artificial dyes have their applicability reduced.

The principal groups of colours naturally occurring in foods are carotenoids, anthocyanins, porphyrins and chlorophylls. The carotenoids, being found throughout the vegetable kingdom, are especially widespread and important. Because other colours which may occur, particularly chlorophyll, can mask the carotenoids, their presence is not always obvious. Nevertheless, these compounds are responsible for many of the brilliant red, orange and yellow colours of edible fruits and berries, vegetables and mushrooms, as well as flowers, insects, birds, fish and other animals. Some idea of the importance of carotenoids may be gained from the estimate (probably conservative) which puts nature's own production at around 100 million tonnes per annum.[1,2] Among the components of this impressive quantity it is fucoxanthin, the characteristic pigment of many marine algae, which is most abundant. As may, perhaps, be expected, it is the three main carotenoids of green leaves which are next in order of magnitude. These are lutein, violoxanthin and neoxanthin.[2] Others are produced in smaller quantities although, from the viewpoint of food technology, their importance is much higher. Some of the carotenoids, such as β-carotene and zeaxanthin, are very widely distributed and so become important as components of many foods. Others, for example lycopene and bixin, may achieve their importance and magnitude by being the main colours of a particular fruit or vegetable.

Carotenoids are also found in combination with proteins as carotenoproteins. These compounds are common to a wide variety of animals, notably the invertebrates. For example, the blue carapace pigment of lobsters is crustacyanin. The same prosthetic group, astaxanthin, appears in the green carotenoprotein of the lobster egg, ovoverdin. Carotenoproteins are an important group of animal colours whose functions are not well understood. Nevertheless, they may well be more important, functionally, than the carotenoids in the animal body.[3]

Various natural extracts containing carotenoids have been used as food colours for centuries. Examples include the yellow colour of saffron (crocetin), the pinkish yellow of annatto (bixin or norbixin, depending on the application type), the orange–red of paprika (capsanthin and capsorubin), various colours obtained from extracts of leaves (xanthophylls), orange–yellow extracts of carrots (carotenes) and rich yellow, formerly used in margarine, of red palm oil (carotenes).

An indication of the widespread distribution of carotenoids in human food may be gained from Table 1. The figures given in the table are mostly for β-carotene, the rest are total carotenoids. Columns B and E give the contents in μg/100 g. Roels[49] originally composed the table in order to

TABLE 1
'CAROTENE' OR 'PRO-VITAMIN A' CONTENT OF VARIOUS FRUITS AND VEGETABLES

Food	'Carotene' or 'Pro-vitamin A' value					
	Source 1[a]			Source 2[b]		
	A	B	C	D	E	F
Fruits						
Apples (raw)	50	30	17	90	50	278
Apricots (raw)	2 500	1 500	833	2 700	1 620	900
Bananas (raw)	333	200	111	190	110	61
Blackberries (raw)	165	100	56	200	120	67
Cherries (raw)	200	120	67	191	110	61
Gooseberries (raw)	300	180	100	290	170	94
Melons (raw, yellow)	3 333	2 000	1 111	251	150	83
Olives (green, canned)	250	150	139	300	180	100
Oranges (raw)	84	50	28	200	120	67
Orange juice (raw)	84	50	28	200	120	67
Orange juice (canned)	84	50	28	200	120	67
Peaches (raw)	833	500	278	1 330	800	444
Peaches (raw, dried)	3 333	2 000	1 111	3 900	2 340	1 300
Pears (raw)	17	10	6	20	10	6
Pineapple (raw)	100	60	33	70	40	22
Pineapple juice (canned)	67	40	22	50	30	17
Plums (raw)	367	220	122	300	180	100
Prunes (raw, dried)	1 666	1 000	556	2 170	1 300	722
Raspberries (raw)	133	80	44	130	80	44
Rhubarb (raw)	100	60	33	100	60	33
Strawberries (raw)	50	30	17	60	40	22
Tangerines (raw)	156	100	56	420	250	139
Vegetables						
Asparagus (raw or boiled)	833	500	278	900	540	300
French beans (raw or boiled)	833	500	278	600	360	200
Beet greens (raw or boiled)	8 333	5 000	2 778	6 100	3 666	2 033
Broccoli tops (raw or boiled)	4 166	2 500	1 389	2 500	1 500	833
Brussels sprouts (raw or boiled)	666	400	222	550	330	183
Cabbage (raw)	500	300	167	130	80	44
Carrots (raw, young or boiled)	10 000	6 000	3 333	—	—	—
Carrots (raw, mature or boiled)	20 000	12 000	6 667	11 000	6 600	3 667
Carrots (canned)	11 666	7 000	3 889	15 000	9 000	5 000
Cauliflower (raw or boiled)	50	30	17	60	40	22
Endive (raw)	3 333	2 000	1 111	3 300	1 980	1 100
Kale (raw or boiled)	8 333	5 000	2 778	9 000	5 400	3 000
Leeks (raw or boiled)	67	40	22	40	20	11
Lettuce (raw)	1 666	1 000	556	970	580	322
Mint (raw)	18 333	11 000	6 111	—	—	—

154   J. N. COUNSELL

TABLE 1—*contd.*

| Food | 'Carotene' or 'Pro-vitamin A' value | | | | | |
| | Source 1[a] | | | Source 2[b] | | |
	A	B	C	D	E	F
Vegetables—contd.						
Mustard and cress (raw)	8 333	5 000	2 778	7 000	4 200	2 333
Parsley (raw)	13 333	8 000	4 444	8 500	5 100	2 833
Peas (raw or boiled)	500	300	167	590	350	194
Pumpkin (raw)	2 500	1 500	833	1 600	960	533
Spinach (raw or boiled)	10 000	6 000	3 333	8 100	4 860	2 700
Sweet potatoes (raw)	6 666	4 000	2 222	8 800	5 280	2 933
Turnip tops (raw or boiled)	10 000	6 000	3 333	7 600	4 560	2 533
Watercress (raw)	5 000	3 000	1 667	4 900	2 940	1 633

[a] Source 1 corresponds with data published by McCance and Widdowson[5] and
[b] Source 2 with Watt and Merrill.[7]
Note: In the original table[49] and later quoted by Kläui[6] the values in the two
columns headed A and D are attributed incorrectly.

allow comparison of the pro-vitamin A values. To do this, he took the
figures of Watt and Merrill[7] which were published in terms of IU/100 g. In
turn, these authors had used an equivalence of 0·6 µg β-carotene and 1·2 µg
other carotenoids to 1 IU of vitamin A. Roels used the same β-carotene
activity relationship to convert the original β-carotene equivalents of
Barrett and Widdowson.[5] These derived vitamin activity levels are given in
columns A and D. Reversing the calculation gives the weights of B-carotene
equivalents, columns B and E. The remaining columns C and F show the
equivalent vitamin A activity calculated using the usual ratio of 6 to 1 (see
section on vitamin A activity). The figures given in the latest version of
McCance and Widdowson's The Composition of Foods (Paul and
Southgate[4]) are slightly different for some of the foods but, in the main,
agree.

Information published which relates to carotenoid contents often, as
may perhaps be expected, appears in terms of its dietary value. It is
essential, when using such figures, to understand the basis of the calculation
made by the authors.

While Table 1 gives an idea of the widespread presence of carotenoids in
our normal foods, there are also to be considered two other aspects: the
complexity of the mixture of carotenoids in some foods and the variations

TABLE 2
CAROTENOIDS IN CAROTENOID FRACTIONS OF ORANGE PULP AND FRESH ORANGE PEEL

Constituent	Orange pulp (%)	Fresh orange peel (%)	Constituent	Orange pulp (%)	Fresh orange peel (%)
Phytoene	4·0	3·1	Capsanthin-like	—	0·3
Phytofluene	13	6·1	Antheraxanthin	5·8	6·3
α-Carotene	0·5	0·1	Mutatoxanthins	6·2	1·7
β-Carotene	1·1	0·3	Violaxanthin	7·4	44
ζ-Carotene	5·4	3·5	Luteoxanthins	17	16
OH-α-Carotene-like	1·5	0·3	Auroxanthin	12	2·3
Cryptoxanthin epoxide-like	—	0·4	Valenciaxanthin	2·8	2·2
Cryptoxanthin	5·3	1·2	Sinensiaxanthin	2·0	3·5
Cryptoflavin-like	0·5	1·2	Trollixanthin-like	2·9	0·5
Cryptochrome-like	—	0·8	Valenciachrome	1·0	0·7
Lutein	2·9	1·2	Sinensiachrome-like	—	0·2
Zeaxanthin	4·5	0·8	Trollichrome-like	3·0	0·8

which can occur, for example, during a season. The former is illustrated by Table 2 which lists the carotenoids identified in oranges.[8]

Bauernfeind[9] in a paper on carotenoids in fruits, juices and concentrates reviewed the seasonal colour fluctuations and carotenoid changes during growth and maturation. Variations in the total carotenoids and β-carotene contents of citrus fruit juices[10] based on published figures[11-13] illustrate the differences to be found even in a small related group of foods.

While there are other, speculative functions assigned to the carotenoids, those established include protective agents preventing damage to cells by photodynamic action and as accessory pigments involved in photosynthetic organisms.

SYNTHESIS

Although β-carotene is by no means the most abundant carotenoid in nature, it was the first to be synthesised commercially. Synthetic β-carotene was first marketed in 1954. Some eight years later β-apo-8'-carotenal (C_{30}) followed and then, in 1964, canthaxanthin appeared. The pro-vitamin A activity of β-carotene makes it of special interest. Apocarotenal (β-apo-8'-carotenal, C_{30}) and apocarotenoic ester (ethyl β-apo-8'-carotenoate, C_{30})

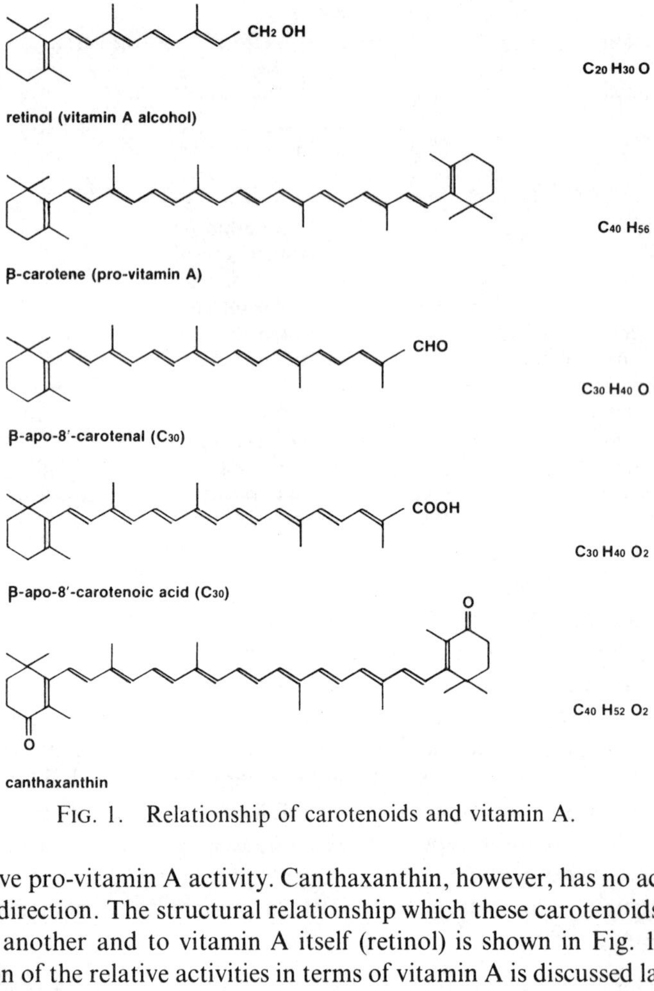

retinol (vitamin A alcohol)

$C_{20} H_{30} O$

β-carotene (pro-vitamin A)

$C_{40} H_{56}$

β-apo-8′-carotenal (C_{30})

$C_{30} H_{40} O$

β-apo-8′-carotenoic acid (C_{30})

$C_{30} H_{40} O_2$

canthaxanthin

$C_{40} H_{52} O_2$

FIG. 1.   Relationship of carotenoids and vitamin A.

also have pro-vitamin A activity. Canthaxanthin, however, has no activity in this direction. The structural relationship which these carotenoids bear to one another and to vitamin A itself (retinol) is shown in Fig. 1. The question of the relative activities in terms of vitamin A is discussed later in this chapter.

The synthesis of β-carotene presented a natural challenge to the ingenuity of the organic chemist, particularly because of its potential commercial importance. The first total syntheses were published in 1950[14,15] and were relatively quickly followed by the successful industrial synthesis by Isler and his team.[16] As a result, the large-scale commercial production of pure crystalline β-carotene was made possible. Resulting from this success was not only the large international trade which has grown in the intervening 23 years but also the rapid development of a wide range of carotenoids. Details of the fundamental research and the chemistry involved are to be found in publications by Isler and his colleagues.[17-25] An outline of the complexity of the route to β-carotene, other carotenoids of commercial significance and vitamin A is given in Fig. 2. The scheme has been assembled from several sources and should not be taken as necessarily representing normal practice.

The synthetic routes to many other carotenoids are known: some of these undoubtedly will be of interest potentially as food colours. However, such is the general climate of opinion, these days, that only those which have identity with carotenoids forming a part of the normal human diet will be likely to enter commercial development.

PROPERTIES

In general, it is a characteristic of carotenoids that they are insoluble in aqueous media, have a low solubility in oils and a very slow rate of dissolution. The more pure the carotenoid compound is, the more limited its solubility. When in the pure, crystalline state, the carotenoids are very sensitive to oxidation. It is necessary for them to be kept under vacuum or inert gas. The oxidation is accelerated by light and, where oils are present, by metallic catalysts, especially copper, iron and manganese. Exposure to fatty acid hydroperoxides can initiate radical decomposition. In the right circumstances the hydroperoxides can directly attack carotenoids. As may be expected, enzymic reactions involved in the decay of vegetable matter may also cause the destruction of carotenoids. Through secondary reactions, the carotenoids are destroyed by gamma radiation.

The sensitivity of carotenoids to oxidation makes the use of antioxidants desirable. In this connection, the value of vitamin C and its derivatives and tocopherol is considerable and not least because of their widespread acceptance.

The more important physical properties of three pure synthesised carotenoids are given in Table 3.[1] It must be remembered that the carotenoids are not normally available in the pure forms. Stability and difficulty of application preclude this although for the research worker, samples can usually be obtained from the manufacturer.

Many publications also list properties for a fourth commercial carotenoid—β-apo-8'-carotenoic acid (C_{30}) ethyl ester. The information is included in this review although the use of this carotenoid, at least in Europe, is not large in direct food addition terms. It is one of the substances

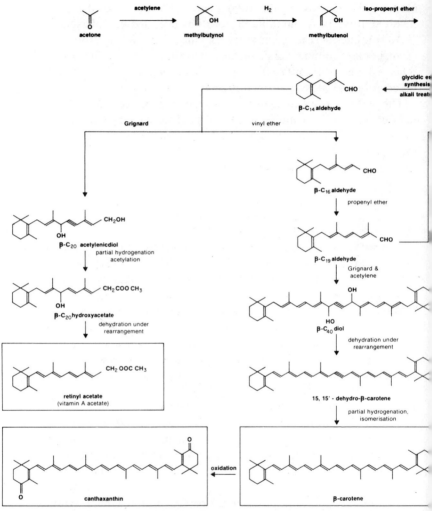

FIG. 2.   Some synthetic routes to carotenoids and vitamin A.

acceptable for marking intervention butter oil within the EEC. The level recommended, however, makes the colour level a little too high for applications where colour level is required to be low; shortbread being a good example.

It will be clear from the foregoing that in the pure state synthetic carotenoids do not have properties which favour their direct use as food

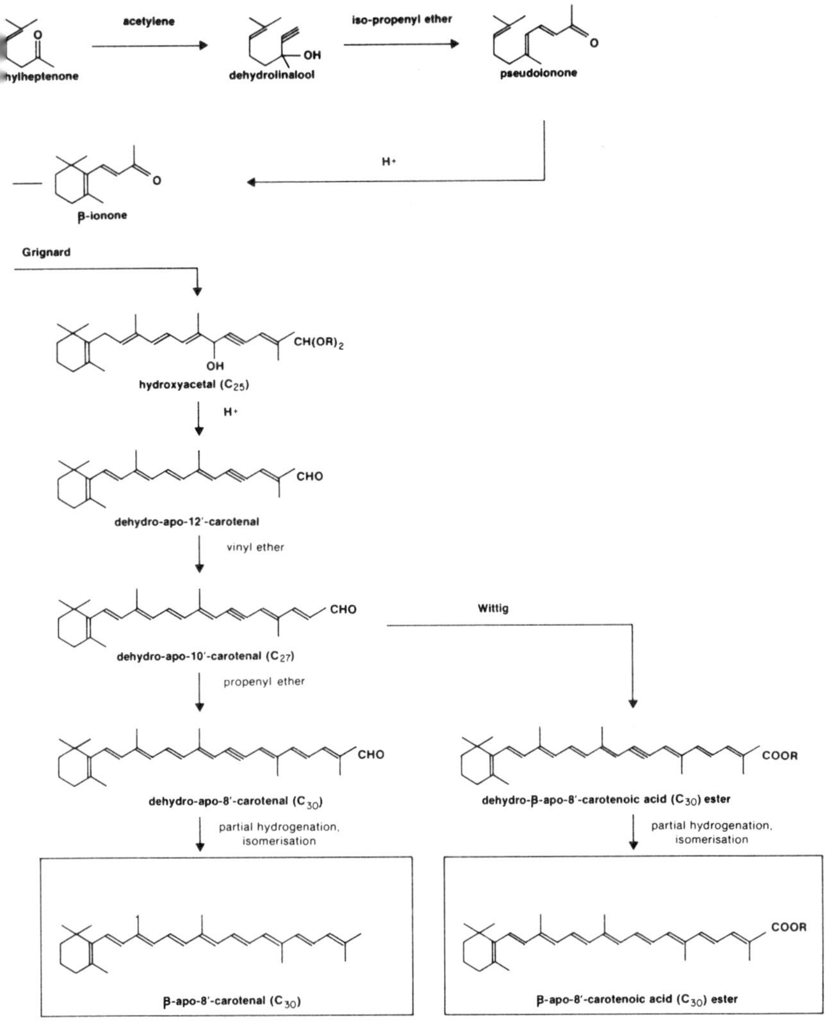

FIG. 2—contd.

colours. A very large technology has grown up which involves the preparation of application forms which not only improve stability but also allow their use in many kinds of food products. Naturally, much of this application technology is of a commercially sensitive nature. A very useful summary was given by Kläui et al.[26] of the methods used which, while mainly for fat-soluble vitamins, are also applicable to carotenoids.

TABLE 3

PHYSICO-CHEMICAL DATA AND BIOLOGICAL PROPERTIES OF CAROTENOIDS

	β-Carotene	Apocarotenal	Apocarotenoic ester	Canthaxanthin
Colour of oily solution (different concentrations)	yellow to orange	orange to orange-red	yellow to orange	orange to red
Melting point of crystalline compound	176–182°C	136–140°C	134–138°C	approx. 210°C
Vitamin A activity	yes	yes	yes	no
Solubility (g/100 ml solution, 20°C)				
Fats, oils	0·05–0·08	0·7–1·5	approx. 0·7	approx. 0·005
Orange oil	0·2–1·0	approx. 3·1	3·4–4·4	approx. 0·04
Water	insoluble	insoluble	insoluble	insoluble
Glycerol	insoluble	insoluble	insoluble	insoluble
Ethanol	below 0·01	approx. 0·1	below 0·1	below 0·01
Cyclohexane	approx. 0·1	approx. 0·8	approx. 2	below 0·01
Ether	approx. 0·1	approx. 1·5	approx. 2·5	approx. 0·03
Chloroform	approx. 3	approx. 20	approx. 30	approx. 10
Acetone	approx. 0·1	approx. 1·8	approx. 1·2	approx. 0·03
Spectrophotometric data[a]				
λ max. (in cyclohexane)	455–456 nm	460–462 nm	448–450 nm	468–472 nm
E_1^1 max. (in cyclohexane)	456 nm > 2 400	461 nm > 2 530	449 nm > 2 440	470 nm > 2 110
	485 nm > 2 030	388 nm > 2 030	475 nm > 2 000	

[a] The carotenoids isomerise in solution during storage or on heating; the predominant isomer in the equilibrium mixture is the *trans* compound. The values given correspond to the *trans* isomer.

In general terms, there are two main fields of application for any food colour: those involving aqueous systems and those which are essentially non-aqueous. The former predominate. Thus, commercial products tend to follow these two lines. For convenience, the same division will be adopted here, although the fat-soluble products will be considered first.

CAROTENOIDS IN FAT-BASED FOODS

Carotenoids are particularly potent colours. At the levels at which, for example, β-carotene is added to fat-based foods, solubility is not a major problem. The very slow dissolution rate of the crystalline substance is a disadvantage. The simple expedient of reducing the crystal particle size will overcome this problem but clearly, due to its consequently greatly increased exposure to oxygen, it will be less stable. The particles of about 2–5 μm size are produced in practice by grinding in an attritor-type mill under a nitrogen atmosphere while suspended in an edible oil. The end product is normally packed under oil and nitrogen which retard the oxidation enough to enable the product to be distributed, stored and used with very few problems.

Of the four commercially available carotenoids, β-carotene and apocarotenal are distributed in suitable application forms for fat-based foods. The remaining two, apocarotenoic ester and canthaxanthin, are not normally sold for such applications. This is primarily because of the duplication of colour shade.

Micronised crystals of β-carotene and apocarotenal are available as 20 % suspensions in an edible vegetable oil. In addition, β-carotene is available as a 30 % suspension for large-scale application where the more difficult handling characteristics are not a disadvantage.

1. Margarine and Butter

When the dairy cow is on a good summer pasture she produces cream of a rich yellow colour which, in turn, gives a deep yellow butter. The colour is due primarily to β-carotene which has escaped conversion to vitamin A. In the winter, however, when, in some countries, the cow is on grain and dry roughage, the cream and corresponding butter are very pale. Seasonal variation in butter carotenoids is shown in Fig. 3.[51]

It is possible, at least in theory, to increase the colour of the cream and

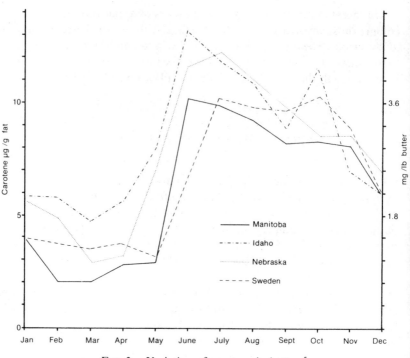

FIG. 3.   Variation of carotene in butter.[5]

butter during these winter months by feeding a high level of stabilised β-carotene in concentrated form. In practice, however, the levels required in the animal's feed are so high to achieve a measurable result that the idea must be ruled out on economic grounds. It is easier, cheaper and more controllable to make the addition to the butter. In the first year of its commercial introduction, now a quarter of a century ago, successful industrial trials of β-carotene for colouring butter and margarine took place.[27] While the standardisation of butter colour is relatively easy[28] it is not always necessary. It is effective to add a solution of β-carotene in a suitable oil to the churning mass. Provided that the microcrystals are fully predissolved, the butter will be suitably tinted. Any undissolved crystals will lead, over a period of storage, to small intensely coloured spots in the butter. This is caused by the slow dissolution and diffusion of the colour in the cold fat.

As a colour, β-carotene has become the accepted standard for margarine in many countries. The application is still one of the more important in commercial terms. In a considerable number of countries vitamin A is added to margarine.[29] In Denmark, a part of the activity of this vitamin is in β-carotene. In the UK the use of β-carotene is allowed and its activity, as vitamin A, may be taken into account when assessing the vitamin A level to ensure conformity with the statutory compositional requirements.[30] The stability of the β-carotene in this application is excellent.[31,32]

The correct colour for margarine is achieved using only some 3 to 6 g pure β-carotene per tonne of product. In some markets, the consumers may prefer even more. It is only necessary to add the calculated quantity of the microcrystal suspension to the warm oil (usually at about 40–55 °C) and stir thoroughly.

In practice, it is usual to use a proprietary mixture of the β-carotene with vitamin A, vitamin D, vitamin E and other trace ingredients. Such a mixture has obvious advantages in process and process control simplification. Such mixtures are based on a suspension rather than a solution of β-carotene. While it is possible to prepare relatively concentrated solutions, these have a short storage life. This is not a reflection on the stability of β-carotene. Over a period far too short to enable concentrated solutions to be of any practical value, the β-carotene recrystallises. When this happens the crystals will be much larger and their rate of redissolving will be correspondingly very much lower. The advantages of the microcrystals in rapid dissolution are obviously lost. Apocarotenal is sometimes used in margarine colouring either alone or in combination with β-carotene. The resultant colour level may be much more intense and so suitable for specialised markets. Alternatively, the combination may show an economic advantage even though the vitamin A value is lower.

'Margarines' with higher water content which have been whipped may need more colour due to the physical effect of lightening.

2. Other Shortenings, Fats and Oils

The addition of colour to other food fats and oils beyond the butter and margarine markets is often practised. While free from the compositional requirements of margarine such shortenings can be used for catering and industrial manufacture of cakes, pastry and biscuits.

Again, β-carotene provides an excellent colour for the purpose. By adjusting the concentration involved, the effects of variations in the colour of the egg yolk supply can be countered through the addition of carotenoids to the fat.

Some liquid vegetable oils used domestically for frying etc., are often coloured naturally. Others may be devoid of colour and consequently not appear so attractive at the point of sale. The colour may easily be standardised by the use of β-carotene.

3. Processed Cheese

β-Carotene and apocarotenal are used, especially in the USA, for colouring processed or process cheese. Apocarotenal is particularly useful for achieving the darker orange colour which is so characteristic of many products in this group. The colour or colours may simply be added to the hot melted cheese directly. Provided that the mixing is adequate, this method is acceptable. Any risk of possible uneven distribution may easily be avoided by predissolving the carotenoid suspensions in some of the melted cheese or in butter oil.

4. Other Fat-based Products

In general, the micronised crystal suspensions of the carotenoids have a commercial advantage over the types developed for non-aqueous applications. This is understandable when the very much greater processing and other ingredients are taken into account. Thus, there is an incentive to try to colour foods with an oil component through the use of the oil-soluble colours. A great deal will depend on the nature of the product and the stability of the oil. For example, by colouring the oil the appearance of French fried potato and potato crisps (chips) may be considerably improved. Such an application is clearly not easy in view of the high temperature of the frying bath and the very easy availability of oxygen. As a result it is not practised in countries where high levels of antioxidants are not allowed. It has been suggested[33] that this process could be extended to such items as fish, meat and poultry products coated with breadcrumbs. Usually, however, this is better achieved, particularly where the retail market is involved, by adding the colour in a suitable form to the bread from which the crumbs are prepared. Colour may be added to popcorn either by using coloured fat for heat transfer or by spraying a coloured oil after the corn has popped. In the latter method the shelf-life will be short and so oxidation is not such a problem. For the candied variety, of course, the colour is incorporated into the boiled sugar mass and a water-dispersible type is used.

Canning and freezing vegetables in butter sauce can represent a problem when water-soluble dyes are used to enhance the sauce colour. Often, the colour migrates on storage to the vegetable tissue to the detriment of the appearance of the product. The carotenoids, being oil soluble, do not exhibit this effect.

Through the addition of a small amount of β-carotene to the oil phase the appearance of imitation creams can be considerably improved. The amount of colour added is usually just enough to take away the otherwise unappetising whiteness of these products.

Apocarotenal and β-carotene may be successfully used for colouring French dressings. The stability using a 0·5 % solution of apocarotenal in oil was good when stored in glass bottles. Prolonged exposure to sunlight must, however, be avoided.[35] Finberg[36] reported the results of an important study based on comparisons made in seven companies between paprika, paprika oleoresin and apocarotenal. The improved colour uniformity and the stability of apocarotenal were judged to be of major value for dressings, especially when packed in plastic containers.

In most of the applications so far discussed, there has been a stage where sufficient heat and agitation have been involved to ensure the complete dissolution of the added microcrystalline carotenoid suspensions. When processing frozen raw egg yolks, however, it is usually advisable to ensure adequate premixing of the carotenoid into a portion of the liquid yolk. Where high capacity, multiple plate heat exchangers are used at a temperature of about 60 °C, there is usually enough heat and agitation to ensure solution. Some of the special forms of β-carotene developed primarily for aqueous-based foods are even more suitable both for this application and also for spray dried egg yolk.

Pasta products made in the normal way from durum wheat have a characteristically rich, light yellow colour. The natural carotenoid content of wheat is responsible for this shade. However, when soft wheat is used, the naturally lower carotenoid content produces correspondingly pale pasta products. One method of overcoming this problem is through the use of specially coloured flour or starch premix. This idea, first described by Schuchardt[27] in 1954 may also be extended to dry cake mixes and other similar products. A coloured flour premix may also be prepared using the method of spraying an oil solution of β-carotene into the agitated carrier. A level of 200 mg/lb (440 mg/kg) has been reported by this method.[34]

The oil-soluble forms of carotenoids have also been used in various ways for colouring soft drinks. Rather than divide the topic, consideration of all forms will be given under the aqueous food heading.

CAROTENOIDS IN WATER-BASED FOODS

Devising application methods for oily foods where the carotenoids have some, albeit not often high, solubility was a challenge. In this area, where the solubility in water is virtually zero, new techniques have had to be devised and, indeed, are still being developed.

Nature does not restrict the occurrence of carotenoids to lipid systems. Large amounts of carotenoids occur in the form of very fine dispersions and as such are capable of colouring aqueous media. Common examples of this are to be seen in the carotenoid colouring of the juices of the tomato, orange and carrot. The well-recognised stability may be due to the carotenoids being present in the form of complexes with proteins or lipoproteins. The submicroscopic structure may also be a factor in their outstanding stability.

Methods of application of carotenoids to aqueous systems include the formation of emulsions, colloidal suspensions and dispersions in suitable colloids, particularly when a surface active agent is present.

Dissolving the carotenoid in a suitable water-miscible solvent, such as alcohol or acetone, pouring the solution into water and then evaporating the solvent gives a colloidal suspension.

Emulsions are generally useful but limited due to the low solubility of the carotenoid in oil which, of necessity, results in low potencies. Applying heat, e.g. above 100 °C, will enable the concentration to be raised but great care has to be exercised to ensure that more than the minimum isomerisation does not occur. Alternatively, other solvents can be used but a number of those which have advantages in this direction have obtrusive odours. The use of a surface active agent results in very fine dispersions. The emulsions obtained are quite stable. The carotenoid can be further stabilised by the addition of ascorbic acid. By the process most widely used for commercial carotenoids and for vitamin A, the products are obtained as free-flowing powders. These are, in fact, reversible, dried emulsions. The carotenoid is dissolved in a suitable oil using various techniques as outlined above. If necessary, suitable oil-soluble antioxidants may be added—in order to preserve the wide regulatory acceptance of the colour the antioxidants will usually be ascorbyl palmitate and tocopherol. The aqueous phase comprises a solution of a film-forming, hydrophilic colloid such as gelatin with a plasticiser or humectant, e.g. sugar. Water-soluble antioxidants (ascorbates) and other substances may be added in this phase.

The two phases are emulsified and then homogenised in a high-speed homogeniser until the average diameter of the oil droplets is below about five microns. Such a particle size helps to ensure a good physical strength of the colloidal matrix when dried as well as a good emulsion quality when reconstituted.

After homogenisation, the emulsion is subdivided into small droplets, usually by spraying. It is necessary, after spraying, to keep the droplets separated from each other in order to prevent them sticking together. This is usually achieved by using a suitable powder or liquid medium to catch the particles. Powders will adhere to the surfaces of the particles and liquids will form a film around them. Both media, but especially the powder, will contribute a dehydrating effect. After separation from the catch medium, the particles are dehydrated and so form the characteristic very hard beadlets. These beadlets commonly contain 10 % of the carotenoid.

These beadlets, provided they are kept dry have a very good stability and, although rather more clumsy to handle compared with most of the artificial dyes, are nevertheless capable of use in very many foods. Although in practice the method may be varied, it is normally suggested that the beadlets are wetted with 10 to 15 times their weight of water at about 50 °C and stirred until completely dissolved. For experimental work or trials in processing, filtering through a very fine sieve is suggested in order to ensure no undissolved particles remain.

Because of the physical properties of the particles of coloured material resulting in a dispersion of these beadlets, the colour of the emulsion will be darker in shade than would be expected in a true solution. Using the idea of a much more dilute emulsion with more readily soluble base colloids can permit the preparation of cold-water-dispersible powders. Such powders are different from the beadlets by being much less concentrated, about 1 % compared with 10 % for beadlets, and by being lighter, not only in intensity but also in shade.

In aqueous systems a great deal will depend upon the product involved and the colour shade desired. Generally, however, it may be said that shades from light yellow through to tomato red are possible with the commercially available synthetic carotenoids.

The following applications are mainly drawn from the application studies of the Roche organisation. Many have not previously been published. It is necessary to sound a word of caution, however, regarding the application of carotenoids to food products. The basic physical and chemical properties of carotenoids are vastly different from those of the artificial dyes. Similarly, the need, as described earlier, for supporting and protecting colloids makes for even greater differences. It would hardly be reasonable, therefore, to expect a weight for weight substitution of carotenoid preparation for artificial food dye to be possible. It is not. A certain amount of common sense has to be brought to bear. Nevertheless, many excellent results have been achieved already and, as the restrictions of legislation become more difficult still, more of the presently laboratory results will be transferred to production practice.

1. Confectionery—Hard Candy

In the normal process, the sweet mass, consisting principally of sugar, glucose and water, is boiled to the correct point and deposited on to an oiled slab. Flavour, colour and acids are mixed into the hot mass by kneading. When adequately mixed and when the correct temperature is reached, the mass is pressed into shapes and wrapped. At levels from 1·5 mg/kg to 20 mg/kg of pure substance, the carotenoids give truly beautiful colours. The cold-water-soluble β-carotene gives pale, slightly yellow sweets at the 1·5 mg/kg level. At 15 mg/kg, the colour is a strong but distinctly lemon yellow. Where the gelatin-based beadlets are involved, however, the colours of the sweets have a distinct red component.

Apocarotenal and canthaxanthin can be used to take the colours forward through a more reddish orange to an intense orange–red rather like a rich tomato shade.

By using an appropriate grade of chlorophyll with the canthaxanthin, very attractive shades of brown can be achieved. On the other hand, using a low level when added to β-carotene, one can obtain an even more lemon yellow. Provided that certain obvious incompatibilities can be avoided, such mixtures are capable of reproducing a great many of the attractive shades previously considered impossible without recourse to the artificial dyes.

The advent of the new continuous depositing technique for the production of high quality hard candy (e.g. the continuous depositor made by Baker Perkins) puts a higher demand on the colour—and on the flavour as well as other ingredients. By this method the liquid mass is cast in moulds. It is necessary for colours and other additions to be made when the temperature is as high as 140 °C—some 50 °C higher than in the more conventional process. Experiments on a laboratory scale have shown that the carotenoids are capable of withstanding the heavy demands of this process.

In the slab technique, the resulting sweets are rarely transparent. The cloudiness which may result from the use of some carotenoid preparations is therefore no disadvantage. The continuous depositing method, however, produces candy in very smooth and clear pieces. The slight turbidity caused by the carotenoids may represent a slight drawback.

2. Confectionery—Fruit Jellies

A typical fruit jelly will contain sugar, glucose, sorbitol and agar-agar. The general principle of adding the sensitive ingredients after most of the heating has finished is employed here. The colour solutions and the flavours are added after boiling and before pouring and casting.

The colours obtained with the carotenoids are similar to those produced in the hard candy. Slightly lower concentrations of carotenoids give excellent results. The cold-water-soluble preparation of β-carotene gives yellows ranging from pale at $1 \cdot 5$ mg/kg up to an intense yellow at 10 mg/kg. As before, a red element is introduced by the gelatin beadlet product resulting in a definite orange. Apocarotenal and canthaxanthin in the beadlet form can produce interesting and useful shades of reddish orange through to orange–red. As a general guide, a concentration of 10 mg/kg for the carotenoids in this application gives a reasonable range of product colours.

Pectin jellies made to a conventional recipe and coloured with β-carotene and canthaxanthin as well as other natural colours show excellent stability over six months stored in daylight and darkness. A form of chlorophyll used to shade some samples was tested on its own. It showed a little loss of brightness and, towards the end of this exacting test, a shift of shade towards yellow–brown.

3. Confectionery—Marzipan

Marzipan products may be coloured either on the surface only or throughout the mass. Alternatively, of course, both techniques could be used.

After the marzipan has cooled down to about 50 °C the surface may be painted with predissolved carotenoids. Towards the end of the mixing when the mass has cooled, some powdered sugar is added. This improves adhesion of the colour preparation. Usually, the solution strength used is in the region of $0 \cdot 1$ to $1 \cdot 0 \%$. The surface is then dried and may be given a coat of protective varnish. Once again, beautiful shades from yellow through to red are obtained with the three carotenoids using the different types available. Mixtures of canthaxanthin with a suitable type of chlorophyll enable rich brown shades to be obtained.

To colour the mass of the marzipan, the colour solutions are added with the powdered sugar when the product has cooled to about 50 °C. The commercial carotenoid forms used at levels to give between 3 and 10 mg/kg pure substance give attractive shades from pure yellow through to orange.

4. Sugar-coated Tablets

The water-soluble or dispersible forms of the carotenoids may be used to obtain especially attractive colours for sugar-coated sweets. These products include the chocolate beans, chewing gum, nuts and so on which are coated by a process essentially the same as that used for sugar-coated pharmaceutical tablets. The standards of finish may not be the same in the two industries but the successful application of the carotenoids and other natural colours is a point in common.

Before application to the tablet with a white sub-coating, the carotenoid preparation will have been dispersed in water in the ratio of 1:4. At about 20% this is double the concentration usually recommended for aqueous applications. While not so easy to achieve, the higher concentration is necessary to avoid over-dilution of the syrup. The concentrate is then mixed with hot sugar syrup containing 100 parts sugar in 40 parts of water at 106 °C. The coloured syrup is then applied to the sub-coated tablets by the conventional technique. The number and thickness of the layers will be determined by the quality standard required and, of course, the economic demands of time and material in process. At the pharmaceutical end of the scale, some 60 or more coats will produce a very high quality tablet while at the confectionery end an adequate result can be obtained with, say, six to eight coats.

The colour range includes shades between yellow and red according to whether β-carotene, apocarotenal or canthaxanthin is used. The addition of a suitable grade of chlorophyll enables interesting variations to be made. By this means, not only can attractive brown shades be made but also the reddish overtones of β-carotene may be toned down to create more yellow results.

Using newly developed application forms, canthaxanthin in particular can be applied to produce especially attractive shades ranging from pale peach through to a strong, almost purple shade.

The stability of these colours in this application is excellent. With some tablets, only the slightest change is noticeable after some 15 years or so.

It is not so easy to give concentrations in this application. Using a tablet core of 9 mm diameter, the amount of colour expressed as pure substance per tablet will mainly lie in the range of 5 to 50 μg depending on the shade and the application type used.

5. Confectionery—Fondant

Having made fondant in the usual way, the colour is added in the predissolved form while the mass is still warm and reasonably fluid. When the distribution is complete, the fondant is deposited into starch moulds, allowed to set and finally wet crystallised. An attractive range of pastel shades is possible with the water-dispersible carotenoids. Concentrations of 3 to 50 mg/kg will cover most of the colour range desired. Shading with other natural colours, especially chlorophyll, will increase the range.

6. Confectionery—Chocolate

While, strictly, it should be included under the oil-soluble applications heading, 'white' chocolate seems more logically placed under confectionery. The carotenoids can be used to give pleasant pastel shades to this confection. Some trials have given results with rapid colour loss on storage while others have been remarkably stable. No direct evidence is available to allow this conflict to be explained.

However, there can be little doubt that the responsible factor is oxidation of the carotenoid. In the successful trials, the fat used was a hard type intended for export to very warm climates. It was also fresh and the product processed on a small scale whereas the unsuccessful trials involved a cheap commercial product where formulation and other details were not known.

7. Ice-cream

The carotenoids, β-carotene, apocarotenal and canthaxanthin may be used simply to give very attractive shades from vanilla yellow through to a reddish orange. By careful shading with other natural colours, a very useful range of colours for ice-cream can be made. The coffee and chocolate browns, for example, are particularly good.

Concentrations, depending on the end result desired and the colour involved will be mainly in the range 10 to 30 mg/kg. The stability is excellent.

In the products known as sorbet ices (or, if frozen without agitation and, usually, on a stick, lollies) the shades of vanilla yellow through to a red can be obtained using lower concentrations. In this case 3 to 10 mg/kg will probably suffice.

Sherbet ices fall in between these groups of frozen products. The presence of some fat and milk solids may be expected to raise the colour concentration. This is so but, depending of course on the amounts of these ingredients, the levels will be nearer to the plain water ice than to ice-cream.

8. Yogurt

For the trials which were carried out on yogurt, 1 to 2 % of skim milk powder was added to whole milk. The end product contained 3·5 % fat. The milk was incubated in large tanks at 42–45 °C. After the fermentation was complete, sugar, flavour and colour were added with stirring.

Quite low concentrations, 2 to 8 mg/kg of the carotenoids in water-dispersible forms, were adequate to produce an attractive range of colours from lemon yellow through apricot and peach to redder tints.

9. Cheese

It may be expected that β-carotene might lend itself ideally to achieving a suitable colour in hard cheeses such as Cheddar, Red Leicester and Double Gloucester. As a result of success at the bench level with various experimental application forms of β-carotene, a trial was set up at a pilot level. The results were highly encouraging in that the distribution of the colour was strongly towards the curd rather than the whey. From this viewpoint, the concept may prove useful commercially because of the increased value of whey when it has a lower colour level. Losses proved to be very small and stability during the normal shelf-life of the cheese was excellent.

While the results for Cheddar cheese were generally considered to be first-rate, the particular shade of yellow did not lend itself to being used at higher concentrations. When increased to the level usual in, say, a Scottish cheddar, the yellow was rather too low in red component for the cheese to have been accepted. Further trials using mixtures of the carotenoids are expected to bring the colour nearer to the ideal and at the same time to reduce the cost in use in the darker cheeses.

10. Bakery Products

The natural presence of β-carotene in many of the ingredients used in baking makes its addition, when necessary, an advantage. It provides a convenient and practical way of giving a rich golden colour to cakes and other baked foods.

Quite low levels, in the region of 4 to 12 mg/kg are usually quite enough to achieve an excellent end result. When the product contains fat or shortening, the colour could be added by using the fat-soluble form and predissolving it in the fat. Alternatively, and usually preferably, the β-carotene is used in water-dispersible form. The beadlets are predissolved in water and added with the other liquids.

Some colour loss may occur during long baking times and also when the temperature is unusually high. Should this occur, the effect may be compensated for by adding a suitable overage. Usually, 10–15 % is enough. In the finished product in normal commercial packings, the stability of the colour is good. If the product is exposed to sunlight for extended periods, some surface fading may occur. In normal handling, fading is not a problem.

Interesting results in brown biscuit shells have been obtained using canthaxanthin in the presence of caramel. Shade variations and dulling can be made with a grapeskin anthocyanin and a carbon black of vegetable origin.

Canthaxanthin and β-carotene have been used as colours for wafer biscuits. After predissolving in water, the colours were added to the separately prepared batter and thoroughly mixed. The wafer was cooked for 90 s: the plate temperatures were 220 °C lower and 200 °C upper.

The β-carotene results were very successful not only in shade but also in evenness of coloration across the sheets. Canthaxanthin showed a slight change of colour towards the yellow end of the spectrum. This was probably due to its being extracted into the fat used in the recipe. A particularly satisfactory chocolate-coloured wafer was made with a blend of canthaxanthin and caramel.

The carotenoids also provide a particularly attractive range of colours for breadcrumbs. Coloured breadcrumbs are an important article of commerce in these days when so many breaded products are distributed through the frozen food chain. Such items include the ubiquitous fish fingers as well as many other meat and fish preparations. Crumbs coloured in this way stand up to the preheating, freezing and subsequent cooking very well.

The stability of β-carotene in cake mixes is good. In products of this type, the conventional gelatin-based beadlets are not normally used. This is because there is a wide discrepancy between the particle sizes of the colour and the mass of the mixture. While there may be a problem of separation in handling dry mixtures, the presence of fat would be expected to prevent this. Greater problems are represented by the inevitable presence of visible dark spots in the mixture. Consumer reaction is likely. Similarly, due to the relatively slow rate of dissolving, particularly when the batter is prepared cold, the colour will progress through local spots and streaks to an even result. These intermediate stages are not likely to create confidence on the part of the housewife. It is therefore necessary to employ the rapid dissolving type with finer particle size. The benefits of this type are increased in this application by the lower concentration.

11. Baked Goods—Icings and Fillings

Many cakes and biscuits are decorated or filled. Strictly, these decorative items are not baked but they fit here with their associated bases.

The cream filling of a biscuit sandwich is usually made up of fat of suitable plasticity and sugar. Skimmed milk powder may also be added. The colour, in the form of strong solutions of the water-dispersible types, may be added after the mix is otherwise complete. The small amount of water involved does not affect the product adversely. It is essential, however, to continue mixing long enough to ensure an adequate distribution of the colour. If this is not done and the cream cools too much, the result may be rather streaky.

Many biscuits containing cream fillings are packed for distribution in transparent wrappings. In order to show the intending purchaser the true nature and high quality of the product, manufacturers not only use such wrappings but also pack the biscuits end on. The practice not only exposes the cream to the consumer but also to the demanding lighting conditions of the modern supermarket. As a result, the carotenoid creams tend to fade. At the same time there may be demonstrable changes in the fat component. The use of a suitable protective agent such as sodium ascorbate, tocopherol or ascorbyl palmitate with tocopherol can do a great deal not only to delay the colour change but also to prolong the shelf-life of the biscuit cream. Where the artificial dyes are used in biscuit creams, the oxidation of the fat still takes place. There is, however, no colour change observed.

Some biscuits are filled with a jam-like preparation. Canthaxanthin and apocarotenal may be used to colour this jam depending on the shade needed. The stability is improved by the addition of ascorbic acid to a point where the biscuit shell is likely to fade first.

Fondant-type icing used on cakes for distribution to the retail trade can be coloured successfully with carotenoids. The addition of β-carotene gives a pleasant warm yellow which may be made more 'lemon' in character by adding a little of a suitable chlorophyll type. Canthaxanthin used with vegetable carbon black gives a very useful chocolate-brown shade. The icings used on biscuits, while of a harder consistency and subject to a longer shelf-life, may also be successfully coloured with carotenoids. In some cases, where gelatin is a component of the icing, the gelatin in the protective matrix of the carotenoid may have to be taken into account otherwise changes of consistency may result.

12. Fruit Juices
Bearing in mind the importance of carotenoids in the make up of the natural colour of oranges (Table 2) it is not unexpected that the synthesised carotenoids should have found application in orange juice from an early date. During the course of a season variations in colour of juice occur. Differences of colour occur also due to the varieties grown and the place

where they are grown. Producers and, perhaps, more especially distributors like to decrease the variation in product colour at the point of sale. There can be little doubt that the purchaser is considerably influenced by colour. The influence is obvious when the product is offered in a transparent pack. While presentation in cans may seem to change this, the product is subject to the same scrutiny when poured out. It is, therefore, by no means an uncommon practice for juices to be standardised in colour before packing whether the pack is to be glass or tin plate.

Fruit juices, and particularly orange, are generally accepted as valuable items of the diet. The addition of β-carotene is in no way inconsistent with this. Its presence enhances the nutritive value of the juice, the addition of a suitable quantity of ascorbic acid not only improves the stability of the carotenoid but also, of course, enhances still further the nutritional value.

There are many published reports of the addition of β-carotene to orange and other fruit drinks. Nearly twenty years ago[37] the stability of β-carotene was demonstrated. In glass packs and in various types of tin-plated and enamelled cans the stability was good. In glass, the products were stored for three weeks at 104 °F and for three months at 86 °F. In the former group only one sample fell below 90 % retention while in the latter, only two were below 90 % retention. The averages for the whole trial were 96 % and 95 % retention respectively. In the experiment with cans, the retention was better. There was some scatter of analytical results but the averages for retention over six and twelve months at 75 °F were very close to 100 %.

Although canthaxanthin may not have a ready identification with the natural colour of the tomato (mainly lycopene) its colour is remarkably close. For this reason, canthaxanthin enjoys wide use for the standardisation and enhancement of the colour of tomato juices.

Clearly in such applications, the suspectibility of β-carotene to oxygen has to be remembered. Three points particularly should be remembered when processing fruit juices. Firstly, deaeration by mechanical means, secondly, reduction of headspace to the lowest amount practicable and thirdly, the use of ascorbic acid which is particularly effective.

13. Soft-Drink Powders

The incorporation of carotenoids in soft-drink powders represents no particular difficulty. It will be important, naturally, to ensure that an appropriate commercial type is used. The conventional beadlet has a large particle size of intense colour. Consequently, the end product will be uncoloured and have dark spots which will dissolve only slowly in cold water. Some of the more recent types with good cold water solubility and fine yellow particles are much more suited. The carotenoid could be dissolved in a suitable small amount of water and sprayed on the sugar crystals in a trough mixer. The effect of the small addition of water on the sugar flowability could be negated by adding a little tri-calcium phosphate, followed by the other ingredients. It would be necessary to conduct suitable trials in order to ensure that the colour stability was good.

14. Soft Drinks

A number of techniques are available for the successful incorporation of carotenoids into soft drinks. These involve the application of different ways of overcoming the basic difficulty: that of the insolubility of carotenoids in water.

The first method involves using the essential oil in citrus drinks as a solvent. The 20% suspensions of micronised carotenoids (the usual oil-soluble application forms) can be used to colour the flavouring oil prior to emulsification. The low solubility of the carotenoids in essential oils, Table 4, and the heat sensitivity of these oils presents a difficult problem. The apocarotenoids have a significantly higher solubility in these oils and this allows their inclusion in tinctorially useful amounts.

The solubilities mentioned in Table 4 have been determined in orange and lemon oils without heating. Canthaxanthin and β-carotene are obviously unsuitable for addition via the essential oil because the amounts which can be incorporated are far too low. However, their use in conjunction with the two apocarotenoids will enable suitable variations in colour shade to be obtained in the pale yellow to dark orange range.

In the second method, the water-dispersible forms of carotenoids are used. This is, indeed, a most important application in commercial terms. The water-dispersible beadlets, predissolved, may be used at various levels, alone or in combination with one another or other natural colours to obtain most, if not all, shades required in this area of the food industry.

As a very approximate guide, carotenoid additions for an orange drink will be in the range of 1 to 5 g per 1000 litres. Particularly, it is strongly recommended that the colour solution added should be homogenised with the pulp, the fruit concentrate or a mixture of the concentrate, sugar syrup and citric acid before dilution to the bulk beverage. Not only does this homogenising step greatly enhance the appearance by producing particularly brilliant results, it can also contribute to a reduction in the amount of added colour needed to obtain a given colour intensity. Through the action of the homogeniser which encourages the carotenoid to 'stick' to the fruit particles, the stability is very much improved.

In order to match this induced physical stability, the addition of ascorbic acid to the beverage greatly reduces losses due to oxidation. The presence of dissolved oxygen and free oxygen in the headspace are often responsible for the loss of colours. Even where the loss of colour may not immediately be

TABLE 4
SOLUBILITY OF PURE CRYSTALLINE CAROTENOIDS

	Lemon oil ('Citronenkonzentrat' Givaudan-Esrolko)	Orange oil ('Orangenkonzentrat' Givaudan-Esrolko)
β-carotene	approx. 0·3 %	approx. 0·3 %
β-apo-8'-carotenal	approx. 4·5 %	approx. 3·2 %
β-apo-8'-carotenoic acid ethyl ester	approx. 5·0 %	approx. 4·4 %
canthaxanthin	approx. 0·1 %	approx. 0·04 %

SOLUBILITY OF 20 % MICRONISED SUSPENSIONS OF CAROTENOIDS

β-carotene	approx. 0·2 %	approx. 0·2 %
β-apo-8'-carotenal	approx. 3·9 %	approx. 3·1 %
β-apo-8'-carotenoic acid ethyl ester	approx. 4·0 %	approx. 3·4 %
canthaxanthin	approx. 0·08 %	approx. 0·05 %

noticeable, there is very often a marked change in the flavour. The fact that ascorbic acid helps to enhance colour stability is useful in the following respect. It is far from uncommon to find that ascorbic acid is added in order to avoid unpleasant flavour changes. If the beverage is coloured with artificial dyes, these can be bleached very rapidly in sunlight. The manufacturer has thus to face the choice between colour and flavour. Carotenoids clearly are an advantage in these circumstances.

The presence of the fruit pulp in beverages of this type is also advantageous for stability reasons. Many 'lemonades' and similar beverages containing no fruit concentrate (or only very small amounts) when coloured with β-carotene will bleach in sunlight in a relatively short time.

Kläui and Manz[10] described some experiments set up to demonstrate the excellent stability of carotenoids in soft-drink products. They prepared, under production conditions, a drink containing 1·2 % orange concentrate, 35 mg/litre ascorbic acid, 0·2 % citric acid and sugar to make a syrup. The

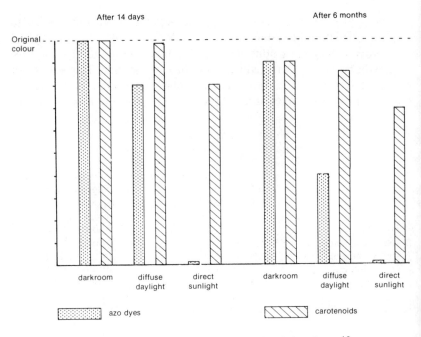

FIG. 4.   Effect of light on stability of soft-drink colours.[10]

syrup was coloured with β-carotene and canthaxanthin at a level sufficient
to ensure that, after dilution and processing, each one litre bottle contained
1 mg each of the two colours. The coloured syrup was intimately
homogenised with a pressure homogeniser, pasteurised at 60 °C for 30 min
and deaerated. The apparatus, pipework and so on was of stainless steel.
Coloured syrup in the bottles was diluted with cold, carbonated water,
stoppered and inverted several times to ensure adequate mixing. Reference
samples were prepared in the same way with the same raw materials but
coloured with tartrazine and sunset yellow. The results of an exposure test
to direct sunlight and diffuse daylight are shown in Fig. 4. Although the
results of this test were only reported after six months' storage, the test
continued for several years. The reported results were still valid after that
extended period.

The conditions of this test were rather extreme as it would hardly be
normal for beverages to be exposed to direct sunlight for half a year. The
rate of loss of the artificial dyes, however, is very well within the normal shelf-
life of such products. The loss is very rapid, even where no ascorbic acid is

added. The fruit pulp or concentrate will invariably contain some vitamin C, usually quite enough to cause decoloration.

In canned beverages, the effect of sunlight is absent, apart of course from temperature rise if the cans should be left exposed to the sun. Canned products containing azo dyes and ascorbic acid may be subject to another problem due to the causative effect of azo dyes on can corrosion. Sunset Yellow FCF is particularly bad in this respect. β-Carotene, on the other hand, is much less corrosive.

Sulphur dioxide is often used as a preservative in some squashes and concentrates. The carotenoids are stable to levels between 50 and 100 mg/kg of SO_2. Using the carotenoids in the gelatin protected beadlet form has the advantage that, being in effect dried reversible emulsions, they impart a certain cloudiness to the product. It is often enough at least to allow a worthwhile reduction in added clouding agent, if not its exclusion.

Sometimes, over a period of storage, a colour change may occur. Usually, with β-carotene which has been added in the gelatin protected form, the change is from the normal orange–yellow towards the more pure yellow. The change is not usually great and may be shown to be due to the solubilising effect of oils in the formulation, e.g. the orange oil of the orange flavour base.

The rather pale, slightly greenish tint of 'bitter lemon' can be achieved, as may be expected, by using β-carotene with a small addition of chlorophyll. With some added ascorbic acid, the stability is particularly good.

New, water-dispersible powders which give optically clear results in beverages were described by Emodi et al.[42] Based on a gelatin–carbohydrate matrix, the powders were reported to disperse easily in hot and cold water and to distribute very readily in other solids such as sugar 'plating'. These spray dried, 'micro-colloidal dispersions' give haze-free optically clear aqueous preparations in the colour range yellow to cherry red. The third application method[1] makes use of the increased solubility of carotenoids in suitable vegetable oils on heating. The necessary amount of β-carotene is dissolved in a vegetable oil (such as groundnut oil) by heating strongly for a few minutes ideally under nitrogen. When the carotenoid has fully dissolved there will be a visible change of appearance. In the suspension state the β-carotene will be an opaque brick-red colour but, when dissolved, the solution is a clear dark red. It is especially important to avoid overheating to reduce the chance of oxidation and also of isomerisation. When large amounts of such a solution are to be made it is worth doing so in small lots or even resorting to a continuous flow process in order to reduce the risks of overheating.

The concentrated oily solution is cooled a little but while still very hot is added to the orange concentrate together with the orange oil, if used. It is immediately follpwed by emulsification into aqueous gum acacia solution and then passed through a two stage high pressure homogeniser. The resulting base is then mixed with a suitable sugar syrup and diluted with cold carbonated water. The end products are especially attractive and, in spite of a low fruit content, very stable. Final concentrations in the region of 2 to 10 mg/kg of carotenoid are usually quite enough by this method.

Obviously, this basic process is capable of modification when certain clouding agents are permitted. Brominated vegetable oil and abietates are relatively good solvents for carotenoids.

The amount of vegetable oil introduced in this way is not large but will usually necessitate a slight adjustment of the specific gravity by increasing the proportions of the heavier ingredients.

Another possibility for applying carotenoids to soft drinks was mentioned by Kläui[6] quoting a Japanese patent.[38] The process involves heating the carotenoid with hydrogenated castor oil and polyoxy-ethylene ether at 100–150 °C under nitrogen. Aqueous dilutions of such solutions are stable and transparent. As Kläui points out, while such solutions look quite appealing, such non-ionic emulsifiers are not permitted for inclusion in foods in most countries. There is, however, scope for the application of this idea in countries where the available permitted emulsifiers can be used effectively in the process. It can be argued that the use of an artificial emulsifier is hardly a suitable vehicle to promote the use of natural colours. This is, however, a matter for the user and his local legislation rather than for the supplier to decide.

15. Tomato Products

The advantage of canthaxanthin in standardising and enhancing the colour of tomato juices has already been mentioned under the heading of fruit juices. It is perhaps obvious that this use extends into the processed tomato-based products industry. The now ubiquitous baked bean and its fellow, spaghetti (in whatever shape it manifests itself), may have their enrobing tomato sauce colour adjusted by the addition of canthaxanthin.

Similarly, other products based on the tomato, including dehydrated tomato powder, are standardised with canthaxanthin. In some countries, the usage of canthaxanthin in rapid preparation soups is very considerable indeed. The practice does not seem to be very common in the UK however.

The stability of canthaxanthin added to canned tomato soup is excellent.[39] It was found that only about 10 % loss had occurred after heat processing and storage for a year at room temperature, the canthaxanthin retention was still well above 90% of the initial value. During the work, variations in tomato content were examined and the conclusion reached that it would be possible to allow a reduction of perhaps as much as 40% of the tomato solids. The comment was also made that the canthaxanthin product was markedly superior in colour, after storage for 14 months at room temperature, to the high solids control.

As long as tomato concentrates remain relatively very cheap, such a substitution is not likely to become widespread. Should the situation change, careful consideration will have to be given to the appropriate labelling regulations. Lycopene measurement is often taken as an indicator of tomato content. Canthaxanthin is structurally different from lycopene.

16. Soups and other Canned Products

Small additions of the appropriate carotenoid can improve the appearance of soups in both canned and packet forms simply by taking away the otherwise pale, unappetising colour.

As a general rule the effect mentioned earlier under the fat solution applications is useful. This is where use is made of the inability of vegetable tissues to absorb the carotenoids from solutions.[50] In the example quoted, β-carotene added to butter sauce did not migrate to the vegetables in the can. It has been reported, however, that a 'dispersible liquid concentrate' of canthaxanthin can be used to colour maraschino-type cherries.[40] The colour was reported to be an attractive red similar to that obtained by current FD and C dyes. A slight bleeding of colour was observed when the cherries were placed in water. The normal methods of application do not exhibit this effect.

Canthaxanthin has been used to produce a particularly attractive colour in canned frankfurter sausages. Canned cod roe is another application for canthaxanthin, so also are prawns and shrimps where, by adjusting the conditions suitably the carotenoid will adhere to the surface.

Some promising results were obtained by Billings[41] in adding colour to Pacific pink salmon before canning. Unfortunately, the initially good results obtained on the bench were too slow for the production line. The effects of many ways of dipping and spraying contain encouraging elements which will, no doubt, lead eventually to success.

17. Dessert Products

The newer cold-water-soluble application forms are especially suited to the milk-based dessert powders. This is particularly so of those, such as instant puddings, which are prepared with cold milk. The simpler pregelatinised starch puddings are only whisked for a minute or two before being left to stand prior to eating. Speed of dissolving is therefore of primary importance. Some of the more recent products are based on various applications of the dried emulsion concept. These often take a little longer to prepare and the problem is not so acute.

Pudding products where either hot milk is used or the mixture is heated do not usually cause difficulty.

Canned dessert products, canned custard, rice and other puddings may be coloured or simply made slightly creamy in appearance with carotenoids. The fat-soluble colour can be incorporated by emulsification into the milk or alternatively the predissolved water-dispersible form can be added to the milk.

Jellies based on gelatin are usually distributed in one of two forms. In the world at large the product is known as jelly crystals and consists simply of a dry mixture of the various ingredients. In the UK, especially, this form is not so popular. The usual product is a jelly tablet—a highly concentrated block of the dissolved ingredients. Whichever form is involved, they have one principal characteristic in common: when made up, they must have virtually absolute clarity. The tablet product, in particular, is often presented as containing fruit juice and, indeed, the concept of both is fruity. Nevertheless, turbidity is not appreciated.

Through the use of the carotenoids, there is a small potential clouding. Bunnell and Borenstein[39] tried to overcome the difficulty by mixing the carotenoids with azo dyes in jelly crystal. If the present legislative changes continue, the choice is not so much likely to be whether carotenoids can substitute for azo dyes but whether natural colours are better than no colour at all.

Carotenoids may be used to colour jam-like products which are incorporated into yogurt-based desserts. Canthaxanthin is particularly interesting in this respect.

INTERNATIONAL LEGAL STATUS

The carotenoids are widely accepted as food colours. As a guide to the international status, the latest position is summarised in Table 5. The peculiarities of the regulations of any country compared with another are a subject more suited to another place, as is the matter of the individual regulations themselves. The table, therefore, is given as a guide. Some countries may only have omitted a carotenoid because its inclusion was not

TABLE 5
INTERNATIONAL STATUS OF CAROTENOID FOOD COLOURS, 1979

+ = Permitted   − = Not permitted

Country	β-Carotene	Apocarotenal	Ethyl ester of apocarotenoic acid	Canthaxanthin
Argentina	+	+	+	+
Australia	+	+	+	+
Austria	+	+	+	+
Brazil	+	+	+	+
Canada	+	+	+	+
Chile	+	+	+	+
Colombia	+	+	+	+
Costa Rica	+	+	+	+
Cyprus	+	+	+	+
Czechoslovakia	+	−	−	−
Democratic Republic of Germany	+	−	−	−
EEC Member Countries	+	+	+	+
El Salvador	+	+	+	+
Finland	+	+	+	+
Greece	+	+	+	+
Guatemala	+	+	+	+
Honduras	+	+	+	+
Hungary	+	−	−	−
India	+	+	+	+
Indonesia	+	−	−	−
Iran	+	−	−	−
Israel	+	+	+	+
Japan	+	−	−	−
Libya	+	+	+	−
Malaysia	+	+	+	+
Malta	+	+	+	+
Mexico	+	+	−	+
New Zealand	+	+	+	+
Nicaragua	+	+	+	+
Norway	+	+	+	+
Panama	+	+	−	+
Paraguay	+	+	+	+
Peru	+	+	+	+
Philippines	+	+	−	−
Poland	+	−	−	−
Portugal	+	+	+	+
Rumania	+	−	−	−
South Korea	+	−	−	−
Spain	+	+	+	+

TABLE 5—contd.

Country	+ = Permitted β-Carotene	Apocarotenal	− = Not permitted Ethyl ester of apocarotenoic acid	Canthaxanthin
Sweden	+	+	+	+
Switzerland	+	+	+	+
Taiwan	+	+	+	+
Thailand	+	+	+	+
Turkey	+	−	−	−
USA	+	+	−	+
USSR	+	−	−	−
Union of S. Africa	+	+	+	+
Uruguay	+	+	+	+
Venezuela	+	+	+	+
Yugoslavia	+	−	−	−
Zambia	+	+	+	−

requested. Others may permit a carotenoid but not for certain applications. To say that the situation is confused and confusing is an understatement of considerable magnitude. For the food manufacturer hoping to export his product, it is necessary to establish the exact position for each individual colour which he may wish to use and also for the application. Colour manufacturers with world-wide organisations can often help in this direction: their local agencies and offices may be able to give interpretive advice not readily obtainable elsewhere.

VITAMIN A ACTIVITY

The carotenoids we eat are obtained from two sources: those made by the plants in our diet and those which were made in a chemical factory. The two types are identical chemically and physiologically.

In considering how much benefit the body will obtain from a given intake of carotenoid, one has to take into account the following points:

i. Has the carotenoid any pro-vitamin A activity?

ii. Can the digestive system extract the carotenoid from the plant tissue?

iii. Will the extracted carotenoid be absorbed?

iv. Is the body able to convert the absorbed carotenoid into vitamin A?

TABLE 6
VITAMIN A ACTIVITY OF β-CAROTENE

β-Carotene	Vitamin A	Reference
6 μg	1 μg retinol	43
1 μg	0·167 μg retinol[a]	44
2 μg	1 μg	44
6 μg	1 μg	45
6 μg	1 μg	46
0·000 66 mg[b]	1 IU	47
0·555 6 μg	1 IU	5
0·75 μg	1 IU	30
0·6 μg	1 IU	7
0·6μg	1 IU	48

[a] In the diet.
[b] See text.

It is not enough to have a positive answer to each question: there is also the extent to which each may apply to be considered. The situation is very complicated and well beyond the scope of this chapter. Nevertheless, some indication of the confusion and some guidance is given. Table 6 summarises some of the more common sources of reference on the equivalence of β-carotene to vitamin A.

In most diets the major source of vitamin A activity is β-carotene. It is doubtful if any diets are exclusively retinol containing. The question, therefore, of the value of β-carotene in terms of retinol equivalent is very important. A succint account of various trials is given in the WHO report.[44] The two problems were recognised—firstly, the ability of the animal to remove and absorb carotene from the food and secondly, the ability of the animal to convert the absorbed carotene to vitamin A. In the report it was concluded that, having emphasised the probable errors involved, only one-third of the ingested β-carotene was available and only half of it would be converted to vitamin A in the body. A conversion factor of six to one was recommended for humans (i.e. 6 μg β-carotene = 1 μg retinol). The other carotenoids were assumed to have only half of the activity of β-carotene.

It is interesting to note the differentiation made in the Swiss regulations[47] between the β-carotene dissolved in fats or oils and that present in vegetables or supplied without fat where, it is said, the absorption is usually very low (often below 10%). In such cases, it is recommended that only biological tests with animals can give an accurate answer.

The UK regulations seem to support this point. The Margarine Regulations, 1967,[30] define vitamin A and include β-carotene on the basis that 0·75 μg shall be regarded as equivalent to 1 IU of vitamin A. (i.e. 2·5 μg β-carotene equals 1 μg retinol). The Labelling of Food Regulations, 1970 etc.,[46] however, allow β-carotene to be converted on the basis of 6 μg β-carotene equals 1 μg retinol.

A collection of a large number of reported experimental results is given in Appendix 3 of the WHO report.[44] Taking the values reported which were sufficiently firm to be used, the average is indeed very close to the one-third in the recommendation for availability. It is, however, interesting to note that the collected values include, for example, cooked carrot where the average value is nearer to one-quarter. Similarly, taking only the various control experiments where an oil solution of carotene was used, a value nearer to two-thirds would be obtained. As the use of synthetic carotenoids increases, this may need to be taken into account in assessing the dietary intakes.

REFERENCES

1. Kläui, H. and Raunhardt, O., *Alimenta*, 1976, **15**, 37.
2. Weedon, B. C. L., in *Carotenoids*, Ed. O. Isler, 1971, Birkhaüser Verlag, Basel.
3. Lee, W. L., *Carotenoproteins in Animal Coloration*, 1977, Dowden, Hutchinson & Ross, Stroudsburg, Penn.
4. Paul, A. A. and Southgate, D. A. T., *McCance and Widdowson's The Composition of Foods*, 1978, HMSO, London.
5. Barrett, I. M. and Widdowson, E. M., in *The Composition of Foods*, R. A. McCance and E. M. Widdowson, 1960, HMSO, London.
6. Kläui, H., in *Fette als Funktionelle Bestandteile von Lebensmitteln*, Ed. J. Solms, 1973, Forster Verlag, Zurich.
7. Watt, B. K. and Merrill, A. L., *Composition of Foods*, 1963, US Department of Agriculture, Washington DC.
8. Curl, A. L. and Bailey, G. F., *Food Research*, 1956, **22**, 63.
9. Bauernfeind, J. C., in *Symposium on Fruit Juice Concentrates*, 1958, Juris Verlag, Zurich.
10. Kläui, H. and Manz, U., *Beverages*, 1967, **8**, 16.
11. Benk, E., *Deutsche Lebensm—Rundshau*, 1961, **57**, 324.
12. Higby, W. K., *Journal Food Science*, 1962, **27**, 42.
13. Matzik, B., *Fruchsaft Ind.*, 1962, **7**, 317.
14. Karrer, P. and Jucker, E., *Carotenoids*, 1950, Elsevier, New York.
15. Inhoffen, H. H., *et al.*, *Liebigs Ann. Chem.*, 1950, **570**, 54.
16. Isler, O. *et al.*, *Helv. Chim. Acta*, 1956, **39**, 249.
17. Isler, O. *et al.*, *Helv. Chim. Acta*, 1957, **40**, 1242.
18. Isler, O. *et al.*, *Recent Advances in the Chemistry of Colouring Matters*, 1956, Chemical Society, London.

19. Isler, O. *et al.*, *Helv. Chim. Acta*, 1956, **39**, 449
20. Isler, O., *Verhandl. Naturforsch. Ges. Basel*, 1956, **67**, 379.
21. Isler, O. *et al.*, *Liebigs Ann. Chem.*, 1957, **603**, 129.
22. Isler, O., Offner, A. and Siemers, G. F., *Food Technology*, 1958, **12**, 520.
23. Isler, O., Ruegg, R. and Schudel, P., *Chimia*, 1961, **15**, 208.
24. Isler, O. and Zeller, P., *Vitamins and Hormones*, 1957, **15**, 31.
25. Zeller, P. *et al.*, *Helv. Chim. Acta*, 1959, **42**, 841.
26. Kläui, H., Hausheer, W. and Huschke, G., in *International Encyclopaedia of Food and Nutrition*, 1970, Vol. 9., Ed. R. A. Morton, Pergamon Press, Oxford.
27. Schuchardt, W., *Die Ernährungsindustrie*, 1954, **56**, 986.
28. Riel, R. R. and Johns, C. K., *J. Dairy Science*, 1957, **40**, 192.
29. *Vitamin Compendium*, Vitamins and Chemicals Department, F. Hoffman-La Roche & Co. Ltd., Basel.
30. *The Margarine Regulations*, 1967, SI 1967, No 1867, HMSO, London.
31. Marusich, N., de Ritter, E. and Bauernfeind, J. C., *J. Am. Oil Chem. Soc.*, 1957, **34**, 1.
32. de Ritter, E., 1976, *Food Technology*, 1976, **30**, 48.
33. Kläui, H., *Proc. I.F.S.T.*, 1968, **1**(5), 23.
34. Siemers, G. F. and Parman, G. K., *The Macaroni Journal*, April 1958.
35. Bauernfeind, J. C. and Bunnell, R. H., *Food Technology*, 1962, **16**, 76.
36. Finberg, A. J., *Food Prod. Dev.*, 1971, **5**, 46.
37. Bauernfeind, J. C., Oscada, M. and Bunnell, R. H., *Food Technology*, 1962, **16**, 101.
38. Japanese Patent No 6986/69, 1969.
39. Bunnell, R. H. and Borenstein, J. C., *Food Technology*, 1967, **21**(3A), 13A.
40. Emodi, A., *Food Technology*, 1978, **32**, 38.
41. Billings, F., private communication.
42. Emodi, A. *et al.*, *Food Technology*, 1976, **30**, 58.
43. Dept. Health and Social Security Reports on Public Health and Medical Subjects, No. 120. *Recommended Intakes of Nutrients for the United Kingdom*, 1970, HMSO, London.
44. WHO Technical Report Series No 362, *Requirements of Vitamin A, Thiamine, Riboflavine and Niacin*, 1967, FAO, Rome.
45. WHO Monograph Series No 61, *Handbook of Human Nutritional Requirements*, 1974, FAO, Rome.
46. *The Labelling of Food Regulations*, 1970, SI 1970, No 400, HMSO, London.
47. *Verfügung des Eidenössischen Departmentes des Innern über Zusatz und Aupreisung von vitaminen bei Lebensmitteln*, 1957, Bern.
48. Schwieter, U. and Isler, O., in *The Vitamins*, Ed. W. H. Sebrell, Jr. and R. S. Harris, 1967, Academic Press, New York.
49. Roels, O. A., in *The Vitamins*, Ed. W. H. Sebrell, Jr. and R. S. Harris, 1967, Academic Press, New York.
50. Weckel, K. G., Huang, T. T. and Ziemba, J. V., *Food Eng.*, May, 1967.
51. Reinhart, A. and Brown, R. W., *Proc. Int. Dairy Congress, The Hague*, 1953, **3**, 1233.

Chapter 7

MISCELLANEOUS NATURALLY OCCURRING COLOURING MATERIALS FOR FOODSTUFFS

J. COULSON

Pointing Ltd, Prudhoe, Northumberland, UK

SUMMARY

Colours extracted from naturally occurring materials were the first products used to improve the appearance of Man's food supply. Interest in the usage of natural colours has been reviewed in recent years due to their continued permitted use in certain markets in which synthetic organic colours are prohibited.

The legislative positions concerning the use of the natural colouring extracts, particularly in the UK, the EEC, and the USA, are discussed. The major classes of permitted oil-soluble and water-soluble natural organic colours, apart from the anthocyanins, are considered, including their methods of manufacture or extraction, their properties and stabilities towards food processing conditions, and their applications in food products.

The naturally occurring inorganic materials used in foodstuffs are also briefly described.

Natural colouring materials of vegetable, animal and mineral origin have been added to Man's food for centuries. Originally the use of these colours was to disguise the signs of spoilage and other deficiencies in the product, such as lack of butter, chocolate, egg and fruit content. Improvements in food hygiene and the desire not to deceive the consumer have made these uses of added colouring unnecessary. Synthetic colouring materials, because of their superior properties and cost effectiveness, are now used extensively to enhance the appearance of nutritious but unattractive foods

189

and to realistically replace food's inherent natural colour lost during processing and storage. The synthetic colourings currently permitted in food, however, differ substantially between countries and the number allowed is gradually being eroded by legislation. This is a particular problem for the food manufacturer dealing with international markets and, until a greater degree of international harmonisation on colouring materials is achieved, only limited blends of synthetic colourings will be available for widespread use in export markets. The natural colouring materials, however, are approved food additives in most countries where regulations are in force and interest in their use as sensory additives has greatly increased.

The natural colours added to foodstuffs are the oil- or water-soluble extracts, and in some cases their lakes, of natural organic colouring materials and the insoluble pigments of natural mineral or inorganic colouring materials. The extracts may be the products of simple physical extraction or they may be chemically modified to make them suitable for food use. In many cases the colours, in their natural state, are bound to protein or carbohydrate residues and during extraction these linkages are, in most cases, broken.

LEGISLATION ON NATURALLY OCCURRING COLOURING MATERIALS FOR FOODSTUFFS

In the United Kingdom the first regulations on food colourings in 1925[1] prohibited the use of harmful colourants including the vegetable colouring matter Gamboge and compounds of antimony, arsenic, cadmium, chromium, copper, lead, mercury and zinc. In 1954 the Food Standards Committee (FSC) Report on Colouring Matters was published,[2] recommending the positive listing and permitted use of the following colours of natural origin: Alkannet, Annatto, Caramel, Carotene, Chlorophyll, Cochineal, Flavine, Orchil, Persian Berry, Saffron, Turmeric, Bole or Iron Oxide and Carbon Black; the colours that were in use for colouring food at that time. It was noted that no question arises as to the suitability for use in food of any colour which is a normal constituent of edible products, but that this generalisation does not apply to all colours derived from natural sources. It was recognised that the chemical structure and biological action of many of the colouring matters extracted from the root, bark, fruit, leaves, petals, or stems of plants were unknown. These recommendations were implemented, with some amendments, in the first positive list of permitted natural food colours in the UK, in Part II of the

First Schedule of the Colouring Matter in Food Regulations 1957.[3] All of the recommended colours of natural origin were included and in addition Indigo, Osage Orange, Safflower, Sandalwood, Titanium Dioxide, Ultramarine and colouring matter natural to edible fruits and vegetables were added to the list for generally permitted use, while Silver and Aluminium were permitted for external colouring of certain confections. The aluminium or calcium lakes of any permitted water-soluble colours were also permitted.

In Germany at that time the only natural colours permitted appeared to be Carotene, Chlorophyll and Cochineal, while in France, synthetic Indigo and Alizarin and their sulphonic acid derivatives were classified as vegetable colours and their use in food allowed.

A further review[4] of colouring matters was conducted in the UK by the FSC between 1961 and 1964 and the only change recommended concerning natural colours was that Titanium Dioxide should be restricted to the surface colouring of food, as in the European Economic Community (EEC) at that time. As a result of the review new regulations were made in 1966[5] in which the FSC recommendations were implemented and Charcoal and Gold were added to the permitted list, the latter with restrictions on its use.

In 1973,[6] UK legislation on food colours was harmonised with that of the EEC and following deletion of Orchil, Channel Black and Burnt Umber in 1976[7] and the addition of Riboflavin-5'-phosphate in 1978,[8] the permitted list of natural colours for food use was as shown in Table 1.

In the EEC, a Council Directive in 1962[9] was issued dealing with colouring matter which may be used in foodstuffs intended for human consumption. Following the Sixth Amendment[10] to that Directive in 1978, the only differences between EEC and UK legislation were the following:

For general use in the EEC	*EEC No*
Persian Berry	—
Alkannet	—
For restricted use in the EEC	
Calcium Carbonate	E170
Ultramarine	—
Not mentioned in the EEC Directive	
Paprika	—
Turmeric	—
Saffron	—
Sandalwood	—

The Color Additives Amendment 1960[13] in the USA provisionally listed

TABLE 1

Colouring material	EEC No
Natural colouring materials	
Curcumin	E100
Riboflavin	E101
Riboflavin-5'-phosphate	E101
Cochineal	E120
Chlorophyll	E140
Copper complexes of Chlorophyll and Chlorophyllin	E141
Caramel	E150
Vegetable Carbon	E153
Beetroot Red	E162
Carotenoids (specified)	E160 (a)–(f)
Xanthophylls (specified)	E161 (a)–(g)
Anthocyanins (specified)	E163
Natural substances with secondary colouring effect	
Paprika	—
Turmeric	—
Saffron	—
Sandalwood	—
Inorganic colouring materials	
Titanium Dioxide	E171
Iron Oxides and Hydroxides	E172
Inorganic colouring materials for restricted use	
Aluminium	E173
Silver	E174
Gold	E175

the natural colours in prior use in that country. At the present time the following natural colours are permitted[14] for food use and do not require certification:

For general use in the USA
Annatto extract
Dehydrated Beet (powder)
Caramel
Cochineal extract, Carmine
Toasted partly defatted cooked cottonseed flour
Fruit and vegetable juices
Carrot oil
Paprika and its oleoresin

Riboflavin
Saffron
Titanium Dioxide
Turmeric and its oleoresin
For restricted use in the USA
Ferrous Gluconate
Grape skin extract
For animal feed in the USA
Ultramarine Blue
Synthetic Iron Oxide
Dried algae meal
Tagetes
Corn endosperm oil

CLASSIFICATION OF NATURAL COLOURING MATERIALS FOR FOODSTUFFS

The natural colouring materials may be grouped into those of organic and those of inorganic origin. Further classification of the organic naturally occurring colouring materials for the purposes of this chapter is according to their chemical structures (Table 2).

TABLE 2
ORGANIC NATURALLY OCCURRING COLOURING MATERIALS

Class of colouring matter	Examples	Major colouring principle	EEC No	1971 CI No
Flavonoids	Anthocyanins	(Considered in Chapter 5)	E163	—
Carotenoids	Annatto	Bixin, norbixin	E160(b)	75120
	Paprika	Capsanthin, Capsorubin	E160(c)	—
	Saffron	Crocetin	—	75100
	Tagetes	Lutein	E161(b)	—
	Alfalfa	Lutein	E161(b)	—
	Carrot	β-Carotene	E160(a)	—
	Palm oil seed	β-Carotene	E160(a)	—
	Orange peel	Violaxanthin	E161(e)	—
	Tangerine peel	β-Citraurin	—	—
	Maize	β-Carotene	E160(a)	—
	Tomato	Lycopene	E160(d)	—

TABLE 2—contd.

Class of colouring matter	Examples	Major colouring principle	EEC No	1971 CI No
Melanoidins	Caramels	Melanoidin	E150	—
	Toasted cottonseed	Melanoidin	—	—
	Molasses	Melanoidin	—	—
Porphyrin	Chlorophylls	Phaeophytin	E140	—
	Chlorophyllins	Phaeophorbide	E140	—
	Cu Chlorophylls	Cu Phaeophytin	E141	—
	Cu Chlorophyllins	Cu Phaeophorbide	E141	—
	Blood pigments	Haemoglobin	—	—
Betalines	Beetroot	Betanin	E162	—
	Pokeberry	Betanin	—	—
Quininoids	Cochineal	Carminic acid	E120	—
	Kermes	Kermesic acid	—	—
	Lac	Laccaic acid	—	—
	Alkannet	Alkannin	—	—
Miscellaneous	Riboflavin	Riboflavin	E101	—
	Riboflavin-5'-phospate	Riboflavin-5'-phosphate	E101	—
	Turmeric	Curcumin	E100	75300
	Orchil		E121	—
	Indigotine		E132	73015
	Vegetable carbon	Carbon	E153	—
	Logwood	Haematin	—	—
	Brazilin	Brazilein	—	—
	Carthamus	Carthamin	—	—
	Tea extracts	Tannin–catechin complexes	—	—
	Ferrous gluconate	Ferrous gluconate	—	—
	Fruit and vegetable juices		—	—

The E references are those numbers allocated in the EEC Directive of 23.10.62 (as amended) to the colouring matters listed in Annex 1 to that Directive.[9] The 1971 Colour Index (CI) numbers of the Society of Dyers and Colourists (UK) and the American Association of Textile Chemists and Colourists (USA)[11] are included in the classification where appropriate.

CAROTENOID PIGMENTS

The Carotenoids are one of the most important groups of natural pigments used as food colourants. The group comprises both the hydrocarbon carotenes and the oxygenated xanthophylls and they are responsible for most of the yellow, orange and red shades so common in living organisms. The Carotenoids are present in the plant chloroplast and all green tissues in the higher plants contain the same major Carotenoids, viz. β-carotene (Fig. 1), lutein (Fig. 2), violaxanthin (Fig. 3), and neoxanthin (Fig. 4), and less frequently the pigments α-carotene (Fig. 2), β-cryptoxanthin (Fig. 1) and zeaxanthin (Fig. 1). Carotenoids contribute to the vivid colouring of many fruits, seeds, roots, flower petals, autumnal foliage, feathers and skin and may be extracted from a wide variety of sources. The most commonly used

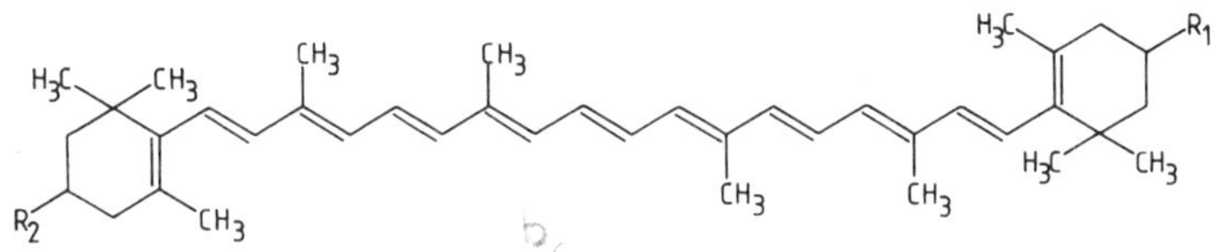

FIG. 1. β-Carotene, $R_1 = R_2 = H$; β-cryptoxanthin, $R_1 = H$, $R_2 = OH$; zeaxanthin, $R_1 = R_2 = OH$.

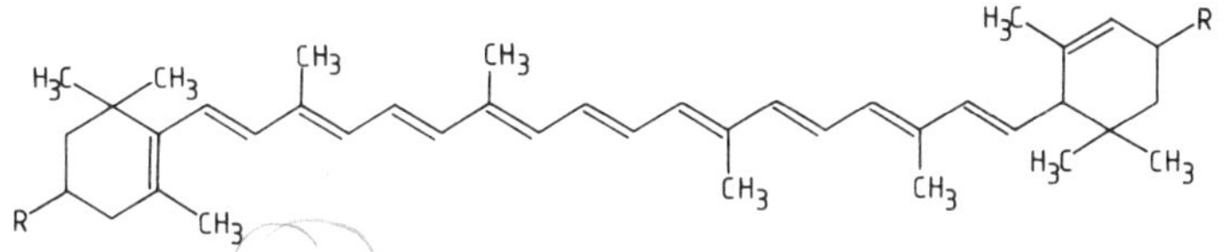

FIG. 2. α-Carotene, $R = H$; lutein, $R = OH$.

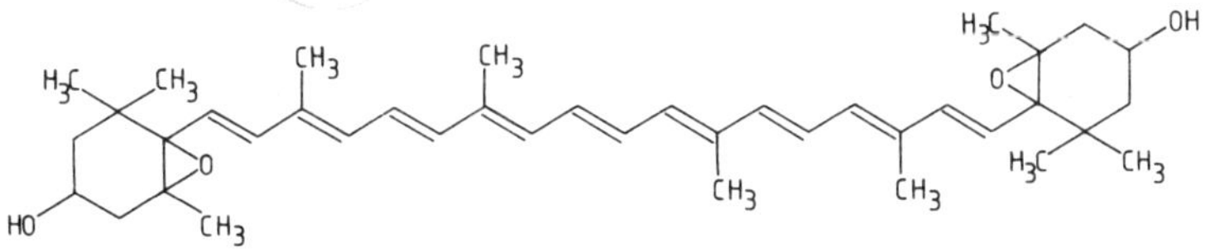

FIG. 3.   Violaxanthin.

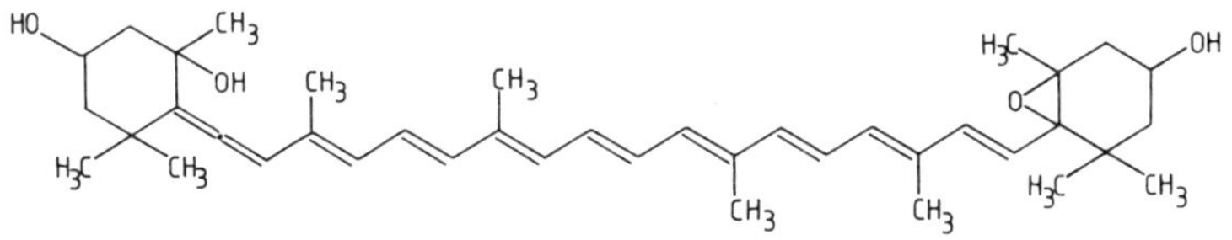

FIG. 4.   Neoxanthin.

natural Carotenoid extracts for foodstuffs are those of Annatto, Paprika and Saffron, but many other sources are utilised including tagetes, alfalfa, carrot, palm oil seed, citrus peel, maize and tomato. All of these contain a number of different Carotenoids and the extracts frequently contain a combination of all the Carotenoid pigments originally present in the extracted material.

Most of the Carotenoid pigments suitable for food use are fat soluble and may be isolated by extraction with a suitable solvent, such as diethyl ether, petroleum ether, methanol, ethanol or chloroform (acid-free). Evaporation of the volatile solvent affords a crude extract which may be further purified and crystallised if required. It is usually advantageous to conduct a preliminary purification, such as treatment with 10% methanolic potassium hydroxide solution, to hydrolise lipids or esters of hydroxylated Carotenoids. Rough separation of the various Carotenoids present in the extract may be achieved by partitioning the crude mixture between two immiscible solvents, such as petroleum ether and a 90% solution of methanol in water, which will separate, and take up into solution, non-hydroxylated Carotenoids and Carotenoids containing two or more hydroxyl groups, respectively. The Carotenoids that contain a single hydroxyl group partition between the solvents and are not separated.

Annatto, 1971 CI No 75120, E160(b)
Annatto is the orange–yellow oil-soluble natural colouring material extracted from the pericarp of the seed of the *Bixa orellana* L. tree. This small tree or shrub is cultivated primarily in Central and South America. The major colouring component is the diapocarotenoid, bixin (Fig. 5), while several other pigments, chiefly degradation products of bixin, are also present, including *trans*-bixin, norbixin and *trans*-norbixin. Bixin is a dibasic fatty acid which, on treatment with alkalis, is hydrolysed to water-soluble norbixin (Fig. 5), a yellow colouring material. Two types of commercial Annatto extract of different shades are therefore available; an

FIG. 5.   Bixin, R = CH₃; norbixin, R = H.

oil-soluble extract containing bixin, and a water-soluble extract containing norbixin as the major pigment.

In the extraction of oil-soluble Annatto, the seeds are pretreated with steam and the resulting swollen seeds are extracted either with a volatile solvent, such as a mixture of ethanol and a chlorinated hydrocarbon, or with vegetable oil at an elevated temperature. The filtered solution is concentrated, if appropriate, and standardised.

Oil-soluble Annatto is somewhat unstable under oxidative conditions and the degradation is accelerated by light and catalysed by metals. A wide-range of antioxidants, including ascorbic acid, tocopherols and polyphenolics, help to suppress this oxidative degradation. Compared to other Carotenoids, Annatto shows a surprising stability to exposure to the air. Stability to heat is moderate and pH changes have little effect, although low pH foods may turn pinkish in shade on storage. Sulphur dioxide, however, can cause decolorisation.

The major uses of oil-soluble Annatto are in dairy and fat-based products, such as butter, margarine, processed cheese, yogurt, creams, desserts, baked goods and snack foods. Annatto may be used in combination with Paprika oleoresin if redder shades are required, such as in processed cheeses, and in combination with Turmeric oleoresin if yellower shades are needed. In addition, Turmeric may have some stabilising action on the Annato extract.[12]

A water-soluble Annatto food colourant can be produced by extracting steam-swollen *Bixa orellana* L. seeds with propylene glycol containing potassium hydroxide, and filtering and standardising the resultant solution.

The stability properties of water-soluble Annatto are similar to those of the oil-soluble extract. Usage is mainly in smoked fish, cheese, baked goods, cereals and ice-cream; in each case the pigment is absorbed on to the protein and carbohydrate components of the foodstuff and is not leached out by water.

Water-soluble Annatto is also available as a powder product, containing high proportions of norbixin, useful for colouring dry and instant foodstuffs.

Paprika

Paprika oleoresin is the orange–red oil-soluble extract from sweet red peppers, *Capsicum annum*. The oleoresin contains the xanthophylls capsanthin (Fig. 6) and capsorubin (Fig. 7) as their dilaurate esters as well as β-carotene and characteristic natural flavouring components.

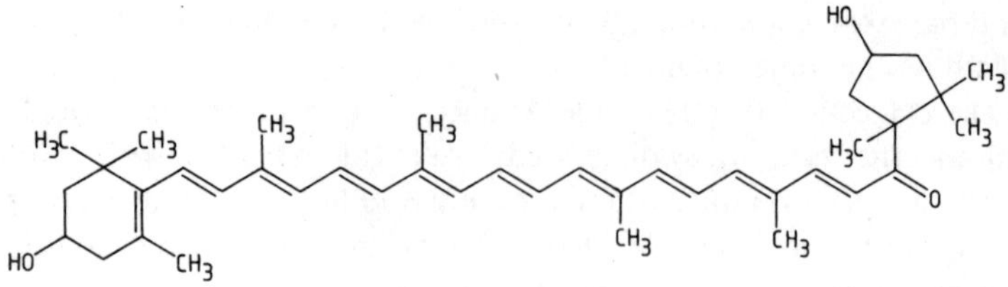

FIG. 6. Capsanthin.

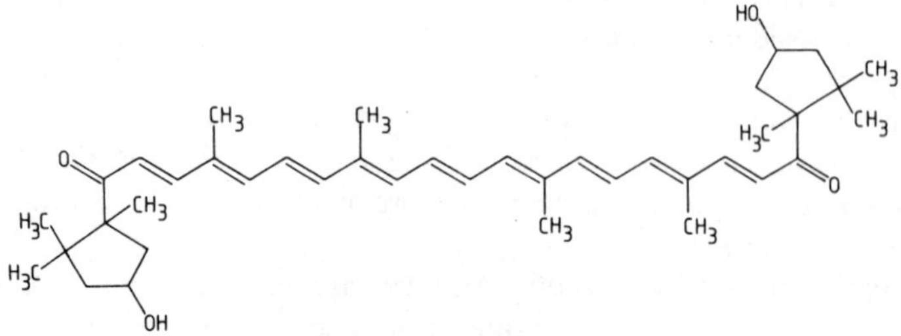

FIG. 7. Capsorubin.

The oleoresin is produced by extraction of ground and dried red peppers with a volatile solvent, such as a chlorinated hydrocarbon, followed by careful removal of the solvent under reduced pressure.

Paprika oleoresin is suitable for colouring sauces, salad dressings, sausages, meat seasonings, snacks, processed cheese, confectionery and baked goods. It colours a deep crimson-red to pale pinkish-yellow depending on concentration and invariably also contributes some of its spicy pungency to the foodstuff.

Saffron
Saffron extract and its oleoresin are the yellow extracts from *Crocus sativus* L, a member of the *Iridaceae* family. The extracts contain the apocarotenoic acid, crocetin (Fig. 8) as well as zeaxanthin, β-carotene and characteristic flavouring components. The flowers of the crocus contain their yellow pigment as crocin, the digentiobioside of crocetin.

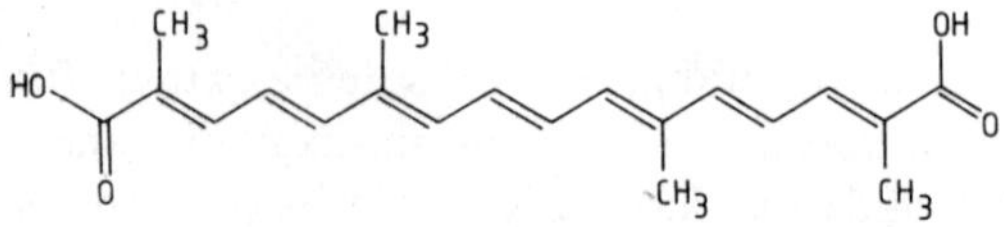

FIG. 8. Crocetin.

The oleoresin is produced by hydrolysis of the natural glycosidic pigment of the dried stylus and stigma of the yellow crocus flower, followed by extraction with a volatile solvent, such as ethanol or acetone, and careful evaporation of the solvent under vacuum. The original pigment, crocin, being a glycoside, is not soluble in oils and fats. Saffron is somewhat sensitive to pH changes and is unstable towards light and oxidative conditions. It exhibits moderately good resistance to heat. The extracts of Saffron exhibit good water solubility and are used in baked goods, soups, meat and curry products, cheese, and some confectionery, where its pure yellow colour and spicy taste are desirable. Its use as a natural colourant is severely restricted by its high price.

Miscellaneous Carotenoid Colours

Tagetes extract, from the flower petals of the Aztec marigold, *Tagetes erecta* L., contains the colouring principles lutein (Fig. 2) and β-carotene (Fig. 1). Carotenoid pigments from flower petals are usually partially or fully esterified, and, in the case of Tagetes, the lutein is in the form of a dipalmitate ester. Usage of this yellow oil-soluble extract is in dairy and fat-based products.

Alfalfa extract is the yellow Carotenoid extract from lucerne grass. It contains the colouring principles lutein (Fig. 2), violaxanthin (Fig. 3), zeaxanthin and β-carotene (Fig. 1). A typical analysis of the percentage of total xanthophylls present in lucerne shows lutein 40%, violaxanthin 34%, neoxanthin 19%, β-cryptoxanthin 4% and zeaxanthin 2%. Usage of the oil-soluble extract is in dairy and fat-based products.

Carrot extract contains the colouring principles β-carotene (Fig. 1) and α-carotene (Fig. 2). Xanthophylls make up less than 5% of the total pigments in commercial varieties. Usage of the yellow, oil-soluble extract is mainly in dairy and fat-based products, soups and beverages.

The major colouring principles of palm-oil seed are β-carotene (Fig. 1), α-carotene and lutein (Fig. 2). Usage of the yellow, oil-soluble extract is mainly in dairy and fat-based products.

Citrus peel extract contains, depending on its origin, violaxanthin (Fig. 3) and β-carotene (from oranges) or β-citraurin (Fig. 9) and β-carotene (from

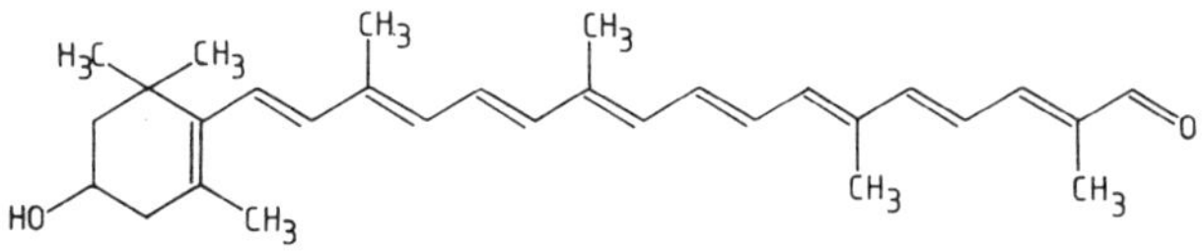

FIG. 9. β-Citraurin.

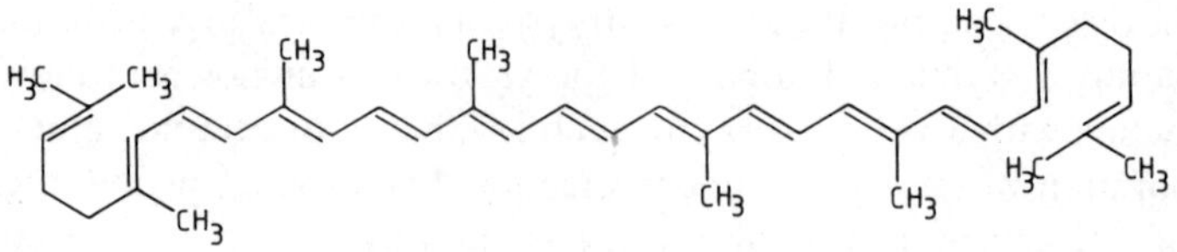

FIG. 10.   Lycopene.

tangerines). Usage of this orange coloured oil-soluble extract is predominantly in soft drinks and preserves.
Maize has a high proportion of Carotenoids in its seed. Its extract contains mainly β-carotene, β-cryptoxanthin and zeaxanthin (Fig. 1). Usage of the yellow, oil-soluble extract is in dairy and fat-based products. Tomato extracts contain lycopene (Fig. 10) as the main Carotenoid pigment. The bright red, oil-soluble extracts are particularly used in soups and meat products.

MELANOIDIN PIGMENTS

The most important way to produce colour in foods that are heated is by non-enzymatic browning reactions. Two main types of reaction are thought to occur:

(a)   The Maillard reaction between a carbonyl compound (usually a reducing sugar) and an amine (usually ammonia, ammonium salt, amino acid or a related compound) followed by polymerisation or condensation to give high molecular weight materials.

(b)   Pure caramelising reactions obtained by heating carbohydrates alone at relatively high temperatures to give aldehydes which subsequently condense to give coloured components.[15] The reactions which produce Melanoidins are complex and their structures are not fully understood. Melanoidin colour may be used as an added colourant to other foodstuffs. The most important example is Caramel formed from sugars often with an accelerator present.

Caramel, E150

Caramel is the name given to the amorphous dark brown colouring material formed by heating food-grade carbohydrates in the presence of selected accelerators. If consists of a mixture of volatile and non-volatile low molecular weight compounds and non-dialysable high molecular weight compounds. The latter, making up 25% of the total solids in commercial products, contribute to the colouration of caramel and are known as colour bodies.

The formation of natural caramel, or the browning reaction, has been observed since cooked food was first prepared. It forms an important natural part of the appeal of foods such as cooked meats, toasted bread, coffee and potato chips. As an added food colourant caramel was probably first used in the form of burnt sugar in alcoholic drinks. Following this, special grades of caramel were developed for the colouring of spirits, particularly rum, and later for other branches of the food industry.

Manufacture of Caramel
Caramel was originally prepared by heating sucrose in an open pan until it frothed and eventually caramelised. In modern caramel processing, a wide range of available carbohydrates including sucrose, invert sugar, and high dextrose—equivalent glucose syrups from the hydrolysis of various starches, are heated in concentrated solution at 120–160 °C, in some cases under pressure, with ammonia, ammonium salts, or other inorganic substances as accelerators, and then rapidly cooled and blended. The caramelisation reaction involves the simultaneous processes of inversion and reversion. The larger carbohydrate molecules are hydrolysed (inversion) to monosaccharides, which are polymerised (reversion) usually in conjunction with a nitrogen source. The variability of the carbohydrate employed, and its effect on the subsequent caramel is the main reason for the empiricism necessary in caramel manufacture.

A wide range of different caramels are produced commercially and they can be classified as electropositive or positively charged caramels which are generally made with ammonia, as electronegative or negatively charged caramels which are generally made with ammonium salts, and as caramels that have little or no charge and are referred to as spirit caramels, since the colour is both soluble and stable in ethyl alcohol.

Processing Conditions for the Manufacture of the Major Caramels
1. Positively charged caramel formed by the ammonia process. Ammonia solution (specific gravity 0·88) is blown into glucose syrups in a vented tank and the reaction allowed to progress on storage for several days. The pH rises to 10, the smell of ammonia disappears and the colour value rises to 5000 EBC (European Brewing Convention Units). The product is pumped into open tanks together with a further charge of ammonia and held for

several hours at 90 °C. The mix is heated steadily while excess ammonia and most of the water are boiled off. A vigorous exothermic reaction then ensues in which one equivalent of ammonia reacts with one equivalent of sugar at a temperature of about 120 °C. The reaction is carefully controlled for several hours and then subsides. The colour increases to about 44 000 EBS and the pH drops to 3·0. Further boiling is carried out to attain maximum colour intensity while maintaining a workable viscosity. Air is blown into the mass to cool it to 80 °C once a colour value of around 60 000 EBC has been reached. Water is added and the batch is standardised by blending with other batches.

2. *Negatively charged caramel formed by the ammonium sulphite process.* Glucose syrup is caramelised at about 120 °C with ammonium metabisulphite (prepared directly from ammonia and sulphur dioxide) as catalyst. The reaction is controlled in the same way as for the positively charged caramel but the reaction is conducted under acidic conditions and the maximum colour value attained for this caramel is of the order of 25 000 EBC.

3. *Spirit caramel formed by the sodium hydroxide process.* Sucrose is dissolved in water to obtain a 66° Brix syrup, which is concentrated in an open pan at 160 °C for several hours to about 80°Brix. A calculated amount of 70° twaddell sodium hydroxide solution is added and a violent reaction ensues with copious release of carbon dioxide. Boiling continues for several hours until the colour reaches about 20 000 EBC, the maximum possible colour value, while maintaining a workable viscosity. An alcohol-soluble caramel is formed to which the minimum amount of water is added and the batch is standardised by blending with other batches.

Properties of Caramel

The physical properties of caramels are related to their electrical properties and the stability of caramel in solution is assessed by the degree of flocculation of the polymeric colour bodies resulting from interaction between the charge on the caramel and its environment. Thus, apart from the intensity of the colour produced, the determination of a caramel's isoelectric point, viz. the pH at which the caramel has no net charge, is necessary to ascertain the compatibility, stability and reaction with other charged materials in the product which is being coloured. Electropositive caramels, usually produced under alkaline conditions using ammonia, exhibit an isoelectric point of between pH 4·0–7·0, but predominantly pH 6·0–7·0. They are particularly suitable for the brewing industry where stability in the presence of positively charged fining colloids is necessary. The electronegative caramels are frequently produced under acidic conditions with inorganic salts, e.g. ammonium sulphite, and exhibit isoelectric points below pH 3·0, and often around pH 1·5. Electronegative caramels are used in the soft drinks industry where stability at low pH is necessary. Spirit caramels differ from positive and negative caramels in that any charge they possess is of a weak ionic character.

Composition of Caramel
The compositions of each of the various caramels in use in the food industry are extremely complex. Low molecular weight compounds are present, some of which are precursors and some by-products of many reactions that occur during its manufacture. These compounds contribute particularly to the aroma of the caramel and consist of components such as alcohols, aldehydes, ketones, fatty acids and furans. High molecular weight polymers and residues are the coloured components and consist predominantly of material having molecular weight in the 5000–10 000 range.

Uses of Caramel
The major uses of caramel are in the meat products, brewing, baking, confectionery, vinegar, pickle, soft drinks and spirits industries.
    In meat products, particularly tinned meats, gravy mixes and soups, caramel provides a desirable colour and is generally used in liquid form.
    In the brewing industry caramel is used to provide both colour and flavour. The caramel chosen must carry a positive charge and remain stable, clear and bright in the presence of alcohol and tannins.
    Caramels find wide use in the bakery and confectionery industries, generally to provide uniformity and darker richness in shade in products such as brown bread, cakes, biscuits, puddings, toppings and sweets. The caramel may provide desirable colour and flavour properties and, in some circumstances, an appreciable quantity of saleable solids. Powder forms of caramel are utilised in dry mixes for bread, cakes and toppings.
    The colouring of vinegar and pickles can be successfully carried out using caramel but the type of vinegar and the stability of the caramel in the individual foodstuff must be thoroughly investigated.
    In carbonated soft drinks, caramel is used to provide colour while maintaining brightness and clarity in the presence of tannins and fruit extracts that have high acid concentrations, such as in cola, ginger ale, sarsaparilla and dandelion and burdock. Thus negatively charged caramels are generally used for colouring soft drinks.

The caramels used to colour whisky and rum must be stable in products with high alcoholic content and the spirit caramels have been developed for this purpose. Similar caramels have good foaming properties and are used in products, such as root beer, where this is desirable.

Other Melanoidin Pigments

A number of other Melanoidin pigments are in use as food colourants. Toasted, partially defatted cooked cottonseed flour is listed as a permitted colour additive in the USA. It varies in shade from light to dark brown and is for general use in foodstuffs.

Molasses is a dark brown material produced by boiling cane sugar in water and evaporating the resulting solution. It is cheaper than caramel and has a characteristic aroma and sweet taste. Usage is mainly in baked goods, sausages, meats and cereals.

PORPHYRIN PIGMENTS

The Porphyrins are macrocyclic materials containing four methine-linked pyrrole rings. Two groups of Porphyrins are commonly used as natural colouring materials for foodstuffs, the Chlorophylls and the Haemes.

The green pigments of vegetables, leaves and fruit, the Chlorophylls, are the magnesium complexes of compounds derived from Porphyrin and its di- and tetrahydroxy derivatives. They all contain a further (fifth) ring referred to as the isocyclic ring. Chlorophylls 'a' and 'b' are both dihydroporphyrins with different substitutes at C-2.

The red and brown pigments of meat, the Haemes, are the iron complexes of compounds derived from Porphyrin.

Chlorophyll and its Derivatives, 1971 CI No 75810. E140 Chlorophyll, E140 Chlorophyllin, E141 Chlorophyll Copper Complex, E141 Chlorophyllin Copper Complex

Chlorophyll is the generally accepted name for the green pigments in any organism capable of photosynthesis. In higher plants and algae, except the blue-greens, Chlorophyll is found in the chloroplast, while in the blue-green algae and photosynthetic bacteria, Chlorophylls are located on intracellular lamellae.[16]

Chlorophyll is the most widely distributed of the natural plant pigments and acts as a catalyst in biochemical photosynthesis, converting solar energy into food in plants. It is always accompanied by carotenoid and xanthophyll pigments in the plant and is found in the cell membrane in association with carbohydrates and proteins. In the plant the chlorophyll is present predominantly as a mixture of two components, Chlorophyll 'a' and Chlorophyll 'b' (Fig. 11). Recently, evidence has been found in all higher plants and algae demonstrating that several chemically different Chlorophylls 'a' and 'b' associate in different ways with fats and proteins to carry out the photosynthetic process.[17] Chlorophyll 'a' is a bluish-green

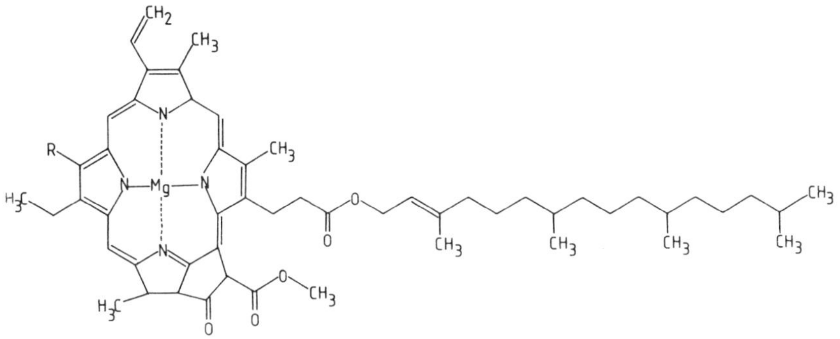

FIG. 11.   Chlorophyll 'a', R = CH$_3$; Chlorophyll 'b', R = CHO.

shade, while Chlorophyll 'b' is a rather more yellowish-green, and they are generally associated with each other in leaves in the ratio 2–3 parts 'a' to 1 part 'b'.

Chlorophyll readily looses its central magnesium ion under even the mildest acidic conditions. Other metals can be introduced into the macrocyclic nucleus using metal acetates in acetic acid solution or in methanolic solution containing pyridine. Replacement of the magnesium ion with a copper ion produces a derivative from which copper ions are not removed to any appreciable extent on metabolism, thus being acceptable for the coloration of foodstuffs. A limit of not more than 200 ppm of free ionisable copper is specified for food use. Chlorophyll, generally as its magnesium free species, Phaeophytin, and its copper derivative Copper Phaeophytin or Chlorophyll Copper Complex, are available for use as food colours (Fig. 12). The phytyl ester on the C-7 propionate group in the Chlorophylls is easily hydrolysed off without affecting the C-10 methoxy-carbonyl group under mild alkaline conditions and an inert atmosphere or by using the natural enzyme, chlorophyllase, affording Chlorophyllin (Chlorophyllide) (Fig. 13). Chlorophyllin readily loses its central

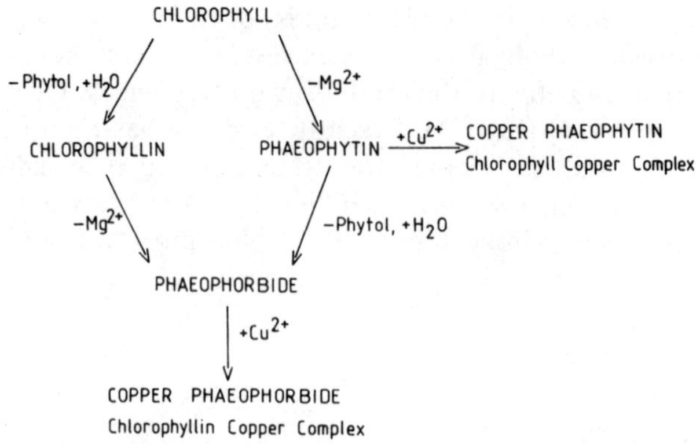

FIG. 12.　Chemical relationship of commercial Chlorophyll colours.

magnesium ion to give, under mild acidic conditions, Phaeophorbide. These mild hydrolysis products readily take up a copper ion to give Copper Phaeophorbide or Chlorophyllin Copper Complex. Both coppered and uncoppered Chlorophyllin are available as food colourants. Under strongly alkaline conditions Chlorophyll's methyl ester group, as well as the phytyl ester group, may also be hydrolysed and ring cleavage may occur destroying the colour molecule.

Extraction of Chlorophyll and Manufacture of Derivatives
Lucerne grass, nettles or other green plant material are harvested, briefly treated with boiling water to prevent chlorophyllase hydrolysis, and immediately comminuted and dried at low temperature in the dark.

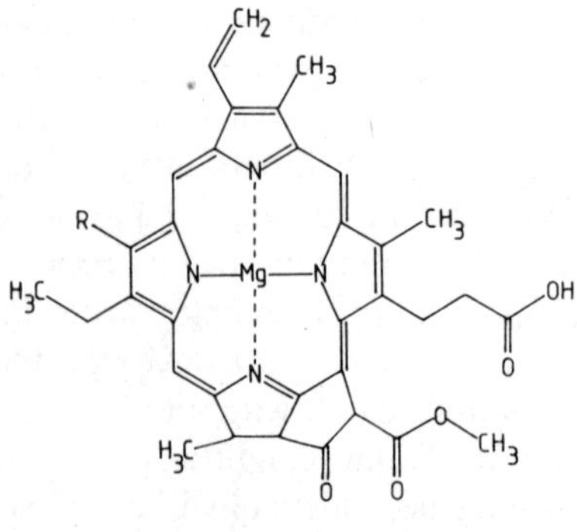

FIG. 13.　Chlorophyllin, $R = CH_3$ or CHO.

Solvent extraction is carried out rapidly using chlorinated hydrocarbons, lower alcohols or ketones, usually with a small amount of water present. Prior extraction with 50% aqueous acetone can be employed to remove phospholipids while partition between a hydrocarbon solvent and 80% methanol in water removes xanthophylls. The waxy Chlorophyll extracts can be purified in diethyl ether–petroleum ether. The physical parameters of the extraction must be strictly controlled as they govern the proportions of Chlorophyll, fats, waxes and phospholipids that are extracted.

The crude extract may be further processed by solvent extraction to give Phaeophytin (commercial Chlorophyll) extract from which a high proportion of magnesium ions have been lost, or the Phaeophytin may be treated with copper acetate to give Copper Phaeophytin (commercial Chlorophyll Copper Complex). Alternatively the crude extract can be acid hydrolysed, solvent extracted, neutralised and solvent evaporated to give a water-soluble Phaeophorbide (commercial Chlorophyllin) or the Phaeophorbide can be treated with copper acetate to give a water-soluble Copper Phaeophorbide (commercial Chlorophyllin Copper Complex).

Uses of Chlorophyll and its Derivatives
The oil-soluble Chlorophylls (uncoppered and coppered Phaeophytin) are not widely used for food colouring as commercial purifications have not proved to be as satisfactory as those for the water-soluble derivatives. Stability is good towards light and heat but poor to both acid and alkaline conditions. Usage levels are around 0·05–0·1% and solubility is very poor in all solvents apart from oils. Applications are found in canned products, confectionery and pet foods.

The water-soluble Chlorophyllins (uncoppered and coppered sodium, potassium or sodium potassium Phaeophorbide) show good stability towards light and heat and moderate stability to both acids and alkalis. Usage levels are around 0·002–0·01% and solubility is only satisfactory in aqueous systems. Food colour usage is in canned products, confectionery, soups and dairy products.

Haem Pigments
Animal blood and its dehydrated protein extracts, which mainly consist of coagulated and stabilised haemoglobin, have potential as sources of red and brown colourings mainly for use in meat and savoury products. Their usage as a food colouring agent is not permitted in most countries but usage as a food ingredient is common place, such as in black pudding in the UK.

BETALAINE PIGMENTS

The Betalaines are the water-soluble colouring materials responsible for the red and yellow shades found in numerous varieties of beetroot and also found in pokeberries.

Beetroot Red, E162

Beetroot Red is the name given to the colouring material extracted from the red beetroot (*Beta vulgaris*). It consists of red and yellow quaternary ammonium amino acid pigments of the betalaine class. The red pigments are betacyanins and the yellow pigments are betaxanthins. The major betacyanin and betaxanthin pigments in beetroot are betanin (Fig. 14) and vulgaxanthin respectively. Of the betacyanin content of the beetroot, 75–95% consists of betanin together with small amounts of isobetanin, prebetanin and isoprebetanin. Betanin may be enzymatically hydrolysed to its aglycone, betanidin, plus glucose, while stronger acid hydrolysis affords betanidin plus isobetanidin, the latter having a different configuration at C-15. Betaxanthins in beetroot consist predominantly of vulgaxanthin I and vulgaxanthin II (Fig. 15).

High levels of pigment concentration, on average 0·1% of the fresh weight or 1% of the total solids, are present in beetroot, making it a valuable source as a food colourant.

Extraction of Beetroot Red

Commercial extraction of beetroot gives rise to three types of Beetroot Red extract:

1. Beetroot juice concentrates, produced by removing water under vacuum to a total solids content of around 60%.
2. Beetroot powder, produced by drying beetroot juice on a drum drier, or similar equipment.
3. Beetroot concentrate powders, usually produced by spray drying the vacuum concentrated beetroot juice.

The beetroots are topped and tailed and thoroughly washed. They are crushed and the expressed juice acidified, usually with citric acid, or extracted under acid conditions. The juice may then be drum dried affording beetroot powder. Alternatively the liquor is clarified and may undergo aerobic fermentation to reduce the sugar level. Concentration of the juice by careful vacuum distillation produces beetroot juice concentrate, while spray drying of the concentrate leads to beetroot concentrate powders.

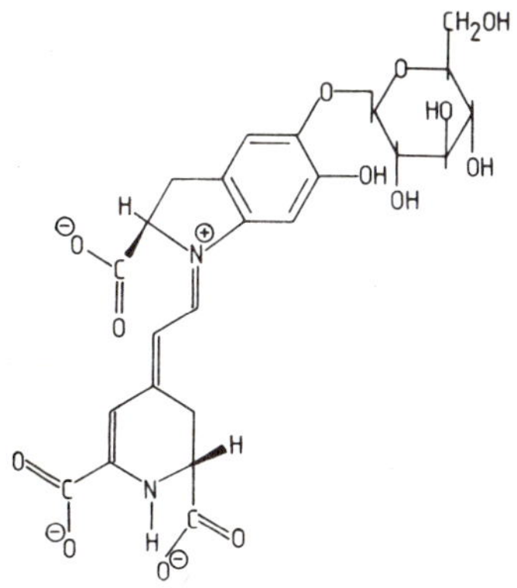

FIG. 14.   Betanin.

Uses of Beetroot Red

Beetroot Red colour is suitable for products having relatively short shelf-lives and where the foodstuff has not to undergo high or prolonged heat treatment. Stability is highest in low moisture foods and in the pH range of 4–5, though stability is reasonable in the pH range of 3–7. The coloration of foods that undergo heat treatment can be successfully carried out with Beetroot Red by adding the colour after heating has ceased. The shade of Beetroot Red coloured food is deep bluish-red and the addition of a yellow tone, such as that from water-soluble Annatto, may be required if a redder hue is desired. Beetroot Red colour is unstable towards air and light and must be protected against long exposure. These effects are cumulative but some protection may be offered by antioxidants such as ascorbic acid.[18] Stability towards benzoate and sorbate preservatives is good. Small amounts of

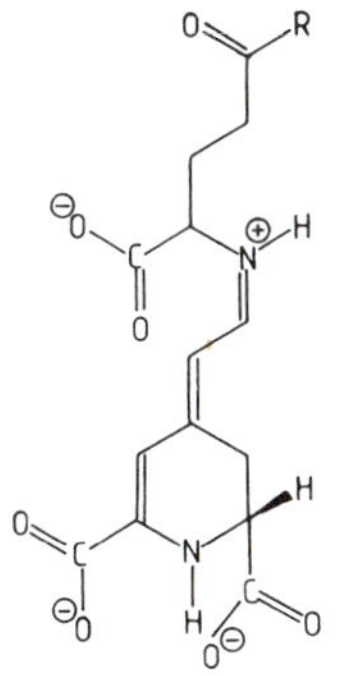

FIG. 15.   Vulgaxanthin I, R = NH_2; Vulgaxanthin II, R = OH.

metallic ions, such as ferric salts, have a detrimental effect on Beetroot Red but chelating agents, such as EDTA at up to 25 ppm, can help stabilise the colour. The major colouring principle of Beetroot Red, betanine, is more stable in beetroot juice, particularly at pH 5, than when extracted from the juice, showing the protective effects of the juice constituents.[19] Many protein systems present in food products also have some protective effect on Beetroot Red colour. In addition, stabilisation of Beetroot Red colour has been demonstrated in solutions containing tea extracts, sorbic acid and ascorbic acid.[20]

Beetroot Red colour may be utilised, with suitable stabilisers, in soft drinks, ice-cream, meat and soya protein products, and in dry mixes, such as gelatin desserts.

Pokeberry

The red-violet natural colouring material from the berries of the shrub-like perennial pokeberry (*Phytolacca americana* L.) from North America contains the pigment phytolaccanin, which has been shown to be identical to the betanin (Fig. 14) pigment of beetroot. The extract may be used to colour wine and foodstuffs that do not undergo heat processing.

QUININOID PIGMENTS

Quininoid pigments exist in large numbers in nature and are widely distributed. They are the major yellow, red and brown colouring materials of roots, wood and bark and they also occur at high levels in certain insects. The largest group is the Anthraquinone pigments, although Benzoquinone and Naphthaquinone pigments are known.

The insect colouring materials are the most important of the commercially available Anthraquinone-containing pigments for use in foodstuffs. Cochineal, Kermes and Lac were previously important food colouring extracts but at the present time only Cochineal remains in use in foodstuffs.

Previously, Madder, the red Anthraquinone-containing extract from *Rubia tinctorum* root, containing alizarin, was used as a food colourant, but its use has long since been superseded. Alkannet, a Naphthaquinone-containing root extract, is still in use for colouring foodstuffs in some countries.

Another Naphthaquinone pigment previously widely used in foodstuffs was Sandalwood or Sanderswood extract containing deoxysantalin.

Cochineal and Cochineal Carmine, 1971 CI No 75470, E120

Cochineal is the red colouring matter extracted from the dried bodies of the female insect of the species *Dactylopius coccus* Costa or *Coccus cacti* L. The insect is cultivated on the cactus plant *Nopalea coccinellifera* and collected by hand and air dried in the sun on trays to one third of its weight. The main centres of cultivation are Peru, Equador, Guatamala, Mexico and the Canary Islands.

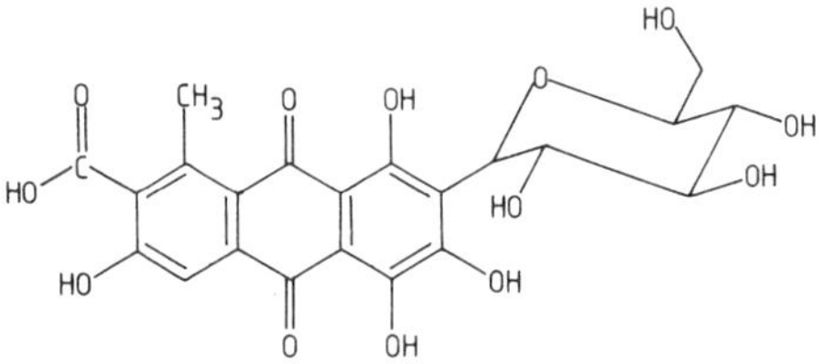

FIG. 16.   Carminic acid.

The major pigment of Cochineal is polyhydroxyanthraquinone C-glycoside, Carminic acid (Fig. 16), which may be present at up to 20 % of the dry weight of the mature insect.

Extraction of Cochineal
The dried bodies of the insects are powdered and extracted with boiling water or with aqueous alcoholic solutions. Higher yields of Carminic acid can be obtained if the insect is treated with surfactants and proteolytic enzymes prior to extraction. For cosmetic use the extract has traditionally been purified as the insoluble lead salt but other metallic complexes are used when the colour is for food purposes. Alternatively, a purified Cochineal may be obtained by acidifying an alcoholic solution of the extract, filtering and drying the product, rewetting and extracting with a solvent, reprecipitating and drying. Approximately 140 000 insects are required to produce 1 kg of Cochineal, containing 10 % pigment.

Properties of Cochineal
Carmine acid has a C-glycoside structure which has been established as 7-D-glucopyranosyl-3,5,6,8-tetrahydroxy-1-methyl-9,10-dioxoanthracene-2-carboxylic acid. It is not known whether the glycoside linkage is α- or β- in configuration and in the insect, the Carminic acid colouring material is associated with protein material. Cochineal extract or Carminic acid are rarely used as colouring materials for foodstuffs but are usually offered in the form of their lake products.

Preparation of Cochineal Carmine
Cochineal readily gives highly coloured complexes with metallic ions. Aluminium complexes (lakes) can be prepared with various ratios of Cochineal to alumina varying from 8:1 to 2:1, having corresponding shades from pale yellow to violet. The aqueous Cochineal extract is treated with an aluminium salt and the lake precipitated with ethanol. The lake may be, in addition, treated with a calcium salt to adjust its properties of solubility.

Properties of Cochineal Carmine
Cochineal Carmine is insoluble in cold water, dilute acids, alcohol, glycerine and propylene glycol, and is slightly soluble in alkali giving a purplish-red solution. The shade becomes more blue at higher pH values.

Cochineal Carmine shows good stability towards light and heat but stability to sulphur dioxide is poor. In the presence of benzoate and sorbate preservatives stability is good.

Cochineal Carmine can be used in powder form for colouring various instant foodstuffs. It can also be used in an alkaline solution in ammonia for colouring a wide range of foodstuffs including baked products, retorted protein products, yogurts, soups, gravies, sauces, desserts, confectionery, syrups and preserves. Precipitation of the pigment at low pH may have to be avoided in certain products, but in some cases fixation of the colour in this way is advantageous. Usage of the colour is generally in the range of 0·04–0·2%.

Kermes and Lac Pigments
Kermes is the solvent extracted red colouring matter from the dried bodies of the female insects of the species *Kermococcus ilices* L. The insect lives on oak trees in the Mediterranean area. The extract is slightly soluble in cold water, and soluble in hot water. It was widely used in foods in the Middle Ages. The major pigment is Kermesic acid (1971 CI No 75460) (Fig. 17), the aglycone of Carminic acid.

Lac is the red colouring matter extracted by dilute aqueous sodium

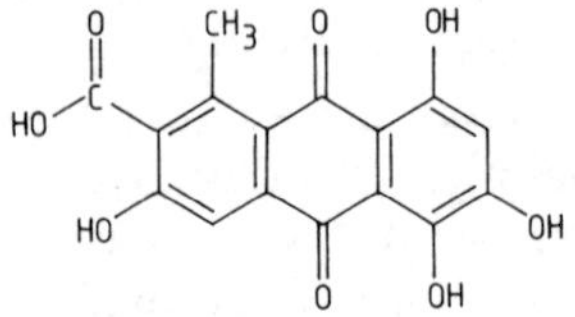

FIG. 17.   Kermesic acid.

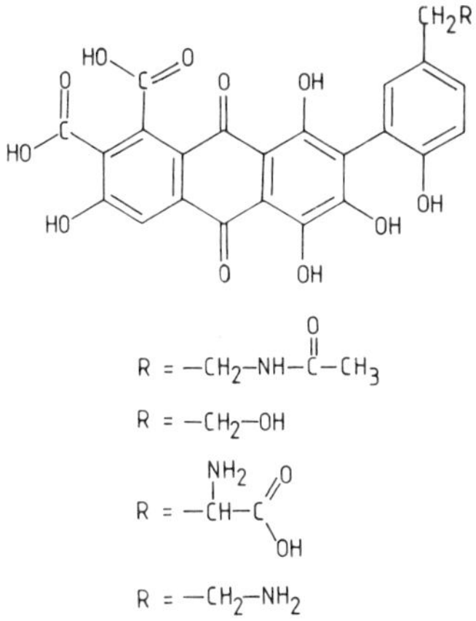

$$R = -CH_2-NH-\overset{\overset{O}{\|}}{C}-CH_3$$

$$R = -CH_2-OH$$

$$R = -\overset{\overset{NH_2}{|}}{CH}-C\overset{\diagup O}{\diagdown OH}$$

$$R = -CH_2-NH_2$$

FIG. 18.   Laccaic acids.

carbonate from the solidified exudate of the insect *Coccus laccae*. The insect lives on various trees in India, Indonesia and Ceylon. The extract is soluble in water. The major pigments are the Laccaic acids (1971 CI No 75450) (Fig. 18). Lac is a by-product of the extraction of shellac resin.

Alkannet, 1971 CI No 75530
Alkannet is the solvent extracted red colouring matter from the roots of the plants *Alkanna tinctoria* Tausch and *Anchusa tinctoria* Lam. found in Southern Europe. The extract is slightly soluble in water but very soluble in organic solvents. The major pigment is Alkannin (Fig. 19). Alkannet can be used in foodstuffs, where permitted, to colour confectionery, ice-cream and wines.

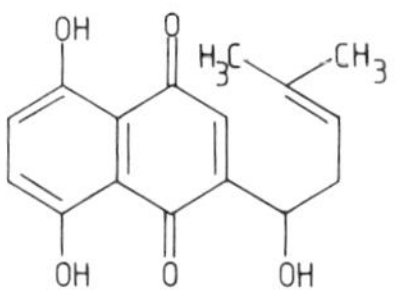

FIG. 19.   Alkannet.

MISCELLANEOUS ORGANIC PIGMENTS

A wide range of organic pigments that have not been included in the classified natural colouring materials are used as food colourants. These include the commonly used additives Turmeric and Riboflavin, used also as a flavouring agent and vitamin, respectively.

Riboflavin and Riboflavin-5′-Phosphate, E101

Riboflavin, Lactoflavin, or Vitamin B_2 (Fig. 20) is a yellow pigment present in plant and animal cells such as milk and yeast. Originally extracted from natural products including quercitron bark it is currently synthesised. It is

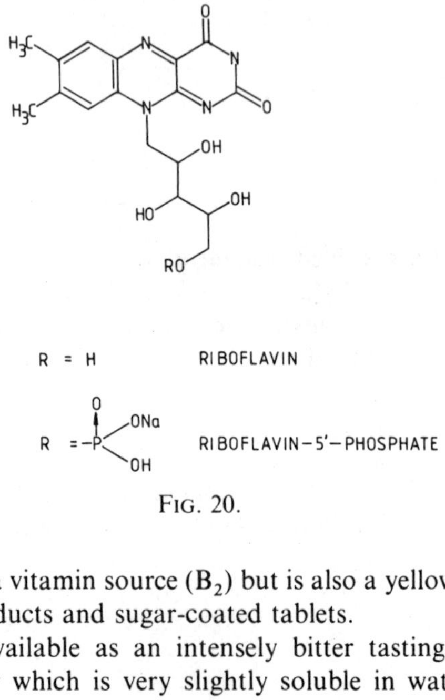

R = H   RIBOFLAVIN

R = —P(=O)(ONa)(OH)   RIBOFLAVIN-5′-PHOSPHATE

FIG. 20.

primarily used as a vitamin source (B_2) but is also a yellow colour mainly used in cereal products and sugar-coated tablets.

Riboflavin is available as an intensely bitter tasting orange–yellow crystalline powder which is very slightly soluble in water and ethanol affording a bright greenish yellow fluorescent solution. It is very soluble in dilute alkalis but the solution rapidly decomposes. Riboflavin shows slight instability when exposed to light, is unstable towards alkali but is stable under acid conditions. Reduction produces a colourless laevo form but colour is regenerated again on exposure to air. Riboflavin-5′-phosphate sodium salt (Fig. 20) is much more soluble in water than the unesterified Riboflavin and is not so intensely bitter tasting. It is one of the physiologically active forms in which Riboflavin exerts its biological functions in an organism. It is rather more unstable to light than Riboflavin. Usage for colouring purposes in foodstuffs is mainly confined to cereals, sugar-coated tablets and dairy products.

Turmeric (Curcumin, 1971 CI No 75300, E100)
Turmeric or Curcuma is the fluorescent yellow coloured extract from the rhizome of various species of Curcuma plant, *Curcuma longa* L. giving the best quality colouring matter. The colouring principle is Curcumin, 1,7-bis-(4-hydroxy-3-methoxyphenyl)-1,6-heptadiene-3,5-dione (Fig. 21). The dried and ground roots of *Curcuma longa* L. are extracted with an alcoholic solvent and the solvent removed under vacuum affording a dark coloured Turmeric oleoresin. Turmeric is insoluble in water

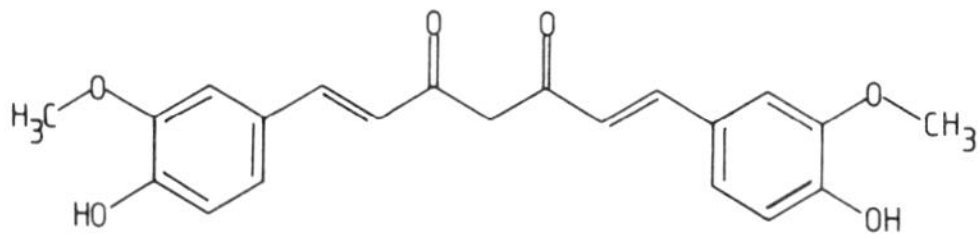

FIG. 21. Curcumin.

but soluble in alkalis, alcohols and glacial acetic acid. The extracts have a strongly characteristic odour and sharp taste associated with them and are utilised for both their taste and colour properties.

Turmeric oleoresins and Curcumin exhibit poor stability to light and to alkaline conditions but stand up well to heat processing and are used in canned products, soups, pickles, mustard, mixes and wrapped confectionery.

Orchil, E121
Orchil is the red extract obtained by extracting with ammonia various species of *Roccella* lichens and *Orchella* mosses from the Azores and Canary Islands. Its colouring component, Orcein, is insoluble in water, but it may be sulphonated affording a water-soluble extract principally used for colouring wines, soft drinks and confectionery.

Indigotin, 1971 CI No 75781, Formerly E132
Natural Indigo (1971 CI No 75780) occurs in precursor form as the glucoside Indican, together with Indirubin (1971 CI No 75790) in various species of *Indigofera*. The colouring principle is present as a glucoside of indoxyl which may be enzymatically hydrolysed by fermentation to free indoxyl and then oxidised by air to Indigo. Sulphonation of the natural Indigo affords its 5,5'-disulphonic acid derivative Indigotin or Indigo Carmine, a water-soluble deep blue colouring material. Indigotin is considered to be a natural colour in a few countries, including France. Usage is in general foodstuffs including ice-cream, desserts and confectionery.

Vegetable Carbon, E153
Vegetable Carbon is produced by fully carbonising vegetable material, such as peat. Usage of this insoluble pigment is primarily in confectionery products.

Other Miscellaneous Organic Colouring Materials
A number of other naturally occurring colouring materials have been previously used in foodstuffs including (i) Logwood, from the heartwood of the tree *Haematoxylon campechianum* L., containing haematoxylin which is readily oxidised to the red colourant haematin; (ii) Brazilin, from the wood of various species of *Caesalpina*, which on oxidation gives the red colourant brazilein; and (iii) Carthamus, from the dried petals of the Dyer's thistle, *Carthamus tinctorius*, containing the yellow colourant carthamin.

Brown and orange extracts, obtained from partially oxidised products of the tannin-catechin complexes from tea, have been tried as food colourants.

Ferrous gluconate is permitted in some countries, including the USA, for the colouring of ripe olives only.

Most countries permit the usage of the common fruit and vegetable juices as food colourants.

INORGANIC PIGMENTS OF NATURAL ORIGIN FOR FOOD

Titanium Dioxide, 1971 CI No 77891, E171
Titanium Dioxide, TiO_2, may be obtained from the natural mineral ilmenite ($FeO \cdot TiO_2$) by digesting it with sulphuric acid, hydrolysing and allowing the Titanium Dioxide to precipitate from the solution. It is suitable for foodstuffs that must undergo the most severe processing conditions, but is often used in any product that is required to be opaque white.

Iron Oxides and Hydroxides, 1971 CI Nos 77489, 77491, 77492, 77499; E172
Natural Iron Oxides and Hydroxides afford a very cheap range of subtle red and yellow colours for use, where permitted, in foodstuffs. The composition of the colour is mainly hydrated ferric oxide ($FeO(OH) \cdot nH_2O$) widely distributed in nature, or various calcined derivatives. It occurs as goethite, $FeO(OH)$, the major constituent of the yellow ochres and siennas, and of the umbers, which also contain manganese dioxide and mangano-

manganic oxide with some alumina and brown haematite. Burnt Umber, produced by roasting umber in air, was previously used as a food colourant. Synthetic products have now predominantly replaced the natural Iron Oxides and Hydroxides but usage may still be found in food that undergoes severe heat treatment, such as retorted and extruded products, mainly for pet foods and fish pastes. High levels of the colour are required as coloration is by pigmentation but its stability properties and covering power are excellent.

Other Inorganic Pigments for Food

Calcium Carbonate, $CaCO_3$ (1971 CI No 77220, E170) occurs extensively in nature as limestone, chalk, marble and calspar. It is used for the surface or bulk coloration (as permitted) of foodstuffs requiring an opaque white appearance, such as in confectionery products.

Ultramarine (1971 CI No 77007) is a polysulphide of an alkali metal aluminosilicate, formed by grinding the precious stone lapis lazuli or by igniting a mixture of kaolin, soda ash, Glauber's salt, carbon, sulphur and kieselguhr in air. It was previously used as a blue colour for foodstuffs, and is still used to some extent in animal foods.

REFERENCES

1. Public Health (Preservatives and Colouring Matter in Food) Regulations 1925, SR & O, London, 1925, No 775.
2. Food Standards Committee Report on Colouring Matters: Recommendations relating to the use of colouring matters in foods, Ministry of Food, HMSO, London, 1954.
3. The Colouring Matter in Food Regulations 1957, Ministry of Agriculture, Fisheries and Food, HMSO, London, 1957, No 1066.
4. Food Standards Committee Report on Colouring Matters, FSC/FAC/REP/4, Ministry of Agriculture, Fisheries and Food, HMSO, London, 1964.
5. The Colouring Matter in Food Regulations 1966, Ministry of Agriculture, Fisheries and Food, HMSO, London, SI 1966, No 1203.
6. The Colouring Matter in Food Regulations 1973, Ministry of Agriculture, Fisheries and Food, HMSO, London, SI 1973. No 1340.
7. The Colouring Matter in Food Regulation 1976, Ministry of Agriculture, Fisheries and Food, HMSO, London, SI 1976, No 2086.
8. The Colouring Matter in Food (Amendment) Regulations 1978, Ministry of Agriculture, Fisheries and Food, HMSO, London, SI 1978, No 1787.
9. EEC Council Directive of 23.10.1962, *Official Journal of the European Communities* L115, 11.11.1962, 2645.
10. EEC Council Directive of 30.1.1978. Sixth Amendment to EEC Colours Directive, No 78/144/EEC.

11. Colour Index, Third Edition, The Society of Dyers and Colourists, Bradford, England and The American Association of Textile Chemists and Colorists, North Carolina, USA, 1971.
12. Todd, P. H., US Patent 3,162,538 1964.
13. Color Additives Amendment to the Federal Food, Drug, and Cosmetic Act of 1938, Public Law No 86–618, 86th US Congress, Washington, DC, 1960.
14. Code of Federal Regulations, Title 21, Food and Drugs, Parts 1–99, April 1, 1979, US Government Printing Office, Washington, DC, 1979.
15. Greenshields, R. N. and Macgillivray, A. W., *Process Biochemistry*, 1972, December, 11.
16. Holden, M., 'Chlorophylls', in *Chemistry and Biochemistry of Plant Pigments*, 2nd edition, Ed. T. W. Goodwin, 1976, Vol. 1, Chapter 18, Academic Press, London.
17. Vernon, L. P. and Seely, G. R. (Eds.), *The Chlorophylls (Physical, Chemical, and Biological Properties)*, Academic Press, New York, 1966.
18. Phillips, M. V., *Food Prod. Dev.*, 1978, September, 24.
19. von Elbe, J. H., Il-Young Maing and Amundson, C. H., *J. Food Sci.*, 1974, **39**, 334,
20. Oragvelidze, N. I., Rizhamadze, Z. A., Kobalava, L. E. and Bokuchava, M. A., USSR Patent 565 049, 25.2.1976.

Chapter 8

TOXICOLOGICAL ASPECTS

J. J-P. DRAKE

The British Industrial Biological Research Association, Carshalton, Surrey, UK

SUMMARY

Animal studies to determine the amount of a substance which may be ingested without obvious ill-effects have been used for about a century. However, it is only over the last 20 years that reliable toxicity data have been obtained and that a wide range of possible effects have been investigated on a large scale. This chapter identifies some of the problems which have confronted those expert committees appointed to reach decisions on the safety-in-use of specific food colours. The implication is that problems on the scale encountered in the past will not be acceptable in respect of any alternative food colourings, particularly when we take into account the comparative shortage of toxicity testing facilities worldwide. This explains the trend towards substances of closely defined specification and metabolic stability in the search for new synthetic colourings.

INTRODUCTION

Public concern over the use of food additives, and colours in particular, may be polarised into questions of need—which will not be considered here —and of safety, which has become an equally emotive issue. The aspect that is perhaps most difficult to explain is the degree of concern expressed over the use of a few man-made chemicals, while hundreds of chemicals made by plants and animals are consumed with little apprehension regarding their effect on health.[1]

Animal studies to determine the amount of a substance which may be ingested without obvious ill-effects have been used for about a century.[2] However, it is only over the last 20 years that reliable toxicity data have been obtained and that a wide range of possible effects have been investigated on a large scale. Deficiencies in early studies, colour specifications and difficulties in extrapolating the results of animal studies to man have created many problems for those experts who have been appointed to reach decisions on the safety-in-use of specific colours.

LEGISLATIVE BACKGROUND

The first legislative restrictions on colours added to food in the United Kingdom were imposed in 1925, when metallic colours, one vegetable colour and five 'coal tar' colours were prohibited.[14] Adequate powers of enforcement were not introduced until the mid-1950s,[15] and of the 98 synthetic colours considered in 1955,[16] only 30 were incorporated into subsequent regulations.[17] Details of the legislative status of colours in other European countries are given elsewhere in this volume.

In the USA, voluntary regulations were introduced in 1907, but certification was only made mandatory for the 15 synthetic colours then on the list in 1938.[10] In 1960, an Amendment to the Food, Drug and Cosmetic Act permitted colours in use at that time to be used provisionally until their safety had been established. Early in 1977, the Food and Drug Administration announced a timetable for testing the safety of the 52 natural and synthetic colours remaining on the provisional list. Since then, 24 colours have been removed from the provisional list—7 terminated and 17 given permanent status. Safety tests on the remaining colours are scheduled to end by 31 January 1981. After that date, colours will either be terminated or placed on a permanent list.[49]

For the last 20 years, the United States has operated the so-called Delaney clause, which has been interpreted to mean that any substance found to induce cancer when investigated at any level is forbidden for use as an additive at any level.[5] Despite the absence of such a clause from European legislation, there is no reason to believe that regulatory bodies in these countries are less vigilant in the protection of our food supply than are their American counterparts. In the UK, for example, the prohibition of Ponceau MX (in 1970) on toxicity grounds was followed by that of Orange RN in 1975.[7] In addition to specific prohibitions, there are numerous examples of deletion of colours for which safety data requested by government experts were not forthcoming within a prescribed period. This is part of a trend towards a more restrictive control of food colours.[1]

SAFETY TESTING REQUIREMENTS

Food additive toxicology began to emerge as a scientific discipline in the early 1960s, with the publication of testing requirements deemed necessary for a 'reliable' evaluation of safety-in-use.[3] The following biological information on colours was sought by the Joint Expert Committee on Food Additives[3] in 1963:

acute toxicity studies;
short-term and long-term toxicity studies (in at least two species);
carcinogenicity studies (in two species);
metabolic studies.

The idea was to use the lowest no-toxic-effect level (NEL) obtained in these animal studies to estimate an acceptable daily intake (ADI) for man. The NEL was divided by an arbitrary safety factor (normally 100), to allow for any differences in sensitivity between the animal species and man, for variations in sensitivity among the human population and for the fact that the animal numbers were small compared with the size of the human population that might be exposed.[7]

Since 1963, numerous additional requirements have been introduced into the testing programmes now demanded by the governments of many countries. These include teratology and reproduction studies, mutagenicity studies and more elaborate chronic toxicity/carcinogenicity studies of increased duration—often taking account of *in utero* exposure.[5,13]

In an attempt to streamline the costly and time-consuming testing programmes now required of food additives, the US Food Safety Council (Scientific Committee) have recently proposed a safety decision-tree approach (Fig. 1). The reader is referred to the report of this Committee[5] for further details of the assessment of hazard to man based on the results of animal studies.

Synthetic Dyes

Over the last 20 years, feeding studies (including carcinogenicity studies) have been, or are being, carried out on every synthetic dye which has endured in Western Europe and North America. Many studies have been repeated in the light of deficiencies identified by successive expert groups. Existing

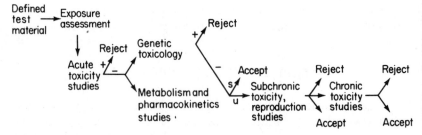

FIG. 1.   Safety decision-tree proposed by the Food Safety Council (as presented in ref. 5) +, Presents socially unacceptable risk; −, does not present socially unacceptable risk; s, metabolites known and safe; u, metabolites unknown or of doubtful safety; ?, decision requires more evidence.

metabolic studies have generally been crude by modern standards, and many mutagenicity, teratology and reproduction studies have only recently been undertaken or completed. The toxicological status of all these colours has been described elsewhere[7-9] and only a summary table will be given here (Table 1).

Natural Colours

In principle, natural colours should be subjected to the same criteria of evaluation as are applied to other food additives.[3] In practice, however, full chemical definitions for most natural colours have not yet been achieved, and the closest description often involves specifying the starting material and the method of preparation.[11] This approach is required for many colourings which are derived from nature by physical processes. For example, a full chemical definition of crude anthocyanin extracts would be extremely complex, since certain tissues contain a variety of flavonoid components—up to 17 being identified in the skin of red grapes alone.[12]

For assessment purposes, the following categories of natural colourings may be distinguished:

Colours derived from natural foods by physical processes. For these colours, acceptance depends partly on assurances that the overall dietary intake is not greatly increased by their use. Thus, for many years, the use of the colouring beet red was evaluated on the basis that the quantities ingested as a result of its technological use were not excessive in comparison to the amounts present in dietary beetroot. Taking into account the increasing interest in the use of this colour, however, the Joint Expert Committee on Food Additives recently concluded that a full toxicological evaluation was required.[13] This was because the major colouring principle, betanin, had

TABLE 1
TOXICOLOGICAL STATUS OF SYNTHETIC FOOD COLOURING MATERIALS

Common name	EEC serial number	Principal chemical constituent (usually as a sodium salt)	Average[a] intake, UK (mg/kg)	Estimated ADI[b] (mg/kg body weight)	Toxicological[c] studies required
Azo dyes					
Azorubine (Carmoisine)	E122	4-hydroxy-3-(4-sulpho-1-naphthylazo)-naphthalene-1-sulphonate	0·32	1·25 (temporary)	M
Sunset Yellow FCF (FD and C Yellow 6)	E110	6-hydroxy-5-(4-sulphophenyl-azo)-naphthalene-2-sulphonate	3·98	5	Currently[d] adequate
Amaranth (FD and C Red 2)	E123	3-hydroxy-4-(4-sulpho-1-naphthyl-azo)-naphthalene-2,7-disulphonate	1·44	0·75 (temporary)	C
Allura Red AC (FD and C Red 40)	—	1-[2-methoxy-5-methyl-4-sulphophenyl-azo]-2-naphthol-6-sulphonate	—	—	
Brilliant Black BN (Black PN)	E151	4-acetamido-5-hydroxy-6-[7-sulpho-4-(4-sulphophenylazo)-1-naphthylazo]-naphthalene-1,7-disulphonate	0·01	2·5 (temporary) (SCF: 0·75 temporary)	M; R
Chocolate Brown HT	—	4,4'(2,4-dihydroxy-5-hydroxymethyl-1,3-phenylenebisazo)-di-(naphthalene-1-sulphonate)	9·76	0·25 (temporary)	M; R
Chocolate Brown FB	—	Product of coupling diazotised naphthionic acid with osage orange extract	<0·005	Not possible	M; R
Ponceau 4R (Cochineal Red A)	E124	7-hydroxy-8-(4-sulpho-1-naphthylazo)-naphthalene-1,3-disulphonate	0·88	0·125	M; C (3rd species)
Brown FK	—	Mixture of sodium 2',4'-diaminoazobenzene-4-sulphonate and five related derivatives	0·21	Not possible (SCF: 0·05 temporary)	R; C[d]
Red 2G	—	5-acetamido-4-hydroxy-3-phenylazo-naphthalene-2,7-disulphonate	0·31	0·0006 (temporary)	R; studies on bone marrow

TABLE 1—*contd.*

Common name	EEC serial number	Principal chemical constituent (usually as a sodium salt)	Average[a] intake, UK (mg/kg)	Estimated ADI[b] (mg/kg body weight)	Toxicological[c] studies required
Red 6B	—	8-acetamido-2-*p*-acetamido-phenylazo-1-naphthol-3:6-disulphonate	—	—	—
Red FB	—	2-[4(1-hydroxy-4-sulpho-2-naphthylazo-3-sulphophenyl]-6-methylbenzothiazole	—	—	—
Fast Red E	—	1-[4'-sulpho-1'-naphthylazo)-2-hydroxy naphthalene-6-sulphonate	—	—	—
Orange G	—	7-hydroxy-8-phenylazonaphthalene-1,3-disulphonate	—	Not possible	Unacceptable[d]
Orange GGN	E111	1-(*m*-sulphophenylazo)-2-naphthol-6-sulphonate	—	Not possible	Unacceptable[d]
Ponceau 6R	E126	1-(4-sulpho-1-naphthylazo)-2-naphthol-3,6,8-trisulphonate	—	Not possible	Unacceptable[d]
Black 7984	E152	6-amino-4-hydroxy-3-[7-sulpho-4-(4-sulpho-phenylazo)-1-naphthylazo]-naphthalene-2,7-disulphonate	—	Not possible	Unacceptable[d]
Chrysoine S	E103	2:4-dihydroxyazobenzene-4'-sulphonate	—	Not possible	Unacceptable[d]
Fast Yellow AB	E105	2-amino-5-(4-sulphophenylazo)-benzene sulphonate	—	Not possible	Unacceptable[d]
Scarlet GN	E125	2-(6'-sulpho-2',4'-xylylazo)-1-naphthol-5-sulphonate	—	Not possible	Unacceptable[d]
Ponceau SX	—	2-(5-sulpho-2,4-xylylazo)-1-naphthol-4-sulphonate	—	Not possible	R; NEL in dog studies
Oil Yellow GG	—	Mixture of 4-phenylazoresorcinol and 4:6 di-phenylazo)resorcinol	—	—	—
Azopyrazolone dyes					
Tartrazine (FD and C Yellow 5)	E102	5-hydroxy-1-(4-sulphophenyl)-4-(4-sulpho-phenylazo)-pyrazole-3-carboxylate	4·63	7·5	Currently adequate
Yellow 2G	—	2,5-dichloro-4-[5-hydroxy-3-methyl-4-(4-sulphophenylazo)pyrazolyl]-benzene sulphonate	1·38	0·025 (temporary)	M

Triarylmethane dyes					
Brilliant Blue FCF (FD and C Blue 1)	—	4',4"-di(N-ethyl-3-sulphonatobenzylamino)-triphenylmethylium-2-sulphonate	<0.005	12.5 (SCF: 2.5 temporary)	Currently adequate
Patent Blue V	E131	Calcium di-4-[diethylammoniocyclohexa-2,5-dienylidene-(4-diethylaminophenyl methyl]-6-hydroxybenzene-1,3-disulphonate	<0.005	Not possible (SCF: 2.5 temporary)	M; S (3rd species C (2nd species)
Green S	E142	4-[4-dimethylammoniocyclohexa-2,5-diethyl-idene-(4-dimethylaminophenyl)methyl]-3-hydroxynaphthalene-2,7-disulphonate	0.08	Not possible (SCF: 5 temporary)	M; C (2nd, 3rd species); R
Fast Green FCF	—	4-([4-(N-ethyl-p-sulphobenzylamino)-phenyl]-(4-hydroxy-2-sulphoniumphenyl)-methylene)-1-(N-ethyl-N-p-sulphobenzyl)-Δ2,5-cyclohexa-dienimine	—	12.5	M
Violet BNP	—	4:4'-di(dimethylamino)-4"-di-(p-sulphobenzyl-amino) triphenyl-methanol anhydride	—	—	—
Violet 6B (Benzyl Violet 4B; FD and C Violet 1)	—	4:4'-di(N-ethyl-4-sulphobenzylamino)-4"-dimethylaminotriphenylmethanol anhydride	—	Not possible	Carcinogenic activity—possibly due to impurity
Indigoid dyes					
Indigotine (Indigo Carmine; FD and C Blue 2)	E132	5,5'-indigotinesulphonate	0.03	5	Currently adequate
Xanthene dyes					
Erythrosine BS	E127	2,4,5,7-tetraiodofluorescein	0.21	2.5	M
Quinaphthalene dyes					
Quinoline Yellow	E104	Mixture of the mono- and disulphonic acids of quinaphthalene or 2-(2-quinolyl)-indandione	<0.005	0.5 (temporary)	C (2nd species)

TABLE 1—contd.

Common name	EEC serial number	Principal chemical constituent (usually as a sodium salt)	Average[a] intake, UK (mg/kg)	Estimated ADI[b] (mg/kg body weight)	Toxicological[c] studies required
Anthraquinone dyes					
Indanthrene Blue (Solanthrene Blue)	E130	6,15-Dihydro-5,9,14,18-anthrazinetetrone (Indanthrone)	<0·005	Not possible	M; S (2nd species) C; R
For certain purposes only pigment rubine (lithol rubine BK)	E180	Calcium and aluminium salts of 3-hydroxy-4-(2-sulpho-p-tolylazo)-2-naphthionic acid	—	Not possible	Migration, M, C (2 species)[d]
Coitrus Red No 2[e]	—	1-(2,5-dimethoxyphenylazo)-2-naphthol	—	Not possible	Not to be used

[a] Corrected average intake of the colour in the UK.[7]

[b] 'Acceptable Daily Intake' as estimated by the Joint FAO/WHO Expert Committee on Food Additives;[3,4,6,27,28] not possible = evaluation not possible on the basis of data available.

[c] 'Toxicological Studies Required' (by the same Committee) are abbreviated as follows: M, additional metabolic studies in several species, preferably including man; S, short-term feeding studies, usually defined as 90 days in rodents; C, long-term feeding studies, usually defined as 2 years in rats and 80 weeks in mice; R, reproduction studies including embryotoxicity and teratology.

[d] Comments of the EEC Scientific Committee for Foodstuffs (SCF, 1975); unacceptable = not acceptable for food use.

[e] Permitted only in the USA for use on orange skins (up to 2 ppm).

TABLE 2

TOXICOLOGICAL STATUS OF NATURAL FOOD COLOURING MATERIALS

Common name	EEC serial number	Composition	Typical uses[a]	Estimated ADI[b] (mg/kg body weight)	Toxicological studies[c] required
β-Carotene	E160a	Mainly *trans* form			
α- and γ- Carotene	E160a	Mainly *trans* form	General	5 (except α-; γ- carotene)	Adequate
β-apo-8 Carotenal	E160e	Mainly *trans* form	Soups, baby foods, desserts		
Ethyl ester of β-apo-carotenoic acid	E160f	Mainly *trans* form	Cheese		
Annatto	E160b	Includes bixin and norbixin	Butter, margarine	1·25 (temporary)	M (now complete)
Capsanthin	E160c	Paprika extract		Not possible	Unspecified
Lycopene	E160d	Mainly *trans* form		Not possible	Acceptable[d]
Xanthophylls	E161	Flavoxanthin, lutein, cryptoxanthin, rubixanthin, violaxanthin, canthaxanthin		Specification only	Oral toxicity not investigated (except canthaxanthin)
Chlorophylls	E140	(a) Phytyl-4-ethyl-10-methoxy-carbonyl-1,3,5,8-tetramethyl-9-oxo-vinylphorbin-7-propionate, magnesium complex (b) Phytyl 4-ethyl-3-formyl-10-methoxy-carbonyl-1,5,8-trimethyl-9-oxo-2-vinylphorbin-7-propionate, magnesium complex	Soups, sauce mixes	NL	Adequate
Copper complexes of chlorophyll + chlorophyll itself	E141	Copper chlorophyll complex and chlorophyllin complex		15 (temporary)	Adequate: specification details required.

TABLE 2—contd.

Common name	EEC serial number	Composition	Typical uses[a]	Estimated ADI[b] (mg/kg body weight)	Toxicological studies[c] required
Anthocyanins	E163	(a) Certain glycosides of 2-phenyl-benzopyrylium salts		From grapeskin—tentative specification only	Studies on known anthocyanins
		(b) Cyanidin, perlargonidin, delphinidin, petunidin, malvidin (Anthocyanidin aglycones)	Wine		Acceptable[d]
Beetroot red	E162	Aqueous extract of red beetroots containing betanine	Yogurt	'Temporary ADI, not specified'	M; C
Orchil or orcein	E121	Extract of the red colouring matter of Roccella, Lechanora and Orchella		Not possible	Unacceptable[d]
Cochineal, carminic acid	E120	Extract of Coccus cacti (ammonium salts included)	Desserts, jellies	Not possible	Temporarily acceptable[d]
Curcumin	E100	1,7-di(4-hydroxy-3-methoxy-phenyl)-hepta-1,6-diene 3,5-dione. Rhizome of Curcuma longa V contains curcumin	Meat products	0·1 (temporary curcumin) / 2·5 (temporary turmeric)	C; R-in progress; M / C-in progress; S (2nd species) acceptable[d]
Riboflavin, lactoflavin	E101	7,8-Dimethyl-10-(D-1-ribityl) isoalloxazine	Flour confectionery	0·5	Adequate
Carbon black	E153	(Vegetable carbon)	Confectionery	—	Specification to be clarified
Caramel colours	E150	Products obtained exclusively by heating sucrose or other edible sugars; or water-soluble amorphous brown products obtained by controlled action of heat on edible sugars (see text)	Dry mixes, confectionery, meat products	100-Ammonium sulphite process only (max. 200 ppm 4-methyl imidazole) / Ammonia process (non-sulphite)—not possible	Identify principle causing reported effect / C, T

Name	E number	Colouring principles/source	Uses[a]	ADI[b]	Comments
Titanium dioxide	E171			NL	Adequate
Iron oxides and hydroxides	E172		Sugar confectionery Meat pastes	'Temporary ADI, not specified	M (for individual oxides—human absorption studies)
Calcium carbonate	E170		Surface use only	NL	Adequate
Aluminium	E173			NL	Adequate
Silver	E174			—	? tissue accumulation
Gold	E175			NL	Adequate
Persian berries extract		Colouring principles rhamnetin, rhamnazin. Extract of the berries of various types of *Rhamnus*	For colouring the whole and the surface	Not possible	Unspecified
Alkannet, alkannin		Extract of the root of *Alkanna tinctoria*		Not possible	Unacceptable[d]

[a] Typical uses of natural food colours in the UK (where permitted).[1]

[b] 'Acceptable Daily Intake' as estimated by the Joint FAO/WHO Expert Committee on Food Additives.[3,4,6,27,28]

[c] 'Toxicological Studies Required' (by the same Committee) are abbreviated as follows: M, additional metabolic studies in several species, preferably including man; S, short-term feeding studies, usually defined as 90 days in rodents; C, long-term feeding studies, usually defined as 2 years in rats and 80 weeks in mice; R, reproduction studies, including embryotoxicity and teratology; T, teratology studies.

[d] Comments of the 1975 Scientific Committee for Food (SCF) are given in cases where JECFA have not made further recommendations. Unacceptable = not acceptable for food use; acceptable = acceptable for food use if derived from natural food by physical processes.

been isolated for commercial use, and few toxicological data were available on this substance. An equally strict ruling has been applied to certain other colours (e.g. lycopene) extracted from edible vegetable products and fruits even though the solvents used (e.g. water and alcohol) would not constitute a toxic hazard.[11]

Colours obtained from natural sources which are not natural foods. For these colours, typified by carmine, a full inventory of toxicity studies is required.

Chemically-synthesised colours claimed to be 'nature-identical' (*whether or not the natural colouring occurs in food*). Once again, the safety-in-use of these materials (e.g. β-Carotene) has to be demonstrated in animal studies.

The toxicological status of natural colours has been described elsewhere[1,7,11] and only a summary table is provided here (Table 2). It can be seen that formal toxicity studies are lacking for many natural colours of defined specification.

SURVEILLANCE BY EXPERT COMMITTEES

Historical Review

The first comprehensive review of safety data on food colours was undertaken in the early 1960s by a meeting of experts convened by the World Health Organisation and the Food and Agriculture Organisation.[3] It was recognised that hundreds of coloured chemicals made by plants and animals had been consumed for centuries with little apprehension regarding their effect on health. However, before principles could be established for assessing the safety-in-use of food colours, it was necessary to identify each colouring, preferably in chemical terms. Bearing in mind available data on toxicity and specification, the Committee felt that they could supply a satisfactory chemical definition for only 20 of approximately 160 colourings considered. In fact virtually no toxicity data were available for about a third of the colourings considered, and for another third of the total, available toxicity data were inadequate for evaluation. At the same time, the UK Pharmacology Panel made their pronouncement on 44 colourings.[20] Among the five colours unreservedly accepted for food use, only Amaranth (FD and C Red No 2) satisfied the requirements of both bodies.

Over the last 15 years, colours have been evaluated many times, by an increasing number of expert groups. Even within Europe, the expert committees of many countries must deliberate against a background of advice from the EEC Scientific Committee for Food (SCF)[31-33] the Joint FAO/WHO Expert Committee on Food Additives[3,4,6,13,27,28] and to a lesser extent the International Agency for Research on Cancer (IARC).[29,30] Not surprisingly, divergent views have often been expressed on the significance of the same toxicity data. For example, Amaranth was banned in Russia and later in the United States, but the SCF[32] as well as the Canadian Food and Drug Directorate (among other agencies) did not consider that a ban was justified on the available scientific evidence. By the same token, the IARC has described Citrus Red No 2 as a carcinogen for rats and mice[29] although the colouring is still permitted for use on orange skins (at up to 2 ppm) in the USA.

Some Problems Encountered
Ignoring any political constraints which may or may not be involved, problems which have been encountered by expert groups in their consideration of the health status of colours include:

Relative Instability of Food Colours
Synthetic dyes. Many azo colours cannot be regarded as highly stable under conditions of varying pH, reduction and oxidation (see Chapter 3). In food media, azo dyes undergo fading to varying degrees on heating or storage, giving rise to colourless and coloured subsidiary products whose toxic properties may not be known.[9] As another example, Indigotine (Indigo Carmine; FD and C Blue No 2) is unstable in aqueous solution, in which it is readily oxidised to isatin-5-sulphonic acid and then to 5-sulphoanthranilic acid, which are less clearly defined toxicologically than the parent molecule.[1]

The sole xanthene derivative accepted for use as a food colour is Erythrosine BS (tetraiodofluorescein), which has been regarded as a probable adventitious source of iodine.[48] Since it has been suggested that iodine supplementation in the diet may be associated with an increased incidence of thyrotoxicosis, it is likely that some restrictions will be placed on the use of this colouring.[7]

Natural colours. It has long been recognised that, because of the poor stability of certain natural colours, their decomposition during the storage of colours/raw materials may produce toxic impurities.[11]

When a natural material is extracted with acid or alkaline solution, with or without heating, the coloured component may be hydrolysed or produce its salt. This explains why bixin, the principal coloured component of annatto, is hydrolysed to norbixin, a symmetrical dicarboxylic acid.[26]

TABLE 3
EEC COLOURS DIRECTIVE (1962)—GENERAL PURITY STANDARDS

I. Inorganic impurities
    (a) No more than 5 mg/kg of arsenic, 20 mg/kg of lead.
    (b) No more than 100 mg/kg of the following products taken separately: antimony, copper, chrome, zinc, barium sulphate or more than 200 mg/kg of these products taken together.
    (c) Must not contain cadmium, mercury, selenium, tellerium, thallium, uranium, chromates or soluble barium compounds in detectable quantities.

II. Organic impurities
    (a) Must not contain 2-naphthylamine, benzidine or 4-amino-diphenyl (or xenylamine) or their derivatives.
    (b) Must not contain aromatic polycyclic hydrocarbons.
    (c) Synthetic organic colouring materials must not contain $>0.01\%$ of free aromatic amines, or $>0.5\%$ of synthetic intermediates or $>4\%$ of subsidiary colours (isomers, homologues etc.).
    (d) Sulphonated organic colouring materials must not contain $>0.2\%$ of substances extractable by diethyl ether.

Chemical modifications also occur in the production of caramels, which are often regarded as natural colours because they can be formed when certain foods are cooked or when sucrose is heated.[11]

Imprecise Specifications
   Synthetic dyes. A synthetic colouring intended for food use may contain coloured compounds of various molecular weights resembling each other in chemical structure, isomers of the same molecular weight but having functional groups (e.g. sulphonate) at different positions on the molecule and unreacted colourless intermediates.[9]
   Since the early 1960s, following the advice of several expert committees, detailed standards of purity have been incorporated into the regulatory requirements of many European countries. In 1962, the EEC Directive on colours[19] defined maximum amounts of trace metals and various organic impurities (based on 100% dye content) (Table 3). However, the EEC specifications are less detailed than those in the US and Canadian regulations on food colours, and are deficient in certain respects. In particular, they incorporate no minimum limit for the total content of dye and give little indication as to the nature and levels of subsidiary dyes, residues of starting materials, intermediates or other contaminants.[7] Not surprisingly, many toxicity reports have given insufficient attention to detail in defining

specifications, and so we cannot exclude the possibility of effects in some studies being related to impurities. For example, in the two Russian studies[21,22] which questioned the carcinogenic status of Amaranth (FD and C Red No 2) doubts have been expressed about the purity of the colouring used, which in one study was no greater than 65–75 %.[23]

The difficulties of toxicological assessment are compounded by a complex manufacturing process. For example, there are as many as six major components of Brown FK and two of these were reported to be mutagenic in an Ames-type assay system.[24] It is clear that reference to manufacturing processes will be an even more integral part of colour specifications and safety assessments in the future. Taking an extreme example, a recent US proposal to remove Orange B from use in sausages was based on the view that even non-detection of β-naphthylamine cannot be taken to indicate that this carcinogenic amine is absent from commercial Orange B.[42] Such a rationale, even if applied to all food colours, could not be used in practice to prohibit all those dietary components which may contain very low levels of a potential carcinogen.

Natural colours. Many of the natural colours in common use have not been evaluated for safety according to the same criteria as are applied for all synthetic colours. The same criteria can be applied when the substance to be evaluated is a single pure compound or its synthetic equivalent, but most natural colours contain more than one, and often several, coloured components as well as non-coloured compounds. In addition, the composition varies substantially, according to the source and the method of preparation, and even the composition of components of the same species of the same plant may vary according to climatic conditions and methods of cultivation. These problems were familiar to the Joint Expert Committee on Food Additives when they first attempted a chemical definition of all natural food colours in 1963.[3] Appropriate specifications were prepared for only 5 natural colours, and in about 20 cases the chemical information available was not adequate to complete such an exercise. A further reason for not preparing specifications was the inadequacy of toxicity data on some colourings. More than a decade later, the expert committee again expressed its concern over the lack of detailed information on the composition of all types of natural colours, and reiterated the old maxim that naturalness *per se* does not assure safety.[13]

Taking a specific example, about 98 % by weight of all colouring matter added to food in the UK are caramels. In a recent report the Food Additives and Contaminants Committee (FACC) questioned the industry's need for over 100 distinct caramel products, not one of which could be defined chemically.[7] The Committee pointed out that an extrapolation of existing safety data could not be made from one product to another in the absence of reliable specifications. In an attempt to resolve this problem, the FACC made a number of proposals to the manufacturers:

1. that caramels should be considered in four categories: burnt sugar, caustic, ammonia and ammonium sulphite;
2. that a limited number of caramels of each type should be permitted;
3. that permitted products should be adequately defined, at *least* by a full process specification;
4. that safety assessment of permitted products be undertaken within a 'reasonable' period.

It appears that the needs of the UK food industry could be met by producing a limited number of caramels to several specifications including one caustic caramel, two ammonia caramels and three ammonium sulphite caramels. The FACC have recommended that caramels of each type should be administered initially to rats at several dietary levels for four weeks. This would give an indication of their tendency to produce lymphocytopenia, as has been observed in some previous studies with ill-defined caramels.[7]

Unfavourable Structural Analogies
Possible carcinogenicity has been the major source of toxicological concern over the years, partly on account of the structural similarity of some azo food colours to known carcinogens such as *o*-aminoazotoluene and *p*-dimethylaminoazobenzene (Butter Yellow). In addition to Butter Yellow, food colours manufactured from β-naphthylamine by interaction with aniline, *o*-toluidine and *m*-xylidine were eliminated from the list of colours authorised for use in many countries.[9] Ponceau 3R,† which was reported to be of low toxicity, was subsequently found to be carcinogenic in Wistar rats, and the carcinogenic effect was related to its metabolites (trimethyl aniline derivatives), produced by reductive cleavage of the azo link.[9]

Questionable Interpretation of Toxicity Data
    Amaranth (FD and C Red No 2). Five years after the publication of a Russian study suggesting that the common azo dye Amaranth may be carcinogenic for rats, the US FDA launched a massive investigation in an attempt to resolve the problem. Five hundred rats were fed Amaranth at dietary levels of 0, 0·003, 0·03, 0·3 % and 3 %. The compound produced no significant differences in total number of tumours (both benign and

† No longer a permitted food colouring in Europe.

malignant) in the high dose and lower dose groups, but there was a significant increase in the number of malignant tumours found in female rats maintained at the 3 % dose level. In 1975 it was revealed that in January of the previous year there had been a 'mix-up' with the animals, as a result of which dye had been administered to some control rats. In December 1975, Dr D. W. Gaylor presented a statistical evaluation of the data, which suggested that (as far as could be ascertained) rats fed 3 % Amaranth in the diet were not involved in the 'mix-up' and that even if some control animals had received the dye it would have been less than 3 %. In Gaylor's original document only the data from the female animals were examined since the male rats showed no significant increase in tumours related to Amaranth in the diet. His conclusion was that the findings of the FDA study confirmed those of the original Russian study.[43]

On the basis of the above study, Amaranth was delisted for food use in the USA,† despite the fact that the tumours were neither organ specific nor unusual for the strain of rat tested. Furthermore, the increased tumour incidence was confined to female rats, and except for mammary tumours, the tumours were not sex related.[9]

A further factor contributing to the FDA decision was a statistical re-evaluation of results obtained in an earlier FDA study in rats over two years. It was found that a significant increase in the number of mammary tumours could be demonstrated provided that only two out of three groups were evaluated. The group which was ignored in the re-analysis showed a higher incidence of tumours in control than in treated animals. When all three groups were evaluated together the increase was not significant.[44]

Of about 20 long-term studies on Amaranth which have been reported to date, only two have given a clear indication of carcinogenic potential and these two have been deemed inadequate for evaluation by several expert groups.[23,27] Despite this wealth of data and the fact that 'the structure of the compound does not indicate that it would be a potential carcinogen when given orally', the 1978 Joint Expert Committee on Food Additives requested further long-term feeding studies.[28]

Not surprisingly, the colouring which appears to be replacing Amaranth in the USA, Allura Red AC, has not yet been subjected to the enormous battery of tests to which its predecessor was exposed. On the evidence of two long-term studies, however, it appears that the possibility of a relationship between exposure to Allura Red and tumour acceleration in mice cannot be firmly dismissed.

† Amaranth is still permitted in many other countries.

Other azo dyes. The choice of experimental animal has been a frequent point of debate, particularly in relation to the testing of azo dyes. The relative susceptibility of laboratory mice towards carcinogenic azonaphthalene derivatives, together with the generally refractory nature of rats to such derivatives,[1] has favoured this combination of small rodents as test species. This has led to conflicting results, as in the case of the model azo colouring Sudan I (1-phenylazo-2-naphthol) (Fig. 2) often quoted to be

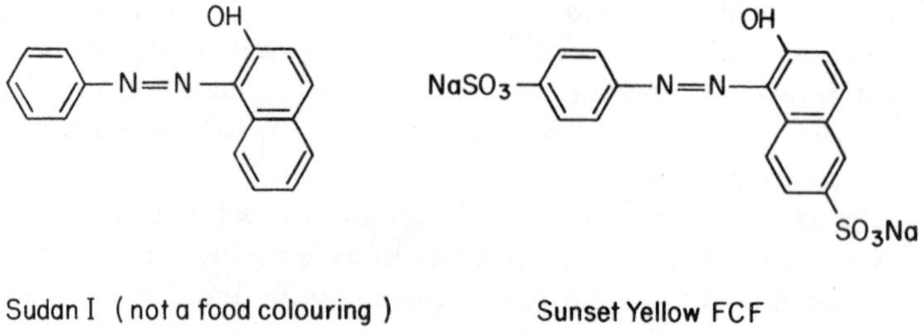

Sudan I (not a food colouring)   Sunset Yellow FCF

FIG. 2.   Sunset Yellow and model azo colouring.

carcinogenic in the mouse but not in the rat. The problem was exacerbated by doubts expressed over the significance of hepatomas in mice following subcutaneous injections with Sudan I, and by clarification of the factors which may complicate the aetiology of tumour production in this species.[1]

The development of short-term screening tests for mutagenicity/carcinogenicity (e.g. the Ames test) has posed questions of some food colours (e.g. Brown FK) even though the *in vitro* tests alone cannot yield definitive results applicable to man.[5] Certain natural colours have also been found to be mutagenic *in vitro*, notably the flavone derivatives kaempferol and quercetin—which are widely distributed in vegetables and other plants.[11]

Triphenylmethane dyes. The constraints imposed on the use of triphenylmethane (TPM) dyes by some health authorities in the sixties were largely the result of disagreement between experts as to the correct regime of safety testing. The central issue concerned the interpretation of carcinogenicity data generated by subcutaneous injection of the test compound.[1] Such findings formed the basis for the removal of Brilliant Blue FCF (FD and C Blue No 1) from 'permitted' lists in the EEC and the United Kingdom. Criticism of these measures stemmed from a growing conviction that the homeostatic balance in an organism is equally sensitive to the physical consequences of administration as to any biological properties of the test compound. In particular, it was alleged that the concentration rather than the dose of an injected compound determined the tissue response.[34] The demonstration that many food additives produced local sarcomagenic effects by virtue of their physico-chemical properties such as surface activity led to the reinstatement of Brilliant Blue FCF in the UK.

Another TPM colour, Violet 6B (FD and C Violet No 1) was also indicted by the demonstration of local sarcoma production following repeated subcutaneous injection in rats. This finding was countered by the demonstration that Violet 6B binds firmly to proteins,[35] a phenomenon now held responsible for the cellular injury leading to sarcoma production.[1] More recently, however, renewed concern was triggered by reports of mammary gland adenocarcinomas and ear duct carcinomas among female rats given 5 % Violet 6B in the diet for a year.[36] In a detailed criticism, BIBRA pointed out that this study fell short of existing standards of carcinogenicity testing in terms of duration and animal numbers used. Strong indications that mammary tumour production in the strain of rat employed are influenced by both hormonal balance and genetic predisposition were also cited as complicating factors in the virtually inextricable aetiology of such tumour formation under the experimental conditions used.[1]

Natural colours. As indicated previously, problems associated with the interpretation of animal data are not restricted to synthetic colours. Similar difficulties have been encountered in the interpretation and comparison of studies on the biological effects of the insect pigment Carmine, which is the only permitted colour to be derived from animal tissue. Complicating factors include variations in the quality and solubility of Carmine, the choice of animal species and the route of administration. For example, foetal malformations ascribed to Carmine were reported in the offspring of mice given a single intraperitoneal injection of the lithium salt[25] but not after oral administration to pregnant rats.[26]

Specious Metabolic Data

Since a thorough metabolic study, which records the progress of different parts of a molecule through the animal body, requires sophisticated analytical techniques, it is not surprising that this type of study has been preceded by expensive but straightforward feeding studies on many synthetic colours. This is unfortunate, if only because the availability of quantitative metabolic data (particularly in man) would palliate the burden of further testing for those colourings which are excreted unchanged in the faeces. In this way precious laboratory facilities might be released for the testing of chemicals which are likely to pose a greater threat to human health than many of the colourings in our food. Possible examples are the triphenylmethane dyes (e.g. Brilliant Blue FCF, Green FCF and Green S) which for many years have been thought to be excreted in a largely unchanged form, although past techniques have not yielded conclusive results. Radiolabelling studies, both *in vitro* and *in vivo*, are currently being

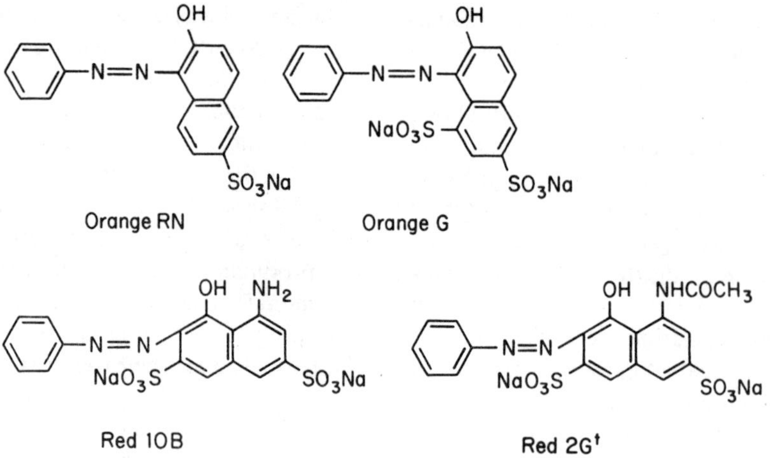

FIG. 3.   Some dyes shown to produce Heinz bodies in animals.

undertaken with a number of these dyes, and studies with human tissues may be contemplated.

The great majority of colourings are biodegraded in the body, and it is the metabolic products which seem to be responsible for effects observed in animals. If this metabolic product is common to a series of dyes, any estimate of acceptable daily intake (ADI) should be made on a collective, and not individual basis. The best example is provided by three dyes which are no longer permitted for food use (Fig. 2) together with Red 2G, which has been assigned a very low ADI by expert groups (Fig. 3).

It seems that a single metabolite, almost certainly aniline (excreted largely as *p*-aminophenol) is primarily associated with disturbance of the integrity of red cells. Effects may include methaemoglobinaemia and the production of 'Heinz bodies'—which are derived from haemoglobin, their formation being largely associated with the β-globulin moiety. Ironically the removal of three of these colourings from permitted lists (notably in the

† Red 2G is still permitted in the UK.

UK) was not a direct consequence of their effects on the blood. In the case of Orange RN, for example, prohibition followed demonstrations of a unique dose-related toxic effect on the liver of a 'sensitive' species, notably proliferation of bile duct epithelial cells, when the colour was fed to pigs.[41] This effect has not been noted in other species tested to date.

The value of comparative metabolic data, preferably with some human correlation, is highlighted by the important species differences which have been encountered in the toxic profile of certain other colourings. For example, Ponceau SX produced adrenal atrophy and chronic follicular cystitis (among other changes) in dogs when fed at 1 % in the diet for seven years. These findings led to the prohibition of Ponceau SX for food use in the USA. It is of interest that no indication of an effect on the adrenal gland was found in long-term studies in the rat.[9]

Non-existent Human Data
Ultimate justification for the choice of animal species rests of course on the extent to which the metabolic steps of a compound resemble those in man. In the few cases where limited human data are available, they tend to refer to acute, rather than to subacute or chronic exposure. A good example is provided by Red 2G which (as has been discussed) may lead to disturbances of red cell function through its metabolism to p-amino phenol. Whereas in rats the no-effect single oral dose for these responses was found to be 20 mg aniline/kg body weight, doses ranging from 25 to 65 mg aniline (up to 1 mg/kg for a 65 kg man) significantly increased the blood level of methaemoglobin in human volunteers. It follows that man is more sensitive to aniline than is the rat (at least on an acute basis), justifying the traditional use of a safety factor in extrapolating results from animals to man.

Extrapolation of Data to Large Populations
A major problem in animal feeding studies lies in excluding the possibility of a very weak carcinogenic effect. This is because difficulties in extrapolating findings in animals to man and the variability of response of individuals make the determination of the safe level of exposure for a carcinogen virtually impossible. This point can be understood if we consider that significant tumour yields in animal experiments usually range from 5 % to 100 %. Vast numbers of animals have to be used to establish the significance of a 1 % tumour yield, and much below this level adequate facilities are not available even on a world-wide basis. Therefore, extrapolating to dose levels including one tumour in a population of 10^6 or 10^8 cannot be confirmed experimentally. In cancer induction the uncertainties

in extrapolating are compounded by the complexity of the process and the vast number of factors, such as promoting agents, which may drastically affect tumour yield.

Variability of Human Response to Chemicals

In extrapolating the results of a toxicity study in animals to man, a safety factor of 100 is usually applied to the 'no-effect level' observed in a sensitive species. This figure is arbitrarily chosen so as to allow a tenfold factor for variations between animals and man, and a tenfold factor to take account of human variability. For example, an evaluation of Red 2G cannot ignore the existence in some areas of the world of a human genetically-determined deficiency of red cell glucose-6-phosphate dehydrogenase, which creates a particular sensitivity to haemolytic amines.[1] Other genetic abnormalities which occur at a very low incidence in human populations include phytol intolerance, abnormalities of copper metabolism (e.g. Wilson's Disease)[3] and beturia—a condition in which beet red pigments are excreted unchanged in the urine.[11] Of slightly greater concern are the possible hypersensitivity reactions to particular colours, of which Tartrazine (FD and C Yellow No 5), is the most familiar example.

In the late 1960s the notion that certain food colours possess sensitising potential was advanced by allegations that a number of allergic conditions appeared to have no possible connection with any causatory factor except

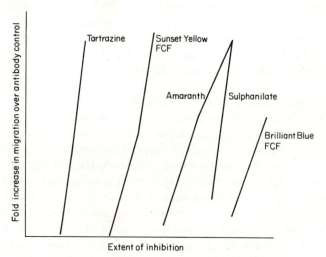

FIG. 4. Haemagglutination inhibition of antigen *p*-azobenzenesulphonate—sheep red blood cells and Tartrazine (modified version of figures in ref. 45).

taking soft drinks. In one Swedish report, urticaria, asthma or both symptoms were noted in 7/8 aspirin-sensitive individuals after challenging with 1–2 mg of Tartrazine.[40] Subsequent studies on the ability of azo dyes to induce the formation of specific antibodies have indicated that the azo group is an important structure in the antigen determinant.[4,5] It was demonstrated by a haemagglutination-migration technique that antibodies with specificity for Tartrazine were produced and that they cross-reacted extensively with p-azobenzenesulphonate (Figs. 4 and 5).

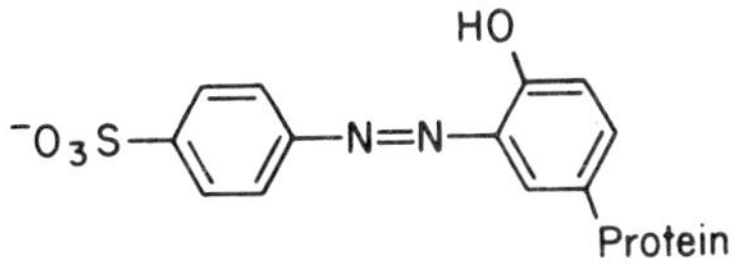

FIG. 5.   Probable structure of antigenic determinant for inhibition of ABS-sheep RBC (see Fig. 3).

It follows that some degree of cross-reactivity might conceivably occur at a clinical level between all the azo dyes. The degree of inhibition determined in an *in vitro* model could possibly be used to predict the extent to which one azo dye might elicit a hypersensitivity reaction in which the original allergic state was established by a different dye. Such a model could possibly be used to evaluate the antigenic potential of any new azo food colour, and could have important implications regarding the need for food labelling. Sublingual testing in humans has also been useful in identifying colours that are allergenic.[9]

NEW FOOD COLOURS

Some Lessons Learnt
The safety assessment of conventional dyes and pigments has indicated that the ideal food colour would be structurally sound (i.e. evince no obvious toxicity or hypersensitivity problems), chemically simple and stable and preferably excreted from the body *per se*. Furthermore, the use of a decision-tree approach to its safety evaluation would be likely to identify major problems at relatively low cost when compared to existing budgets for the testing of colours which may subsequently be found unacceptable for food use.

Synthetic Colours Under Development
The extensive cost of testing a new synthetic colour, together with

uncertainties in the response of expert bodies and government agencies to the results of such studies, has minimised innovation in this area. From the patents which have appeared, it is clear that toxic profile is now being consulted at an early stage in the development of a new dye. Many of these are simple sulphonated monoazo dyes, usually red in colour. Examples are 5-alkyl-2-alkoxyaniline-4-sulphonic acids diazotised and coupled with 2-naphthol-6-sulphonic acid,[37] 4-alkoxyaniline-3-sulphonic acids similarly combined with 1-naphthol disulphonic acids[38] and sulphanilic acid → 1-acetylamino-8-naphthol-3,6-disulphonic acid.[39] It is of interest that every component of these dyes is sulphonated to ensure water solubility of possible metabolites.

One system of food dyes has been specifically designed with due consideration of toxic hazard, namely the so-called 'non-absorbable' polymeric colours. Recent studies have shown that, following oral administration of three [^{14}C]-labelled polymeric dyes to rats and mice, less than 0·5 % of the total dose was absorbed from the gastrointestinal tract, based on radioactivity measurements in the urine, organs and expired CO_2.[46] Furthermore, at least one of these polymers was essentially inert with respect to the gut flora of rats when fed at a dietary level of 5 % for 90 days.[47] However, toxicity studies on selected polymeric colours have not yet been completed, and it would be presumptuous to predict the reaction of government agencies to these new materials.

CONCLUSIONS

By comparison with many other food additives (particularly the enormous range of food flavourings), most synthetic colours have been extensively tested in conventional toxicity studies. Unfortunately, detailed metabolic studies designed to give perspective to the results of these feeding experiments have been hindered by analytical problems, as well as ethical considerations. On the basis of existing data, however, estimates of the probable daily intake of almost every colour permitted in the UK[18] were well within the respective ADI[7] and this statement is likely to be true for other European countries.

Even so, the last 20 years have witnessed a gradual erosion of synthetic colours from the permitted list of many countries, and a vigilant monitoring programme by numerous expert committees (Table 1).

For any new colour, natural or synthetic, formal toxicity tests will be required. It is only the extent of testing which may vary—according to source, preparation, chemical structure and other factors. An ordered consideration of these factors is strongly recommended very early in the development of a new colour.

The intensive surveillance of food colours by expert groups, which is strongly related to public concern over the need for, and safety of these additives has resulted in the duplication of numerous costly investigations. A strong priority for the future must be the co-ordination of data on a world scale, not least to ensure that precious laboratory facilities are not wasted on the testing of any compounds which feature very low on the scale of hazards from food-borne sources.

Duplication of testing is illustrated by the assessment of Amaranth, for which further studies are still being requested—despite the existence of some 16 negative long-term investigations. In view of the many imponderables associated with the design, execution and interpretation of toxicity studies, one may ask how many negative results are required to remove the suspicions cast by one or two studies of dubious validity. Perhaps it is more prudent to enquire how far toxicological resources should be geared to fulfilling demands for increasingly complex long-term studies (now requiring *in utero* exposure) and how much effort should be directed towards investigation of metabolic comparisons and the mechanisms of toxic effects.

One problem with the conventional toxicity study is that the experimental animal exposed to a colouring is not simultaneously exposed to the multitude of environmental hazards that characterise the human condition, and which together may exercise a combined or even synergistic effect on biological systems. These problems are not, of course, restricted to the use of food colours at low dietary levels or even to food additives generally. Nevertheless, the nature and toxicological significance of any reactions, for example between azo dyes and food components during processing/storage, should be examined.

The need for more stringent and uniform EEC specifications for synthetic dyes has now been recognised, and requirements for the identity and purity of substances used in their synthesis are being implemented. Recent advances in analytical chemistry (particularly the development of high-pressure liquid chromatography), together with careful definition of manufacturing procedures, will enable the chemical composition of these colours to be determined more precisely. In the case of natural colours, definitions should again include starting materials and method of preparation.

Many of the difficulties encountered in assessing the safety-in-use of food

244   J. J-P. DRAKE

colours have been compounded by the pejorative and often ill-founded publicity accorded to synthetic dyes in recent years.

Understandably, while the hazard posed by these substances often appears small compared to that of certain other dietary features, it has been assigned a degree of scrutiny which reflects current consumer attitudes to the coloration of food. It follows that if any new colours are to be introduced into our food supply, it will be necessary to demonstrate fewer complications in their safety assessment than has been the case with conventional food colours.

ACKNOWLEDGEMENT

I would like to thank Mr A. Pearce [Williams (Hounslow) Ltd.] for reading this chapter and making helpful comments.

REFERENCES

1. Drake, J. J-P., *Toxicology*, 1975, **5**, 3.
2. Crampton, R. F., 'Colouring agents', in *Why additives. The Safety of Foods*, 1977, The British Nutrition Foundation, Forbes Publications, London.
3. Specifications for identity and purity and toxicological evaluation of food colours, 1964, WHO/Food Add./66.25; FAO Nutrition Meetings Report Series No. 38B.
4. Joint FAO/WHO Expert Committee on Food Additives, 13th Report, 1970, World Health Organisation, Technical Report Series 445.
5. Proposed system for food safety assessment. Prepared by the Scientific Committee, Food Safety Council. *Fd Cosmet. Toxicol.*, 1978, **16**, (Supp, 2), 1–136.
6. Joint FAO/WHO Expert Committee on Food Additives, 18th Report, 1974, World Health Organisation, Technical Report Series 557.
7. Ministry of Agriculture, Fisheries and Food. Food Additives and Contaminants Committee. Interim report on the review of the colouring matter in food regulations 1973. 1979, HMSO, London.
8. Radomski, J. L., *Ann. Rev. Pharmacol.*, 1974, **14**, 127.
9. Khera, K. S. and Munro, I. C., *CRC Crit. Rev. Toxicol.*, 1979, **6**, 81.
10. Committee on Food Protection, *Food Colors*, National Research Council, National Academy of Sciences, 1971, Washington, DC.
11. Kojima, K., 'The toxicological assessment of natural food colorants', in *Chemical Toxicology of Food*. 1978, Elsevier.
12. Markakis, P., *CRC Crit. Rev. Food Technol.*, 1974, **4**, 437.
13. Joint FAO/WHO Expert Committee on Food Additives, 21st Report, 1978. World Health Organisation Technical Report Series 617.

14. Anonymous. *Br. Fd. J.* 1966, **68**, 79.
15. Fairweather, F. A. and Swann, C. A., *Health Trends*, 1978, **10**, 12.
16. Ministry of Agriculture, Fisheries and Food. Food Standards Committee Supplementary Report on Colouring Matters, 1955, HMSO, London.
17. The Colouring Matter in Food Regulations, 1957. Statutory Instrument 1957, No 1066.
18. The Colouring Matter in Food Regulations, 1973. Statutory Instrument 1973, No 1340.
19. Council directive on the approximation of the regulations of member states concerning colouring materials which may be used in foodstuffs intended for human consumption, *J. Off. Commun. Europ.*, 1962, **5**(115), 1645.
20. Ministry of Agriculture, Fisheries and Food. Food Standards Committee Report on Colouring Matters, 1964, HMSO, London.
21. Baigusheva, M. M., *Vopr. Pitan.*, 1968, **27**, 46.
22. Andrianova, M. M., *Vopr. Pitan.*, 1970, **29**, 61.
23. IARC monographs on the evaluation of carcinogenic risk of chemicals to man, Volume 8, 1975, International Agency for Research on Cancer, Lyon.
24. Brown, J. P., Roehm, G. W. and Brown, R. J., *Mutation Res.*, 1978, **56**, 249.
25. Schluter, G., *Z. Anat. Entwickl.-Gesch.*, 1970, **131**, 228.
26. Summary of toxicological data of certain food additives. WHO Food Additive Series, No 12, 1977.
27. Joint FAO/WHO Expert Committee on Food Additives, 19th Report, 1975, World Health Organisation, Technical Report Series 576.
28. Joint FAO/WHO Expert Committee on Food Additives, 22nd Report, 1978, World Health Organisation, Technical Report Series 631.
29. IARC monographs on the evaluation of carcinogenic risk of chemicals to man, Volume 8, 1975, International Agency for Research on Cancer, Lyon.
30. IARC monographs on the evaluation of carcinogenic risk of chemicals to man, Volume 16, 1978, International Agency for Research on Cancer, Lyon.
31. First series of reports on the Scientific Committee for Food—Revision of the Directive on colouring matters authorised for use in foodstuffs intended for human consumption (opinion expressed June 1975).
32. Second series of reports of the Scientific Committee for Food—Amaranth (opinion expressed February 1976).
33. Eighth series of reports of the Scientific Committee for Food—awaiting publication.
34. Grasso, P., Gangolli, S. D., Golberg, L. and Hooson, J., *Fd Cosmet. Toxicol.*, 1971, **9**, 463.
35. Gangolli, S. D., Grasso, P., Golberg, L. and Hooson, J., *Fd Cosmet. Toxicol.*, 1972, **10**, 449.
36. Uematsu, K. and Miyaji, T., *J. natn. Cancer Inst.*, 1973, **51**, 1337.
37. Allied Chemical Corporation, BP 1 164 249 (1966); USP 3 519 617 (1967); USP 3 640 733 (1969).
38. *idem*, BP 1 224 513 (1967).
39. Unilever, BP 1 270 656 (1968).
40. Michaelsson, G. and Juhlin, L., *Br. J. Derm.*, 1973, **88**, 525.
41. Olsen, P. and Hansen, E., *Acta pharmac. tox.*, 1973, **32**, 314.
42. Federal Register, 1978, **43**(192), 45611.

43. Anonymous, *Food Chemical News*, 1976, **17**(43), 68.
44. Anonymous, *Food Chemical News*, 1975, **16**, 28.
45. Johnson, H. M. and Smith, B. G., *Immunochemistry*, 1972, **9**, 253.
46. Enderlin, F. E., Halladay, S. C. and Dollar, L. A., unpublished studies, 1977.
47. Brown, J. P. *et al.*, *Fd Cosmet. Toxicol.*, 1978, **16**, 307.
48. Voight, R. L., Brown, F. A. and Wolf, J. *J. Clin. Endocrin. Met.*, 1972, **34**, 747.
49. Anonymous, *FDA Consumer*, February 1979, p. 5.

Chapter 9

TOWARDS THE FUTURE

J. WALFORD

*Organics Division, Imperial Chemical Industries Ltd, Blackley,
Manchester, UK*

SUMMARY

*The trend towards the use of naturally derived and nature equivalent colours
in place of synthetic colours in food will undoubtedly continue in the future
but a massive shift towards their use is not possible in a matter of a few
months or even a few years. The reasons for this include technical
inadequacy, high cost per colour unit, difficulties associated with financing
the toxicological work required and the unpredictability of political and
legislative climates. An internationally acceptable food colour permitted list
is suggested as one contribution to breaking down the barriers to
international trade in processed food. A plea is made for clear thinking in the
emotive area of food additive regulation when considering both the actual
need for, and the formulation of legislation.*

Food additives in general and colours in particular have been put
increasingly under the safety spotlight during the last two decades. As
toxicological test protocols become ever more rigorous and the analytical
techniques ever more powerful and sophisticated, much needed information on the fate of colours in the manufacturing, storage and metabolic
processes is now becoming available. Even the stability characteristics of
the minor subsidiary colour components present in permitted food colours
are being studied in depth.[1,2] A recent review relating chemical and
biological characteristics of synthetic colours permitted in Canada to their
safety evaluation provides a useful indication of the sort of approach now
being taken.[9]

The results of this increased activity will almost certainly lead to greater restriction of colour usage for both synthetic and naturally derived varieties. Such restrictions will probably take the form of allowing designated colours in specified foods at maximum allowable concentrations, in many cases probably significantly less than 100 ppm. The monitoring of the amount of colour in the many different types of foodstuffs has until recently presented a problem.

New work including that of the Laboratory of the Government Chemist in London should now allow much better estimates to be made of the levels of colour, using enzyme techniques to digest the food before colour extraction.[3]

The likely restrictions have generated interest in identifying alternative colours and methods of colouring food, including altering processing conditions to retain natural colour already present, e.g. high temperature, low dwell time heat treatments.

In the synthetic colour field we have seen that the major initiative is the 'Dynapol' concept of non-absorbable polymeric colours (Chapter 4). There is no doubt that if the colours eventually prove toxicologically acceptable as is confidently expected, they will pose very serious competition indeed both for traditional synthetic colours and to some of the emerging natural derivatives. The concept of polymeric food additives is not of course confined to the colour field alone, as work is at present being undertaken on antioxidants and sweeteners.[4] Further commercialisation of the concept is also being considered by extension to non-food applications. Areas that have been investigated are paper dyes giving non-bleeding effects and plastic stabilisers having non-migratory characteristics. Textile and other substrates could also be a future consideration.

An even more interesting idea is application in the pharmaceutical field— where polymer-bound antibiotics might be used to treat infections of the gastrointestinal tract. The antibiotic would destroy the infection locally and not be absorbed into the patient's systemic circulation. With so many possible opportunities for commercialisation of this idea the future prospects appear encouraging.

In the field of naturally derived colours we have seen that the major effort has been concentrated in the isolation and manufacture of carotenes, anthocyanins and the beet reds, although older, possible second generation colours, also show promise (see Chapter 7). It should be realised however that a massive shift to the use of natural colours is not possible in a matter of a few months or even a few years. The reasons for this can be considered under the headings technical, economic, toxicological and legislative.

From the technical viewpoint, the unsatisfactory stability and solubility characteristics together with low tinctorial strengths and 'off-tastes' associated with many natural colours is well known. Indeed, certain colour effects are simply not achievable at equivalent fastness levels when substituting natural colours for synthetics. Current work aimed at cheaper purification routes and bulk reduction techniques should help to reduce the technical handicaps.[5]

The economic aspects of using natural colours in place of synthetics tend to be unfavourable. Over the last few years there has been increasing activity among natural colour producers to interest the food industry in alternatives to synthetics but the actual increase in the amounts consumed has been rather small.

Increased colour and processing costs together with increased distribution and storage costs owing to shorter shelf-life of foodstuffs using certain natural colours are thought to have been the major reasons.

An interesting approach to calculating the difference in coloration costs when using naturals versus synthetics has been devised recently.[6] This is termed the 'Cost-In-Use-Disadvantage' (CIUD) resulting from the use of naturals.

CIUD is defined as follows:

$$\text{CIUD} = \frac{\text{Natural usage}}{\text{Synthetic usage}} \times \frac{\text{Natural price}}{\text{Synthetic price}}$$

The ratio takes care of the inflationary factor.

Although it should be remembered that the ingredient cost of colour is very low in comparison with the other food components, it has nevertheless been shown that typical 'CIUD Values' for red shades for example are between 6 and 8 and for orange shades between 1·75 and 6.[6]

Much work has been and continues to be carried out on toxicological aspects of food colours. The majority of the work has featured synthetic colours and many of these now have a large dossier of biological evidence supporting their safety in Man, whereas evidence of safety is not nearly so well documented for many natural colours. It does not seem logical to exempt natural colours from the same rigorous test procedures as the synthetics and at least one authority, the EEC Scientific Committee for Food, has stated that if the level of natural colour use increases more than twofold over current consumption, then the full toxicological test requirements demanded for the synthetics should be applied equally to the naturals.

Before embarking on test programmes with natural colours however, the major stumbling block of specification definition is encountered. As may be expected with natural products, differences in plant variety, soil composition, drainage characteristics, and the vagaries of the weather can and usually do lead to end-products of very different characteristics. Take for example the case of grape anthocyanins. The pigment characteristics of grapes from the Burgundy, Bordeaux and Beaujolais areas are different and these are all different to the grapes grown in Northern Italy, California or Australia, for example.

The question arises as to which one should be tested or indeed if they should all be tested. At an estimated cost of £1 million for each series of tests, the economics do not look too attractive, and in practice it is unlikely that a potential colour supplier would risk even the first £1 million, for two main reasons.

In the first place, the unpredictability of the political and legislative climate prevailing at the time the tests are completed would be a major uncertainty. Manufacturers and potential users are still acutely conscious of the 'unscientific' nature of decision making world-wide in the case of the banning of cyclamate sweeteners in 1969, and later in the USA when FD and C Red No 2 (Amaranth) was delisted in 1976. In the second place, even if approval were granted, then any other colour manufacturer could in theory take advantage of the fact and market a similar or even identical product without having contributed to the cost of the test work. And then of course there is always the risk that some unexpected factor will come to light during testing or after product clearance resulting in requests for further expensive toxicological work, or possibly an outright ban.

There are recent signs however of a more realistic approach to the toxicological evaluation of food additives, particularly in the USA where the rigid structure and interpretation of the Delaney Amendment to the Food and Drug Act has been a continuing source of controversy.[7] The Delaney Amendment prohibits the use of any food additive shown to produce cancer in laboratory animals at whatever dose level. Since the amendment was added in 1958, analytical technology has made great strides to the extent that very small amounts (parts per billion or even parts per trillion) of additives can now be detected in food, a situation not foreseen in 1958.

The FDA has now proposed a new approach to food additive regulations in which the carcinogenic potential of a substance is estimated and an assessment is made of the risk involved in its use in food.[8] The establishment of the carcinogenic potential is based on consideration of three factors:

1. An estimate of the probability or extent of human exposure to the substance.
2. The quantity of substance permissible in food in parts per billion.
3. The probable behaviour of the substance as a carcinogen, based on its chemical structure, its probable metabolites and any other relevant information.

It is proposed that each of the factors involved would be given a score, say between 0 and 100, indicating the potential danger. If the total score exceeds a generally agreed figure then full test work would be requested. If not, the substance could be considered for use in specific outlets at maximum permitted levels without further test work.

An important aspect of this procedure is the determination of a safe dose level. A linear risk assessment procedure is proposed when evaluating test results in animals, as it is regarded as the most accurate. In calculating the dose level all tumours found in an animal study, whether benign or malignant, would be considered indicative of carcinogenicity. Proposals such as this are a welcome new approach to the food additive safety debate but are likely to prove highly controversial and the fullest consultations would be necessary in assessment of the actual *need* of the substance as a food additive. Contributions would be essential from many groups including consumer organisations, enforcement authorities in other countries, individual firms, research associations, individual food chemists and technologists, experts from the academic field as well as expert committees.

By the mid-1980s when the results of several series of toxicological tests on both synthetic and naturally derived colours should be available, there is a possibility that a world-wide permitted list could be formulated. Such a list would need the co-operation and agreement of the four major authorities in this field, namely the UK Food Additives and Contaminants Committee (FACC), the EEC Scientific Committee for Food (SCF), the USA Food and Drug Administration (FDA) and the FAO/WHO Joint Expert Committee on Food Additives (JECFA).

The composition of such a world list would be highly speculative, but an attempt is made in Table 1. The list would still be subject to further qualification regarding which food could be coloured and to what extent, but the great benefit would be to facilitate world trade in processed foodstuffs. With the backing of the major regulatory authorities, doubts

TABLE 1
A SUGGESTED WORLD-WIDE FOOD COLOUR PERMITTED LIST FOR THE MID-1980s

Colour	Current status (1979)	
	EEC	FDA
Synthetics		
Allura Red AC	Not permitted	Red No 40
Brilliant Blue FCF	Not permitted	Blue No 1
Carmoisine	E122	Not permitted
Erythrosine	E127	Red No 3
Fast Green FCF	Not permitted	Green No 3
Indigotine	E132	Blue No 2
Ponceau 4R	E124	Not permitted
Sunset Yellow FCF	E110	Yellow No 6
Tartrazine	E102	Yellow No 5
Polymeric colours	Not permitted	Not permitted
Naturals or nature equivalents		
Anthocyanins	E163	Permitted
Beetroot Red or Betanin	E162	Permitted
Carotenoids	E160	Permitted
Chlorophylls	E140	Permitted
Riboflavin	E101	Permitted
Synthetic equivalent of pure colouring principles of the above natural colouring matters	Permitted	Permitted

about the safety of such a group of colours should be minimal, although individual countries would, of course, make their own decisions. Colours not on the world list would no doubt be permitted for internal use as required.

In conclusion it must be stressed that as a means of increasing variety and palatability of processed foods, colours have a significant part to play in mobilising 'non-traditional' food resources such as for example the novel synthetic proteins and the more exotic products of the oceans. In this way, without compromising the safety or legitimate labelling of foodstuff products, colours and other additives such as nutrients, stabilisers, preservatives, and texturisers can, and should be used to improve the quality and increase the extent of the world's food resources. To achieve this, the food industry should have the freedom to innovate and must not be hampered by unnecessary economic barriers or regulations based on unscientific appraisals or be influenced by tenuous and speculative theories.

At the present time it appears that the potential for innovative activity is not being realised as fast as it should be owing to the fact that more and more resources have to be diverted towards coping with the effects of legislation. The severity and complexity of the regulations faced by the food industry will undoubtedly increase in the coming years. The cost of the expertise to deal with such legislation will be high and inevitably it is the consumer who will pay. Hence it must be ensured that these regulations are warranted and properly formulated. It has been argued that fiddling at great cost with the fine tuning of regulations, having in some cases insignificant if any effect on the safety of our food supplies, is not an effective use of scarce resources. Perhaps we should reflect on whether the time and effort would be better spent on the real problem at hand, achieving the permanent demise of hunger itself by whatever means we have at our disposal, and that includes the intelligent use of safe food additives.

REFERENCES

1. Bibeau, T. C. and Clydesdale, F. M. 'Thermal Stability of Subsidiary Dyes in Amaranth (FD and C Red No. 2)', *Can. Inst. Food Sci. Technol. J.*, 1978, **11**, 173–6.
2. Bibeau, T. C. and Clydesdale, F. M. 'Thermal Stability of Subsidiary Dyes in FD and G Yellow No 6', *J. Food Sci.*, 1978, **43**, 521–4.
3. Crosby, N., *Analyst*, 1979, **104**, 472.
4. Anon, *Chemical Week*, 4 August 1976, p. 22.
5. Soukup, R. J. and Maing, I-Y., 'Colour Needs of the Food Industry', in *Current Aspects of Food Colorants*, Ed. T. E. Furia, 1977, p. 77. CRC Press, Ohio.
6. McClelland, C. W., 'Economic Constraint on the use of Naturally Derived Food Colours', in *Current Aspects of Food Colorants* Ed. T. E. Furia, 1977, p. 67. CRC Press, Ohio.
7. Anon, *Chemical and Engineering News*, 19 February 1979, p. 7.
8. Anon, *European Chemical News*, 30 April 1979, p. 20.
9. Khera, K. S. and Munro, I. C., 'A Review of the Specifications and Toxicity of Synthetic Food Colours Permitted in Canada', *CRC Critical Reviews in Toxicology*, January 1979, pp. 81–133.

INDEX